John D. Lenk's
Troubleshooting & Repair
of Audio Equipment

John D. Lenk's Troubleshooting & Repair of Audio Equipment

John D. Lenk

Howard W. Sams & Company
A Division of Macmillan, Inc.
4300 West 62nd Street, Indianapolis, IN 46268 USA

FIRST EDITION
FIRST PRINTING—1987

International Standard Book Number: 0-672-22517-4
Library of Congress Catalog Card Number: 86-63069

Acquired: *Greg Michael*
Editor: *C. Herbert Feltner*
Interior Design: *T. R. Emrick*
Illustrator: *Don Clemons*
Cover Art: *James R. Starnes*
Composition: *Shepard Poorman Communications Corp.,
Indianapolis*

Printed in the United States of America

Contents

Preface

The main purpose of this book is to provide a simplified, practical system of troubleshooting for the many types of audio equipment now available. We concentrate on *modern* audio equipment found in home-entertainment systems, including *integrated amplifiers, linear-tracking turntables,* cassette decks with *noise-reduction,* AM/FM-stereo tuners with PLL *frequency-synthesis,* and *compact disc players.* Of course, it is assumed that you are already familiar with the basics of electronics, including audio. If you are not, you should not attempt troubleshooting or repair of any audio component, either modern or one of the older models.

It is virtually impossible to cover detailed troubleshooting and repair for all audio components in one book. Similarly, it is impractical to attempt such coverage, since rapid technological advances soon make such a book's details obsolete. Very simply, you must have adequate service literature for any specific model or component that you are servicing. You need schematic diagrams, parts-location photos, descriptions of adjustment procedures, and so on, to do a proper troubleshooting job.

Instead of trying to provide such details, this book concentrates on *troubleshooting/repair approaches* that can be applied to any audio component (both those now in use and those to be manufactured in the future). The approaches here are based on the techniques found in the author's best-selling *Handbook of Practical Solid-State Troubleshooting, Handbook of Advanced Troubleshooting, Handbook of Basic Electronic Troubleshooting, Complete Guide to Videocassette Recorder Operation and Servicing, Complete Guide to Laser/Videodisc Player Troubleshooting and Repair, Complete Guide to Modern VCR Troubleshooting and Repair, Complete Guide to Compact Disc (CD) Player Troubleshooting & Repair of Microprocessor-Based Equipment.* However, there is no reference to these earlier books, nor is it necessary to have any other book to make full use of the information presented here.

The approach here is to break each audio component down into its various circuits or sections. All modern audio components have certain circuits and/or sections in common (such microprocessor system control, front-panel operating controls and indicators, amplifiers, and so on) as well as special circuits unique to a particular type of component (such as the oscillators that provide bias and erase currents for cassette decks).

A separate chapter is devoted to each audio component. Individual chapters are divided into sections with a *consistent format.* Using this chapter/section approach, you can quickly locate information you need to troubleshoot a malfunctioning component. For example, if you are servicing a linear-tracking turntable, refer to Chapter 3, and so on.

In each chapter you will find:

● An introduction that describes the purpose or function of the component, including some typical specification.
● A description of the user controls, operating procedures and installation for the component.
● Some typical circuit descriptions or circuit theory (drawn from a cross section of audio components).
● Typical test/adjustment procedures (using actual manufacturer-recommended techniques).
● A logical troubleshooting/repair approach for the component (based on manufacturer's recommendations).

The troubleshooting sections of each chapter are based on *trouble symptoms* (the most common trouble symptoms reported to manufacturer's service personnel).

Chapter 1 is devoted to the basics of audio equipment troubleshooting. Included are such subjects as the basic troubleshooting functions and approach, safety precautions, test equipment, tools and fixtures, cleaning, lubrication, and general maintenance for audio equipment.

Chapter 2 is devoted to integrated audio amplifiers and loudspeakers. Included are such subjects as the general description of a typical integrated audio amplifier and loudspeaker combination, typical amplifier/loudspeaker circuit descriptions, user controls, operating procedures and installation of amplifiers/loudspeakers, typical test/adjustment procedures, and examples of troubleshooting based on symptoms.

Chapter 3 is devoted to linear-tracking turntables, and provides coverage similar to that of Chapter 2, but with additional discussions on the mechanical section of turntables.

Chapter 4 is devoted to audio cassette decks, and provides coverage similar to that of Chapter 2, but with additional discussions of the mechanical functions.

Chapter 5 is devoted to AM/FM-stereo tuners, and provides coverage similar to that of Chapter 2.

Chapter 6 is devoted to compact disc (CD) players, and provides coverage similar to that of Chapter 2, but with additional discussions on the mechanical functions, as well as *laser safety.*

By studying the circuits and mechanical functions found in these chapters, you should have no difficulty in understanding the schematic and block diagrams of similar audio components. This understanding is essential for logical troubleshooting, no matter what type of electronic equipment is involved. Instead of duplicating full schematics, the descriptions are supplemented with *partial schematics and block diagrams* that show such important areas as signal flow paths, input/output, adjustment controls, test points, and power-source connections (those areas you really need to understand to troubleshoot any electronic device).

Many professionals have contributed their talent and knowledge to the preparation of this book. The author gratefully acknowledges that the tremendous effort to make this book such a comprehensive work is impossible for one person, and wishes to thank all who have contributed, both directly and indirectly.

The author wishes to give special thanks to the following: Pat and Roy Wilson; Bob Carlson and Martin Pludé of B&K-Precision Dynascan Corporation; Thomas Roscoe and Eddie Motokane of Hitachi; Ray Blades and Joe Cagle of Alpine/Luxman; Tom Smith of General Electric; Everett Sheppard, Ron Smith, and Jeff Harris of Mitsubishi; Deborah Fee of N.A.P. Consumer Electronics (Magnavox, Sylvania, Philco); John Lostroscio of NEC Home Electronics; Keld Hansson of Bang & Olufsen; Bruce Dorfman of Nagaoka and Microfidelity; Perry Reeves, Jeff Tulley, Greg Kalsow, Mike Fidler, and Diane Fountain of Pioneer; Thomas Lauterback of Quasar; Judith L. Fleming and J.W. Phipps of RCA; Donald Woolhouse of Sanyo; Theodore Zrebiec and Y. Shimazaki of Sony; Justin Camerlengo of Technics, and John Taylor of Zenith.

The author also wishes to thank Ron Bollman, Damon Davis, Herb Feltner, Wendy Ford, Jim Hill, Greg Michael, John Obst, Mavis Robinson, Jim Rounds, Cindy Schlabach, Thomas Surber, and Doris Van Biezen of the Howard W. Sams organization for another opportunity to present his work to the public. The author recognizes that all books are a team effort, and is thankful that he is working with the First Team!

JOHN D. LENK
CONSULTING TECHNICAL WRITER

This book is dedicated to my very special wife Irene, to Karen and Tom, Brandon and Justin, and to our Lambie who is filled with love. And to all the very special people who were nice enough to help me with my book.

Introduction to Audio
Equipment Troubleshooting

This chapter is devoted to the basics of audio equipment troubleshooting. Included are such subjects as the basic troubleshooting functions and approach, safety precautions, test equipment, tools and fixtures, cleaning, lubrication, and general maintenance for audio equipment.

1.1 THE BASIC TROUBLESHOOTING FUNCTIONS AND APPROACH

Electronic troubleshooting is a step-by-step logical approach to locate and correct any fault in the operation of equipment. In the case of audio equipment, the following basic functions are required.

1.1.1 Studying Service Literature

You must study the equipment using service literature, user instructions, schematic diagrams, and so on, to find out how each circuit works when playing normally. In this way, you will know in detail how a given device should work. This is why the *theory of operation* for "typical" audio equipment is included in each chapter. Of course, you must study the service literature for the particular equipment you are servicing, and not rely on typical descriptions. The use of Sams PHOTOFACT®s is highly recommended for this function.

Keep in mind that the functions and features of all audio systems are similar, *but not identical,* to those of other systems. Because the functions are not identical, you will never be able to distinguish what is abnormal if you do not take the time to learn what is normal.

For example, some audio systems simply produce better sound than other systems, even when operating normally. (Frequency response, dynamic range, and signal-to-noise ratio are greater for one system.) You can waste hours of precious time (money) trying to make the inferior system perform like the quality system if you do not know what is "normal" operation. This is especially important when working in audio equipment, where all customers claim to have a "golden ear."

1.1.2 Understanding Operating Controls

You must know the function of, and how to manipulate, all operating controls. This is why the operating procedures for typical audio components are included in the related chapters. Again, you must learn the operating controls for the component you are servicing. It is also assumed that you know how to operate the controls of audio systems in general. An improperly adjusted system can make a perfectly good component appear to be bad. For example, if the equalization controls on a power amplifier are set to some weird combination, a cassette deck can sound equally weird, even though the deck electronics are good.

One suggestion for evaluation of an audio component (in the shop) is to have a complete stereo audio system of known quality. You can substitute the component being serviced into the shop system, and thus compare the suspect component against the same standard. Of course, you must be careful to match inputs and outputs of the components as to impedance, signal level, etc.

In any event, it is difficult, if not impossible, to check out an audio component without knowing how to set the controls, so study the literature. Besides it makes a bad impression on the customer if you cannot find the power switch, especially on the second service call.

1.1.3 Using Test Equipment

You must know how to use test equipment! (If you cannot use test equipment, why are you trying to troubleshoot modern audio equipment?) Because of its importance, we devote all of Sec. 1.3 to audio test equipment. We concentrate on those test instruments that are unique to audio system test and troubleshooting.

1.1.4 Interpreting Service Literature

Along with good test equipment that you know how to use, well-written service litera-

ture is your best friend. In general, audio system service literature is good as far as procedures and drawings are concerned. Unfortunately, audio literature is often weak when it comes to descriptions of how circuits operate (theory of operation). The "how it works" portion of most audio literature is often sketchy, or simply omitted, on the assumption that you and everyone else know audio theory as well as circuit functions.

1.1.5 Applying a Systematic Procedure

You must be able to apply a systematic, logical procedure to locate troubles. Of course, a "logical procedure" for one type of audio component is quite illogical for another. For example, it is quite illogical to check the loading-circuit microswitches for a top-load CD player (since such switches generally do not exist on top-load models). Likewise, many vertical-door CD players do not have laser safety interlock switches, and many CD players do not have disc-detection circuits. However, all front-load CD players with horizontal trays have loading-circuit microswitches as well as laser safety interlocks. For these reasons, we discuss logical troubleshooting approaches for various types of audio components, in addition to basic troubleshooting, in each chapter.

1.1.6 Analyzing Trouble Symptoms

You must be able to analyze logically the information of an improperly operating audio component. For that reason, much of the troubleshooting information in this book is based on *trouble symptoms* and their relation to a particular circuit or group of circuits in the component, as discussed in Sec. 1.1.9.

The information to be analyzed may be in the form of performance (such as failure of a turntable to rotate) or may be indications taken from test equipment (such as waveforms or signals monitored with an oscilloscope). Either way, it is your analysis of the information that makes for logical, efficient troubleshooting.

1.1.7 Performing Checkout

You must be able to perform complete checkout procedures on an audio component that has been repaired. Such checkout may be only simple operation, such as selecting each mode of operation in turn. At the other extreme, the checkout can involve complete adjustment of the component, both electrical and mechanical.

This brings up a problem. Although adjustment of controls (both internal and front-panel) can affect circuit operation, such adjustment can also lead to false conclusions during troubleshooting. There are two extremes taken by some technicians during adjustment.

On one hand, a technician may replace part after part where a simple screwdriver adjustment will repair the problem. This usually means that the technician simply does not know how to perform the adjustment procedure, or does not know what the control does in the circuit.

At the other extreme, the technician may launch into a complete alignment procedure once the trouble is isolated to a circuit. No control (no matter how inaccessible) is left untouched. The technician reasons that it is easier to make adjustments than to replace parts. While such a procedure eliminates improper adjustment as a possible fault, the procedure can also create more problems than are repaired. Indiscriminate adjustment is the technician's version of "operator trouble."

There is a middle ground. Do not make any internal adjustments during the troubleshooting procedure until trouble has been isolated to a circuit, and then only when the trouble symptom or test results indicate possible maladjustment. This middle-ground approach is taken throughout this book.

As a minimum, checkout after troubleshooting should consist of a run-through of the complete operating procedure (not just the area of circuit where the trouble symptom occurred). One reason is that there may be more than one problem. For example, an aging part (say a leaking capacitor) may cause high current to flow through a transistor, resulting in burnout of the transistor. Logical troubleshooting may lead you quickly to the burned-out transistor, and replacement of the transistor restores operation. However, only a thorough checkout can reveal the original high-current condition that caused the burnout.

Another reason for after-service checkout is that the repair may produce a condition that requires readjustment. An example of this is replacement of a major circuit element, such as a turntable motor.

1.1.8 Using Tools

You must be able to use the proper tools to repair the trouble. Audio system services requires all the common hand tools that are found in TV/VCR/video service, plus some special tools unique to turntables, cassette decks, and CD players. Because of their importance, we discuss tools further in Sec. 1.4.

As a minimum, you must have (and be able to use) various *metric tools,* and you must have an assortment of test records, test tapes, and test CDs. (At least, you should have some *known-good* records, tapes, and CDs.) These items are generally not familiar to the average TV service technician (unless that technician also happens to service VCRs, videodisc players, etc.).

1.1.9 The Troubleshooting Approach

The troubleshooting approach in this book is based on *trouble symptoms.* Each chapter has a series of trouble symptoms, listed ahead of the related troubleshooting sections. These symptoms can apply to any similar audio component, but are related specifically (in most cases) to the components described in that chapter. For example, the trouble symptoms and procedures listed in Chapter 2 are related to the amplifiers and loudspeakers described in Chapter 2. Each trouble symptom is referenced to one or more procedures (by section number) that apply to the circuit groups involved.

In some cases, the troubleshooting procedures call for adjustments, both electrical and mechanical. Although the adjustments are given ahead of the troubleshooting procedures, you should not automatically perform all adjustments first. Instead, perform the adjustments only as indicated in the troubleshooting procedures (and in the order recommended).

1.1.10 A Summary of the Troubleshooting Procedures and Approach

Before starting any troubleshooting job, ask yourself these questions: Have I studied all available service literature to find out exactly how the component or system works? Can I operate the audio components properly (*all* components in the system)? Do I really understand the service literature? Can I use all required test equipment and tools properly? Using the service literature and/or previous experience on similar systems or components, can I plan out a logical troubleshooting procedure? Can I analyze logically the results of operating checks, as well as checkout procedures involving test equipment? Using the service literature and/or experience, can I perform complete checkout procedures on the system/component, including electrical/mechanical adjustments, if necessary? Once I have found the trouble, can I use common hand tools, as well as any special tools, to make the repairs?

If the answer is no to any of these questions, you simply are not ready to start troubleshooting any audio system or component. Start studying!

1.2 SAFETY PRECAUTIONS FOR AUDIO TROUBLESHOOTING

Certain precautions must be observed during service of any electronic equipment. Many of these precautions are the same for all types of equipment. Others are unique to special components, such as CD players. Some of the precautions are to prevent damage to the equipment or circuit where service is being performed. Other precautions are to prevent damage to you! This section describes such precautions, particularly as they apply to audio equipment.

1.2.1 General Safety Precautions

The following general safety precautions should be studied thoroughly and then compared with any specific precautions called for in the audio-component or test-instrument service literature, and in the related chapters of this book.

High Voltages Most audio circuits operate at potentials well below the line voltage, since the circuits are essentially solid-state. However, there is always danger in servicing components, if you pull off covers with the power cord connected. A line voltage of 120 V is sufficient to cause serious shock and possible death! Familiarize yourself with the equipment *before servicing,* bearing in mind that voltage may appear at an unexpected point in defective equipment.

Connecting Test Leads Ideally, all test connections should be made with power removed from the equipment under test. Since this is generally impractical, be especially careful to avoid accidental contact with circuits. For example, a screwdriver dropped across a 12-V line in a solid-state circuit can cause enough current flow to burn out a major portion of an audio component, possibly beyond repair. Of course, this problem is insignificant compared to the possibility of injury to yourself! Working with one hand away from the equipment, and standing on a properly insulated floor lessens the danger of electrical shock.

Check all test leads for frayed or broken insulation before working with the leads. Remember that leads with broken insulation offer the additional hazard of voltages at exposed points along the leads.

Capacitors may store a charge large enough to be hazardous. Discharge filter capacitors before attaching test leads. (Make sure that you have turned off the power before you discharge capacitors!)

Disconnect test leads immediately after the test is completed. This habit lessens the danger of accidental shock.

Keep in mind that even a minor shock, or touching a hot spot, can put you in danger of more serious risks, such as a bad fall or contact with a higher voltage.

Use only shielded leads and probes. Never allow your fingers to slip down to the metal probe tip when the probe is in contact with a "hot" or "live" circuit.

Even if you are familiar with all your test equipment, always study the service literature of any component with which you are not thoroughly familiar.

If practical, do not work alone where high voltages are involved.

Ground Problems Many test instruments are housed in metal cases. These cases are connected to the ground of the internal circuit. For proper operation, the grounded terminal of the instrument should always be connected to the ground of the audio component being serviced. Make certain that the component chassis is not connected to either side of the a-c line, or to any point above ground, by means of the leakage check described in Sec. 1.2.2.

One of the most effective means for dealing with ground problems is to use an *isolation transformer*. If practical, use a separate isolation transformer for test equipment and for components being serviced.

Warning Symbols There are two standard international warning symbols found on some test equipment.

A *triangle with an exclamation point at the center* advises you to refer to the operating manual before using a particular terminal or control. The same symbol is often used in audio literature to signify a circuit location or part that is critical for safety.

A *zigzag line simulating a lightning bolt* warns you that there is a voltage limitation to be considered, or that there may be dangerously high voltage at a particular location.

Look for these symbols (and any other symbols), even though they are not universal, particularly on older test instruments.

Mechanical Shock and Vibration Most electronic test equipment and audio components are very delicate. Also, the mechanical portions of turntables, cassette decks, and CD players are vulnerable to any kind of shock or vibration. Not only can the mechanical parts be damaged, but the parts can also be thrown out of adjustment by rough handling. This is particularly true of the turntable tone arm and the optical components of a CD player. (This is the primary reason for the CD player *transit screw* or *shipping screw* described in Chapter 6.) Although the tone arm and optical components are operated continuously, they are not designed to be in contact with the tips of screwdrivers, Allen wrenches, and the like.

1.2.2 Leakage Currents

Before placing an audio component in use for service (or normal home use), it is recommended that you measure for possible leakage current, as follows.

Leakage current indicates that the metal parts of the component are in electrical contact with one side of the power line. If the leakage problem is severe, the component can be damaged. More important, anyone touching the exposed metal parts can be shocked.

There are two recommended leakage current tests: cold-check and hot-check. You should perform at least one of these safety checks before releasing the component to a customer (after service or when the component is first sold).

Cold-Check With the a-c plug removed from the power source, place a jumper across the two a-c plug prongs as shown in Fig. 1.1. Set the a-c power switch to ON. Using an ohmmeter, connect one lead to the jumpered a-c plug, and touch the other lead to each exposed metal part (metal cabinet, screw heads, metal overlays, control shafts, etc.), particularly any exposed metal parts having a return path to the chassis. Always check from the power plug to the outside of any connectors on the rear panel.

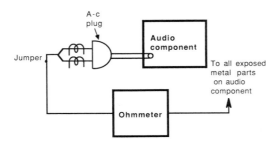

Fig. 1.1. Cold-check circuit for leakage-current tests.

For a typical audio component, exposed metal parts with a return path to the chassis should have a minimum resistance reading of about 500 kΩ. Any resistance substantially below this value indicates an abnormality that requires corrective action (at least some attention).

At the other extreme, exposed metal parts that do not have any return path to the chassis are usually an indication of an open circuit. Generally, any reading above about 5 to 6 MΩ should be suspect.

Keep in mind that there are exceptions. For example, the center terminal of the output connector (both L and R terminals) of a turntable, cassette deck, and CD player could possibly be about 50 kΩ to match the input of a typical stereo amplifier.

Hot-Check Using Fig. 1.2 as a reference, measure a-c leakage current with a milliammeter. Leave switch S1 open and connect the component power plug to the test connector. Immediately after connecting the component, measure any leakage current with switch S2 in both positions. Set the component switches (at least the power switch) to ON when making the leakage current measurements.

Now close switch S1 and immediately

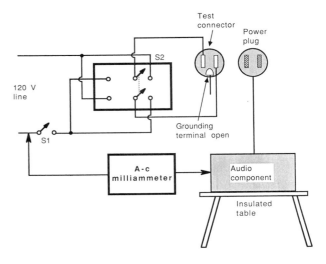

Fig. 1.2. Hot-checking circuit for leakage-current tests.

repeat the leakage current measurements in both positions of switch S2 (and with the component switches on). Allow the component to reach normal operating temperature and repeat the leakage current tests. In any of these tests, the leakage current should not exceed about 0.5 mA (for a typical audio component).

If possible, check the system components (including the loudspeakers) to be used with the component being serviced. To avoid shock hazards, do not connect a component to any audio system that shows excessive leakage current.

There are some practical alternatives if you do not want to use the test setup of Fig. 1.2. You can use a commercial leakage tester (such as the Simpson 229 or RCA WT-540A), or a battery-operated a-c milliammeter (such as a Data Precision 245 digital multimeter). You can also use an a-c voltmeter to measure voltage drop across a resistor (caused by leakage current through the resistor) as shown in Fig. 1.3.

With either the milliammeter or voltmeter, you measure from earth ground to the exposed metal parts, with power applied to the component. If you choose the voltmeter, make sure there is an accurate low-voltage scale, since the voltage indication should not exceed 0.75 V (across a 1.5-kΩ resistor).

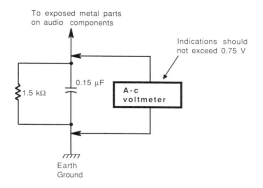

Fig. 1.3. Leakage-current test with a-c voltmeter.

The Simpson 250 or Sanwa SH-63Trd are examples of passive VOMs that are suitable. Most battery-operated digital multimeters (with a 2-V a-c scale) will do the job.

1.2.3 Basic Service Precautions

The author assumes that you are already familiar with good electronic service practices (removing or disconnecting the power cord before replacing circuit boards and modules, installing heat sinks as required on solid-state devices, connecting test-instrument ground leads to chassis ground before connecting the test instrument, and so on). The author also assumes that you can handle electrostatically sensitive (ES) devices (such as FETs, MOS, and CMOS chips, etc.); that you can solder and unsolder ICs, transistors, diodes, and the like; and that you can repair circuit-board copper foil as needed. If any of these seems unfamiliar to you, please, please do not attempt to service any audio system components, especially the author's!

Altering Equipment Do not alter or add to the mechanical or electrical design of an audio component or system. Design alterations, including (but not limited to) addition of auxiliary audio output connections, cables, accessories, and the like, might alter the safety characteristics of the component and create a hazard to the user. Any design alterations or additions may void the manufacturer's warranty and make the *servicer*

responsible for personal injury or property damage resulting therefrom.

Interlocks Do not defeat any type of interlock on an audio component (at least not permanently). If you must override an interlock during service (try to avoid this), do not permit the component to be operated by others without all protective devices correctly installed and functioning. Servicers who defeat safety features, or fail to perform safety checks, may be liable for any resulting damage.

Safety Notices Many electrical and mechanical parts in audio components have special safety-related characteristics, some of which are often not evident from visual inspection. The protection such parts give cannot necessarily be obtained by replacing parts with components rated for higher voltage, wattage, and so on.

Manufacturers often identify such parts in their service literature. One common means of identification is *shading* on the schematics and/or parts list, although all manufacturers do not use shading, nor do they limit identification to shading. For example, some manufacturers use a *dark black* pattern on those areas of the PC board copper patterns that require special care in repair. The exclamation point within a triangle is also used, so be on the alert for any special product safety notices, no matter what the form.

Keep in mind that use of a substitute part that does not have the same safety characteristics (not just the same electrical/mechanical characteristics) might create shock, fire, and/or other hazards. A simple way to solve the problem is to use the part recommended in the service literature.

Condensation Problems Try to avoid using an audio component immediately after moving the component from a cold place to a warm place, or soon after heating a room where it was cold. In rare cases, the moisture condensation can cause possible damage to the printed circuits.

CD players are particularly vulnerable to moisture condensation, which can fog the lenses in the optical system (Chapter 6). You can clean the surface of the objective lens (with a clean, soft, dry cloth), but the remaining lenses are not accessible. You must wait until the condensation evaporates from the internal lenses.

Handling During Service and Use Avoid using or servicing audio components in the following places: extremely hot, cold, humid, or dusty areas; near appliances generating strong magnetic fields (or ones that are affected by such fields); places subject to vibration; and poorly ventilated places. Do not block the ventilation openings. Do not place anything heavy on the component, or place anything that might spill on the top cover. Use an accessory cover (if available) to prevent dust and dirt from accumulating on the component. Use the component in the horizontal (flat) position only.

Reassembling Components When reassembling any component, always be certain that all the protective devices (nonmetallic control knobs, shield plates, etc.) are put back in place. Observe original lead dress (wire routing). Pay particular attention to the wiring associated with components subject to constant movement. (The optical system and the disc compartment drive of a CD player are good examples of such components.) Wire routing is critical in any component subject to movement. For example, wires can be caught in gears or subjected to excessive strain if not properly routed.

Packing/Shipping Always follow any packing/shipping instructions found in the service literature. Look for any transit or shipping screws (such as found on CD players). Such screws hold sensitive parts (such as the optical system in a CD player) in place during transit.

1.2.4 Laser Safety Precautions

CD players have a laser diode that produces an invisible but *potentially dangerous light beam.* Because of this possible service hazard, the subject of laser safety is discussed fully in Chapter 6.

1.3 TEST EQUIPMENT FOR AUDIO TROUBLESHOOTING

The test equipment used in audio service is basically the same as that used in other fields of electronics (television, VCRs, etc.). That is, most service procedures are performed using meters, generators, oscilloscopes, counters, power supplies, and assorted clips, patch cords, and so on. Theoretically, all audio service can be performed using basic test equipment, provided that the generators cover the appropriate frequencies, the oscilloscopes have the necessary gain and bandpass characteristics, etc.

For these reasons, we do not dwell on test equipment in this book. If you have a good set of test equipment suitable for other electronic service, you can probably service most audio equipment. However, there are certain items that can provide considerable help when troubleshooting audio devices.

Typical special-purpose audio test equipment includes the following: wow and flutter meters, distortion meters, wideband a-c meters, shop-standard stereo amplifier and speakers, FM stereo generators, test records, tapes, and discs. We discuss all of these instruments and devices in this section.

1.3.1 Matching Test Equipment to the Circuits

No matter what test instrument is involved, try to match the capabilities of the test equipment to the circuit being serviced. For example, if the circuit under test has a range of measurements to be made (ac, dc, RF modulated signals, pulses, or complex waves), it is usually necessary to use more than one instrument in audio service. If an unmodulated RF carrier is to be measured, use an RF probe. If the carrier to be measured is modulated with low-frequency signals, a demodulator probe must be used.

If pulses, square waves, or complex waves are to be measured, a peak-to-peak meter can possibly provide meaningful indications, but an oscilloscope is the logical instrument. Or you can try a really novel approach and use the test instrument recommended in the service literature!

1.3.2 Wow and Flutter Meters

Wow and flutter are turntable or tape-transport *speed fluctuations* that can cause a quivering or wavering effect in the sound during play. In the case of a tape system, wow and flutter can occur both during record and playback. Wow and flutter are virtually nonexistent in CD players.

The longer fluctuations in sound (below about 3 to 6 Hz) are called wow: shorter fluctuations (typically from 3 to 6 Hz up to 20 Hz, or possibly higher) are called flutter.

Although wow and flutter problems are common to all turntables and cassette decks, it is only when the problems go beyond a certain tolerance that they are objectionable. So, when troubleshooting a complaint of "excessive wow and flutter," first check the actual amount. (This can help settle arguments with "golden ear" customers.)

The basic method for measuring wow and flutter is to measure the reproduced frequency of a precision tone or signal that has been recorded on a test record or tape. Any deviation in frequency of the reproduced or playback tone, from the prerecorded tone, is an indication of wow and flutter.

In the case of a tape system, you can record your own precision signal instead of using a test tape. However, keep in mind that *both* the recorded signal and playback signal are subject to wow and flutter. This may lead you to think that there is a serious wow and flutter problem when the actual fluctuation is within tolerance.

There are four primary standards for wow and flutter measurement: JIS (Japan),

NAP (USA), CCIR (France), and DIN (Germany). With these standards, wow and flutter is measured by playing a test record or tape which has been prerecorded. JIS, NAB, and CCIR use a prerecorded test tone of 3 kHz, whereas DIN uses 3.15 kHz.

A frequency counter (with very good resolution) can be used to monitor the test tone during play. However, a commercial wow and flutter meter is usually more convenient and accurate. Even though the counter may be quite accurate, the problem is one of resolution. For example, the wow and flutter tolerance for a precision home-entertainment turntable is 0.025%. This means that a playback frequency of 3000.75 Hz would be acceptable, but 3000.76 Hz would not be acceptable.

In addition to the accuracy and resolution problems, there is a matter of *weighting*, or test conditions under which wow and flutter are measured. Each standard has its own system or weighting (which we will not discuss here). Likewise, each standard measures wow and flutter in different values. Peak values are used for CCIR and DIN, NAB uses mean values, while JIS uses rms values. Fortunately, all of these weightings and values are accounted for in a commercial wow and flutter meter.

Typical Wow and Flutter Meter   Figure 1.4 shows a typical wow and flutter meter. Six ranges give good resolution for wow and

Fig. 1.4.   Model 1035 wow and flutter meter.
(Courtesy Dynascan Corporation/B&K Precision)

flutter values from 0.003% to 10%. With this particular instrument, the variations in playback or reproduced frequency are separated from the test tone and then measured.

The frequency of the test tone is displayed on a 4-digit frequency counter. The percentage of wow and flutter is indicated on the scale of an analog meter. Filters are used to separate both wow and flutter components (separately, if desired) from the test signal. A mode selector permits the user to select measurement of flutter only, wow only, or combined wow and flutter (weighted or unweighted).

The instrument of Fig. 1.4 accommodates a wide range of input signal levels, permitting measurement at nearly any desired point in the equipment under test. There are two selectable sensitivities of 0.5 to 100 mV and 5 mV to 30 V. This high sensitivity permits measurement of small signals directly from tape heads and phono cartridges if desired.

The level monitor indicator is a time saving feature for setting up tests. The indicator turns on if the input signal level is adequate for wow and flutter measurements; no other measurements or adjustments are required.

Another convenience is the built-in–crystal-controlled oscillators that provide very stable sources of 3 kHz and 3.15 kHz for recording wow and flutter test tapes.

Auxiliary output jacks provide outputs to other instruments, such as oscilloscopes or chart recorders, if desired. These jacks provide a d-c voltage proportional to *rotational speed error or deviation*, and both a-c and d-c voltages proportional to the wow and flutter meter reading.

The a-c wow and flutter voltage is used with an auxiliary oscilloscope, and is about 3 V rms when the meter indication is full scale. The d-c wow and flutter voltage is used with a chart recorder (or perhaps a digital memory oscilloscope) to make a copy of wow and flutter measurements. Output of this d-c voltage is about 1 V for full-scale meter deflection.

The d-c rotational speed error deviation voltage can be used with either a chart recorder or d-c oscilloscope. The output of this d-c voltage is about 1 V for each 1% of speed error.

Note that rotational speed error or deviation is not to be confused with wow and flutter. Speed error (if any) means that the record or tape is not being driven at the correct speed. For example, speed tolerance for a typical turntable is 0.003%. This means that a rotational speed of 45.00135 rpm (for a 45 rpm record) is acceptable. Generally, speed error implies a constant value, or one that changes slowly, whereas wow and flutter implies constant fluctuation.

For added versatility, the built-in-4-digit frequency counter may be used (independently from wow and flutter measurements) for general measurement of audio frequencies. When used as a counter, either a crystal-controlled or a line-frequency (50 or 60 Hz) time base can be selected. An overflow indicator turns on for frequencies higher than 9999 Hz.

Basic Wow and Flutter Measurement We will not go into detailed operation of the meter shown in Fig. 1.4. (Such information is available in the instruction manual.) However, for those totally unfamiliar with wow and flutter measurement, we will run through a typical procedure. Figure 1.5 shows the basic test connections between the meter and the turntable or cassette deck.

1. Set the *indication* switch for the desired type of measurement standard, JIS, NAB, CCIR, or DIN.

2. Use a prerecorded wow and flutter test tape or record on the equipment to be tested.

3. If you want to record a test tape, connect the OSC *output* terminals to the input of the tape recorder as shown in Fig. 1.5. Then set the 3 kHz-3.15 kHz switch to 3 kHz for JIS, NAB, or CCIR. Use 3.15 kHz for DIN.

Keep in mind that wow and flutter present during record are also present during

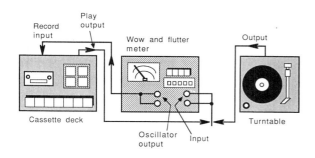

Fig. 1.5. Basic test connections between wow and flutter meter, and the turntable or cassette deck.

playback, and is added to the playback wow and flutter. Under these conditions, measured wow and flutter represents the total wow and flutter introduced for record and playback. One-half the measured value represents wow and flutter for playback only.

4. Connect the output of the equipment under test (cassette deck or turntable) to the INPUT terminal as shown in Fig. 1.5.

5. The *level monitor* indicator should turn on if the signal is of adequate level, and contains the 3 or 3.15 kHz test signal. If the *level monitor* indicator does not turn on, change the *sensitivity* switch setting to 0.5-100 mV. If the *level monitor* still does not turn on, check to make sure that there is some signal present, and that the signal is at the correct test frequency. (It is possible that you are not on the correct portion of the test record or tape, or that there is no signal at the point being measured.)

6. Confirm that the *frequency* (Hz) display indicates the wow and flutter test frequency (approximately 3000 or 3150 Hz). Note that if the signal being monitored is at a high level, the *level monitor* may turn on at frequencies other than 3 or 3.15 kHz.

7. Set the *function* switch for the desired frequency component:

Use WTD for weighted combination of wow and flutter (frequency response of 0.2 to 200 Hz).

Use WOW for wow component only; 0.5–6 Hz for NAB or JIS, 0.3–6 Hz for CCIR or DIN.

Use FLUTTER for flutter component only; 6–200 Hz.

Use UNWTD for unweighted combination of wow and flutter (0.5-200 Hz for NAB or JIS, 0.3–200 Hz for CCIR or DIN).

8. Set the *range* switch for the highest obtainable meter reading, without going off scale. Read the percent of wow and flutter *wow flutter* (%) from the meter, using a scale that corresponds to the range.

1.3.3 Audio Voltmeters

In addition to making routine voltage and resistance checks, the main functions for voltmeters in audio troubleshooting are to measure frequency response and trace audio signals from input to output. Many technicians prefer oscilloscopes for these procedures. The reasoning is that oscilloscopes also show distortion of the waveforms during measurement or signal tracing. Other technicians prefer the simplicity of a meter, particularly in such procedures as voltage gain and power gain. So the choice of meter versus oscilloscope is really up to you.

It is possible that you can get by with any a-c meter (even a multimeter, analog or digital) for all audio work. However, for accurate measurements, the author recommends a *wideband a-c meter*, preferably a *dual-channel* model. The dual-channel feature makes it possible to monitor both channels of a stereo system simultaneously. This is particularly important for stereo frequency response and crosstalk measurements.

Typical Audio Voltmeter Figure 1.6 shows a typical wideband a-c voltmeter, designed specifically for audio work. The instrument has 12 full-scale ranges from 0.3 mV to 100 V. The wideband frequency response permits measurements from 5 Hz to 1 MHz. High sensitivity permits measurements down to 30 μV.

The meter has two voltage scales: a dB scale (0 dB = 1 V) and a dBm scale (0 dBm = 1 mW across 600 Ω). These scales are

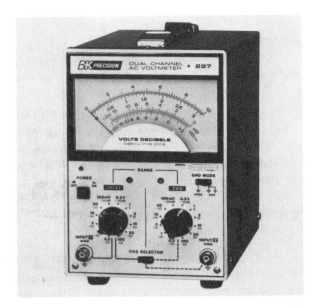

Fig. 1.6. Model 297 wideband a-c voltmeter, dual channel. (Courtesy Dynascan Corporation/B&K Precision)

used for making relative measurements (gain, attenuation, etc.). The meter has dynamic ranges of −90 to +40 dB and −90 to +42 dBm.

A built-in–low-distortion amplifier used to drive the meter movement allows the instrument to serve as a calibrated high-gain preamp. The output is calibrated at 1 V rms for a full-scale reading.

The meter uses absolute mean value (average) sensing, calibrated to read the rms value of a sine-wave voltage. The input voltage is capacitively coupled, permitting measurement of an a-c signal superimposed on a d-c voltage. The 10 MΩ input impedance on all ranges, with low shunting capacitance, assures minimum circuit loading to the equipment under test.

The meter is dual channel, capable of measuring two voltages simultaneously, and had dual pointers (red and black) for convenient direct comparison of two levels (such as is required during stereo balance measurements).

The input attenuator is electronically switched with relays and FET switches, providing higher reliability, improved S/N ratio,

and less crosstalk than with direct rotary-switch methods. The attenuators can be interlocked to permit a single control to select the range for both Channels 1 and 2, or independent ranges may be selected for each channel.

Both channels of the meter operate as preamps. The meter also offers switch-selectable case-ground or floating-reference connections.

Basic Audio Measurements and Signal Tracing The meter is suitable for all forms of audio measurement and signal tracing. It is assumed that you are already familiar with such tests as frequency response, voltage gain, power output and gain, power-bandwidth, load sensitivity, feedback, dynamic output impedance, and dynamic input impedance. However, for those totally unfamiliar with these tests, we run through some basic procedures in Sec. 1.3.10.

It is also assumed that you can trace audio signals from input to output through audio circuits, using a meter or oscilloscope. If not, you may have a problem in troubleshooting modern audio equipment! Read the author's best-selling *Handbook of Electronic Test Procedures* (1982), and Sec. 1.3.5.

Stereo Measurements Two input channels applied to a dual-pointer meter are more useful for direct-comparison measurements than two separate voltmeters. An excellent example is measurement of left- and right-channel characteristics of stereo equipment. To show you the advantages of a dual-channel wideband meter, we describe typical stereo *crosstalk* and *response* measurements, using a meter such as shown in Fig. 1.6.

Figure 1.7 shows the basic test connections for *stereo frequency response*. Connect an audio generator and the dual-channel meter as shown, and apply *equal audio signals* to the left- and right-channel inputs of the stereo amplifier.

Set the CH 2 *selector* switch to the INTER-LOCK position, and select the desired range with the CH 1 & 2 *range* selector.

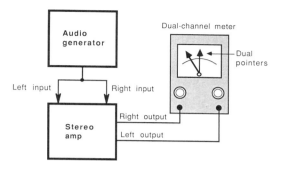

Fig. 1.7. Basic test connections for stereo frequency response.

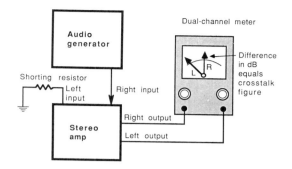

Fig. 1.8. Basic test connections for stereo crosstalk measurement.

Set the GND *mode* switch as required for minimum hum. For a stereo amplifier that has no connection common to the left and right channels, this usually means setting the GND *mode* switch to OPEN. In virtually all other cases (where there is some connection common to both channels), use the GND position of the GND *mode* switch.

Vary the frequency of the audio generator. Note any *differences* in frequency response between left and right channels, as indicated by *unequal deflection* of the two meter pointers. Even those not thoroughly familiar with frequency-response measurements will see how much simpler a dual-pointer meter is to use (than two separate meters).

Figure 1.8 shows the basic test connections for *stereo crosstalk measurement*. Connect an audio generator and the dual-channel meter as shown, and apply an audio signal to one channel. Short the input of the other channel. Typically, the value of the shorting resistor should be equal to the input impedance of the amplifier. However, this should be checked against the value recommended in the service manual.

Set the CH 2 *selector* to INDEPENDENT. Then select the appropriate ranges for each channel with the CH 1 and CH 2 *range* switches. Set the GND *mode* switch for minimum hum as described for the frequency response measurement.

The difference in dB between the signal level measured on the channel with the shorted input, and the signal level on the

channel with the signal input, equals the crosstalk figure. (Crosstalk is generally specified in dB (such as −40 dB).

For a complete crosstalk measurement, reverse the input connections to the stereo amplifier, and repeat the measurement. There should be no substantial difference in the meter readings with the input connections reversed. Make certain that the signal level, frequency, and all other input conditions are identical when the connections are reversed.

1.3.4 Distortion Meters

If you are already in audio/stereo service work, you probably have distortion meters (and know how to use them effectively). There are two schools of thought on distortion meters. One school insists that you must have at least one type of distortion meter. You simply cannot run an audio shop without such an instrument. The other school says you can probably get by without a distortion meter, as a practical matter. If distortion is severe, you will hear it. If the distortion is below a level where it can be heard, you can generally forget the problem. The author has no recommendations either way. However, keep in mind that if you have a customer with a "golden ear," an accurate distortion meter is an excellent tool for settling "discussions" concerning his or her audio system's performance, especially *after* service.

There are two types of distortion measurement: harmonic and intermodulation.

We do not describe any particular meter here. Instead, we include brief descriptions of how harmonic and intermodulation distortion measurements are made.

Harmonic Distortion Measurements In any audio circuit or component, there is always the possibility of odd or even harmonics being present with the fundamental frequency of each signal. These harmonics combine with the fundamental and produce distortion, as is the case when any two signals are combined.

The effects of second and third harmonic distortion are shown in Fig. 1.9. (Second and third harmonics present the greatest harmonic distortion problem in typical home-entertainment audio systems.) As shown in Fig. 1.9, when harmonic signals swing negative simultaneously with a positive switch of the fundamental, or vice versa, the fundamental signal is distorted by the combination.

The *fundamental suppression* principle is used in most commercial harmonic distortion meters. As shown in Fig. 1.10, a sine wave is applied to the circuit input, and the circuit output is measured (on an oscilloscope or meter). The output is then applied through a filter that suppresses the fundamental frequency. Under these conditions, any output from the filter is then the result of harmonics. The frequency of the filter output signal can be checked to determine harmonic content. For example, if the input is 1 kHz and the output (after filtering) is 3 kHz, third-harmonic distortion is indicated.

The *percentage of harmonic distortion* can also be determined by this method. For example, if the output without filter is 100 mV, and with filter is 3 mV, a 3% harmonic distortion is indicated.

In some commercial harmonic distor-

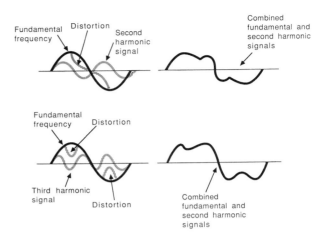

Fig. 1.9. Distortion produced by second and third harmonics.

tion meters, the filter is tunable so that the amplifier can be tested over a wide range of fundamental frequencies. In other harmonic distortion meters, the filter is fixed in frequency but can be detuned slightly to produce a sharp null indication.

When an audio component (preamp, power amp, etc.) is tested over a wide range of frequencies for harmonic distortion, and the result plotted on a graph similar to that of Fig. 1.11, the percentage is known as *total harmonic distortion* (THD). Note that the THD shown in Fig. 1.11 is dependent on frequency and rated power output. However, the THD is less than 0.15% under all conditions.

Intermodulation Distortion Measurements Intermodulation distortion is produced when two signals of different frequency are mixed in an audio component or circuit, and the low-frequency signal amplitude modulates the higher-frequency signal. This can occur in the best of audio systems.

The basic intermodulation distortion test circuit is shown in Fig. 1.12. In a commercial meter, the signal generators are connected so

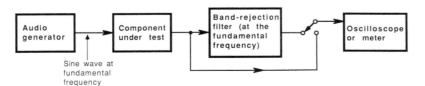

Fig. 1.10. Fundamental-suppression method used to find harmonic distortion.

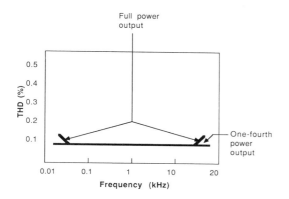

Fig. 1.11. Graph showing relationship of THD to frequency and rated power output.

that a high-frequency signal (typically 7 kHz) is modulated by a low-frequency signal (typically 60 Hz). The mixed signals are applied to the component input. The component output is connected through a high-pass filter to the oscilloscope.

Under these test conditions, the high-

pass filter removes the low-frequency (60 Hz) signal. The only signal appearing on the oscilloscope should be the high-frequency (7-kHz) signal. If any 60-Hz signal is present on the display, the 60-Hz signal is being passed through as modulation on the 7-kHz signal.

Figure 1.13 shows a simple test circuit that you can make up for basic intermodulation distortion tests. The high-pass filter is designed to pass signals above about 200 Hz. The 39 kΩ and 10 kΩ resistors set the 60-Hz signal at four times the 7-kHz signal. Many audio generators provide for a line-frequency output (60 Hz) that can be used as the low-frequency modulation source.

When using the circuit of Fig. 1.13, set the line-frequency output to some fixed value (1 V, 100 mV, etc.). Then set the audio output (7 kHz) to the same value. If the line-frequency output is not adjustable, measure the actual value of the line-frequency output, and then set the 7-kHz output to the same value.

Fig. 1.12. Basic method to find intermodulation distortion.

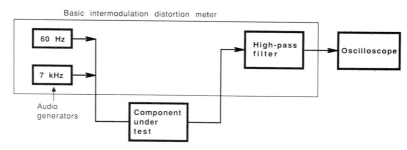

Fig. 1.13. Simple test circuit for basic intermodulation distortion tests.

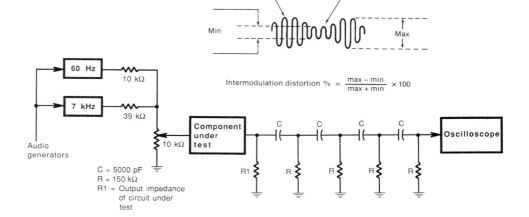

Calculate the percentage of intermodulation distortion using the equation of Fig. 1.13.

1.3.5 Oscilloscopes

The oscilloscopes used for audio work should have the same characteristics as for other electronic service. If you have a good oscilloscope for TV or VCR work, use that scope for all audio troubleshooting and measurements. If you are considering a new scope, remember that a dual-channel instrument permits you to monitor both channels of a stereo system (as is the case with a dual-channel wideband voltmeter). An oscilloscope has the advantage over a meter in that the scope can display such common audio-circuit conditions as distortion, hum, ripple, and oscillation. (However, the meter is easier to read.)

Signal Tracing with an Oscilloscope
Figure 1.14 shows the basic circuits for signal tracing audio circuits with an oscilloscope. A signal is introduced into the input by the audio generator. The amplitude and waveform of the input signal are measured on the scope. The oscilloscope probe is then moved to the input and output of each stage, in turn, until the final output is reached. The gain of each stage is measured as a

peak-to-peak voltage on the scope. It is also possible to see any change in waveform from that applied at the input, making it possible to spot distortion.

Checking Distortion with an Oscilloscope
If you do not have a distortion meter, and plan to troubleshoot audio circuits with an oscilloscope, use square waves instead of sine waves to look for distortion. Unless distortion is severe, it can pass unnoticed in sine wave form. It is much easier to see deviation from a straight line than from a curved line, particularly if the straight line has sharp corners. Also, square waves have a high odd-harmonic content. The third, fifth, seventh, and ninth harmonics of a clean square wave are emphasized. So, if an audio component passes a square-wave signal of some given frequency, and produces a clean square-wave output. It is reasonable to assume that the frequency response is good up to at least nine times the fundamental frequency.

Figure 1.15 shows some classic distortion patterns produced by audio circuits and components. Keep in mind that these patterns are exaggerated. Count yourself as lucky if you get such well-defined indications of square-wave distortion! In Fig. 1.15, it is assumed that a clean square wave is

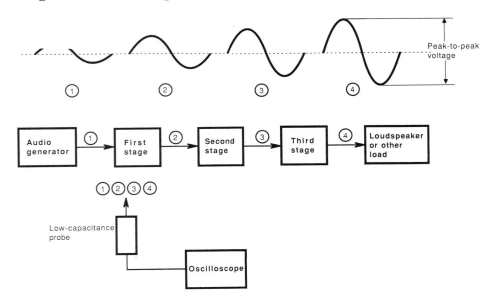

Fig. 1.14. Basic circuit for signal tracing audio circuits with an oscilloscope.

applied at the input, while the output is monitored on an oscilloscope. If the scope is dual trace, you can monitor the input and output simultaneously.

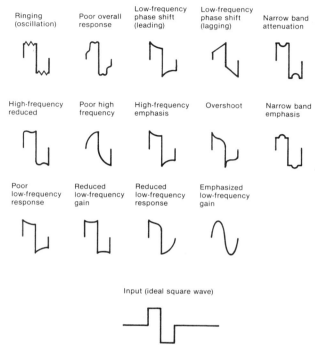

Fig. 1.15. **Classic distortion patterns produced by audio circuits and components.**

1.3.6 FM-Stereo Generator

An FM-stereo generator is essential for troubleshooting the FM-stereo tuners and receivers discussed in Chapter 5. This is because an FM generator simulates the very complex modulation system used by FM-stereo broadcast stations. Without an FM-stereo generator, you would be totally dependent on the constantly changing signals from such stations, making it impossible to adjust FM tuners and receivers, or to measure response after adjustment. So you can put an FM-stereo generator high on your list of test equipment recommended for audio troubleshooting.

The FM-Stereo Modulation System
Before we describe the characteristics of an FM-stereo generator, let us review the basic FM-stereo modulation system (which is quite

complex when compared to that of the AM broadcast system). It is essential that you understand the FM system to troubleshoot any FM-stereo receiver or tuner.

Figure 1.16 shows the composite audio modulating signal used for FM stereo. This FM system permits stereo tuners and receivers to separate audio into left and right channels, and permits monaural FM tuners to combine left- and right-channel audio into a single output.

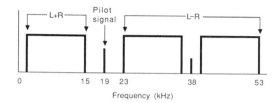

Fig. 1.16. **Composite audio modulating signal used for FM-stereo.**

Figure 1.17 shows the block diagram of a typical FM-stereo modulator and transmitter. Left- and right-channel audio signals are applied through preemphasis networks to a summing network that adds the two signals. A low-pass filter limits this signal to the 0 to 15-kHz audio band, which is the maximum authorized for FM broadcast service. This (L+R) signal contains both left- and right-channel audio in a 0 to 15-kHz baseband.

The left-channel audio is applied to another summing network, along with the right-channel audio, which has been inverted. The summing network effectively subtracts the two signals. The 0 to 15-kHz (L−R) signal is fed to a balanced modulator, along with a 38-kHz sine wave. The balanced modulator produces a double sideband suppressed carrier (DSBSC) subband, centered around 38 kHz. A bandpass filter limits the signal to the 23- to 53-kHz range (±15 kHz of the 38-kHz carrier). The resulting L−R signal is a 23 to 53-kHz subband, with the 38-kHz subcarrier fully suppressed.

When FM-stereo is broadcast, a low-level 19-kHz pilot signal is transmitted simultaneously. The pilot signal is generated by a

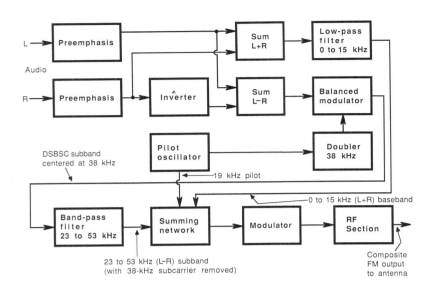

Fig. 1.17. Block diagram of a typical FM-stereo modulator and transmitter.

stable, crystal-controlled oscillator operating at 19 kHz. The 19-kHz pilot oscillator output is also applied to a frequency doubler, providing the 38-kHz carrier for the balanced modulator.

The 0 to 15-kHz baseband (L+R), 23 to 53-kHz subband (L−R), and 19-kHz pilot signal are applied to a summing network, resulting in a composite audio signal consisting of the three components shown in Fig. 1.16. The composite audio signal is applied to the modulator, which FM modulates the RF carrier of the transmitter. For a fully modulated RF carrier, the (L+R) signal accounts for 45%, the (L−R) for 45%, and the pilot for 10%.

Stereo tuners and receivers decode the signal shown in Fig. 1.16, and then separate the audio into original left and right channels. Since monaural FM receivers have only a 0 to 15-kHz audio response, the 19-kHz pilot signal and the 23 to 53-kHz (L−R) subband are rejected. However, the (L+R) baseband signal is accepted, and combines left- and right-channel audio to produce monaural audio.

Figure 1.18 shows the block diagram of a typical FM-stereo receiver, from the discriminator to the audio amplifier inputs. The discriminator output is a composite audio signal similar to that shown in Fig. 1.16.

A PLL locks the sine-wave output of the 38-kHz VCO in phase with the received 19-kHz pilot signal as follows. A divide-by-two circuit converts the 38-kHz VCO output to a 19-kHz sine wave, which is one of the inputs of a phase comparator. The other input to the phase comparator is the received 19-kHz pilot signal. The phase comparator produces an error voltage to lock the VCO in-phase with the 19-kHz pilot signal.

The composite audio signal from the discriminator is applied through a 23- to 53-kHz bandpass filter, which blocks the 0 to 15-kHz (L+R) baseband and 19-kHz pilot signals, while passing only the 23- to 53-kHz subband (L−R) signal. The 23- to 53-kHz subband signal is applied to a balanced demodulator circuit. The other input to the balanced demodulator is a 38-kHz carrier from the VCO. The VCO carrier is locked in phase to the 19-kHz pilot signal by the PLL as described.

During stereo broadcast, with the 19-kHz pilot signal present, the error voltage from the phase comparator approaches zero as phase lock is achieved. This error voltage is applied to a 19-kHz pilot detector, and to the 38-kHz VCO. When the error voltage drops below the threshold of the 19-kHz pilot detector, the stereo indicator is turned on, as is the switch that couples the (L−R) signal from the balanced modulator to the L−R decode matrix.

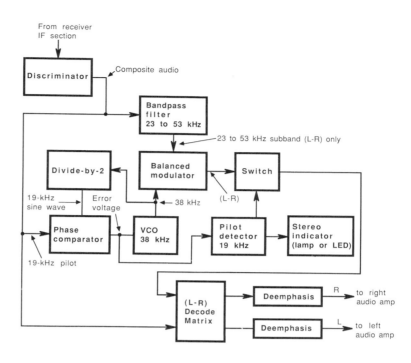

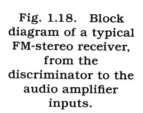

Fig. 1.18. Block diagram of a typical FM-stereo receiver, from the discriminator to the audio amplifier inputs.

The decode matrix separates the L and R components of the (L+R) and (L−R) signals into independent left- and right-channel outputs. When the (L−R) signal is absent, such as during monaural reception, the error signal from the phase comparator does not approach zero, and the 19-kHz pilot detector does not actuate the switch or turn on the stereo indicator. As a result, the (L+R) input is not separated into L and R components within the matrix. Instead, both outputs from the matrix are identical (L+R) signals.

As shown in Fig. 1.17, both the L and R audio signals are subjected to *preemphasis* before reaching the FM modulator circuits. Likewise, as shown in Fig. 1.18, the L and R outputs from the decode matrix are applied to audio amplifiers through *deemphasis* networks. The use of preemphasis and deemphasis is mostly to improve S/N ratio.

Preemphasis increases highs, while deemphasis increases the lows. Frequency modulation (FM) is usually a form of phase modulation (PM). The noise modulation characteristic of PM is not flat, but increases

with noise frequency. So, with deemphasis in the receiver, the high-frequency noise is reduced to the same level as the low-frequency noise, thus improving the S/N ratio.

Remember that noise modulation is essentially an internal modulation of constant level. By preemphasizing the external audio to the transmitter, an overall flat audio response is possible. This compensates for the deemphasis characteristic of the receiver, but does not affect noise modulation.

The RC time constant of the coupling components in a preemphasis or deemphasis network determines the center frequency, and are specified in microseconds (μs). 75 μs is standard for FM broadcasts in the USA. 50 μs is used in some other countries. The standard rolloff rate for both preemphasis and deemphasis is 6 dB per octave.

Typical FM-Stereo Generator Figure 1.19 shows a typical FM-stereo generator, designed specifically for testing, troubleshooting, and adjusting FM-stereo receivers and tuners (as well as monaural FM receivers). The instrument generates a stereo multiplex

FM-modulated RF carrier signal that conforms to FCC regulations, and duplicates the type of signal radiated by an FM-stereo broadcast transmitter.

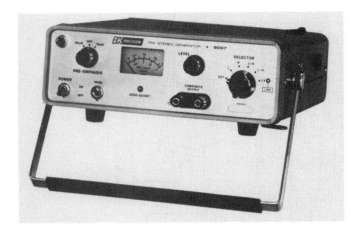

Fig. 1.19. Model 2007 FM multiplex stereo signal generator. (Courtesy Dynascan Corporation/B&K Precision)

External or internal modulating audio is converted to a composite audio signal containing an (L+R) 0 to 15-kHz baseband, and (L−R) 23- to 53-kHz subband. The modulating signal (composite audio) is also available for injection directly into audio and stereo decoder circuits.

The composite audio signal is continuously adjustable. A modulation meter is calibrated to measure the rms value of composite audio on a 0 to 2-V scale. The RF output may be internally or externally modulated. In either case, modulation is continuously adjustable up to 75 kHz. The calibrated modulation meter reads FM deviation in kHz.

For external modulation, independent left and right input jacks permit stereo modulation through selectable 75 μs or 50 μs preemphasis networks, or with no preemphasis. The 50-Hz to 15-kHz audio input bandwidth equals that of a commercial broadcast transmitter, thus permitting full audio-range frequency response test of receivers.

For internal modulation, an internally generated low-distortion 1-kHz signal is

used. A mode-selector switch permits five combinations of internal modulation: left-channel only, right-channel only, (L+R) baseband, (L−R) subband, and L&R (line) with 1-kHz signal applied to left channel and 50/60-Hz line voltage signal applied to the right channel. These combinations permit complete testing of stereo decoder circuits, including channel-balance and channel-separation characteristics. Figure 1.20 shows the composite output signal in various internal modulation modes.

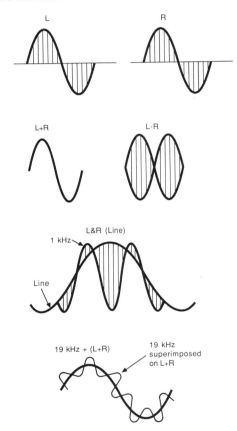

Fig. 1.20. Composite output signal in various internal modulation modes.

During either internal or external modulation, a highly stable 19-kHz pilot signal is generated and combined with the composite audio. The pilot signal may be switched off when desired, such as for testing operation of a pilot detector circuit.

The selectable 85-MHz band or 98-MHz band RF output is tunable within ±2 MHz.

A detachable telescoping antenna is supplied with the instrument. The antenna screws into an antenna jack to simulate an FM-stereo broadcast transmitter. Two antenna receptacles are provided to simulate either a vertically or horizontally polarized antenna. The RF output is also available at balanced 300-Ω output terminals. The RF output may be turned off whenever desired, thus generating the composite audio only.

1.3.7 Shop-Standard Stereo Amplifier with Speakers

You should have at least one good shop-standard stereo amplifier and speaker system. This permits you to check all audio components passing through the shop against a *known standard.* Keep in mind that the amplifier must be capable of handling a wide range of inputs. For example, the line output of a typical cassette deck is in the order of 500 mV, while a turntable produces considerably less output. (The output from a pickup or cartridge is generally less than 5 mV.) The output from a CD player (which may or may not be adjustable) is typically 2 V.

1.3.8 Digital Logic Test Equipment

Many modern audio components use some form of microprocessor (sometimes called a microcomputer) in the system control circuits. More than one microprocessor is used in some cases. While it is possible to monitor most microprocessor signals with an oscilloscope, there are special test instruments for digital troubleshooting.

As a minimum, you should have (and know how to use) a *logic probe.* A *logic pulser* and a *current tracer* are also useful, but not essential. (There are also *logic comparators, logic analyzers,* and *signature analyzers,* but none of these are essential for audio service.)

We do not go into the use of digital test equipment in this book. To do so requires too much space. If you are not familiar with digital troubleshooting techniques, your at-

tention is directed to *John D. Lenk's Troubleshooting & Repair of Microprocessor-Based Equipment* (Howard W. Sams & Co., 1986).

1.3.9 Test Records, Cassettes, and Discs

Many audio component manufacturers provide test records, cassettes, and discs as part of their recommended test equipment and/or tools. (Some manufacturers even recommend the test device of another manufacturer!) There are also some standard test devices available.

These test devices are essentially standard records, cassettes, or CDs with several very useful signals recorded at the factory using very precise test equipment and signal sources. You play the test device on the turntable, cassette deck, or CD player being serviced and note the response, and/or use the signals to perform alignment and adjustment of the component. With the proper test device, you can often eliminate the need for your own signal sources (signal generators, audio generators, etc.).

One major problem with test devices is the lack of standardization. You will probably need several test devices if you are going to service many different models of audio components. The test/adjustment procedures found in some service literature call for signals not available on all test devices. The only way around this problem is to use the recommended test device in all cases. Of course, you can use any known-good test device for a final, after-service check of the component, but this does not give you the necessary signals to perform all test/adjustment procedures.

1.3.10 Basic Audio Amplifier Tests and Measurements

Most of the components described in the remaining chapters of this book contain audio amplifiers of some kind. For that reason, it is essential that you understand how to make basic audio-amplifier tests and measurements. The following paragraphs describe the basics of such procedures, and are included here for those totally unfamiliar with audio work. Detailed procedures for test, measurement, and adjustment of specific audio components are given in the related chapter.

Frequency Response The frequency response of an audio amplifier, or filter, can be measured with an audio signal generator and a meter or oscilloscope. The generator is tuned to various frequencies, and the resultant circuit or component output response is measured at each frequency. The results are then plotted in the form of a graph or response curve, such as shown in Fig. 1.21.

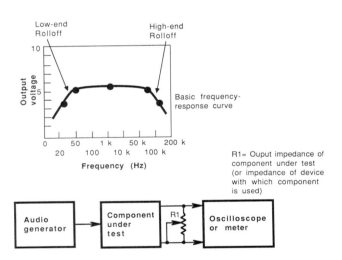

Fig. 1.21. **Basic test connections and curve for frequency-response and voltage-gain measurements.**

The basic procedure is to apply a constant-amplitude signal to the circuit or component input while monitoring the output. The input signal is varied in frequency (but not amplitude) across the entire operating range. A typical audio component has a constant response from about 20 Hz to 20 kHz, but can have a much wider operating range as shown in Fig. 1.21.

The basic frequency-response test procedure is as follows:

1. Connect the equipment as shown in Fig. 1.21. Set the generator, meter, and scope controls as necessary. It is assumed that the audio generator is provided with controls to vary the output in both frequency and amplitude.

2. Initially, set the generator output frequency to the low end of the frequency range. Then set the generator output amplitude to the desired input level. Most audio components are rated as to some specific input voltage for a given output (350 mV input for full output, 100 mV input for 10-W output, etc.).

3. If no particular input value is specified, set the input voltage as follows. Monitor the output and increase the input voltage until the circuit or component is overdriven. Use the center frequency of the circuit or component (or use 1 kHz, whichever is convenient). An audio circuit or component is overdriven when further increases in input voltage produce no further increases in output meter reading (or when the output waveform peaks begin to flatten on an oscilloscope display). Set the input voltage *just below* this point. Monitor the input voltage, and keep the generator at this voltage throughout the test.

4. If the circuit is provided with any operating or adjustment controls (volume, loudless, gain, treble, bass, etc.), set these controls to some arbitrary point when making the initial frequency-response measurement. The response measurements can then be repeated at different control settings if desired.

5. Record the circuit output voltage on a graph. Without changing the generator output amplitude, increase the generator output frequency by some fixed amount, and record the new circuit output voltage. The amount of frequency increase between each measurement is an arbitrary matter. For a typical audio circuit or component, use an increase of 10 Hz at the low end and high end (where rolloff occurs), and an increase of 100 Hz at the middle frequencies.

6. Repeat this process, checking and recording output voltage at each of the check points in order to obtain a frequency-response curve. With a typical audio component or bandpass filter, the curve resembles that of Fig. 1.21, with a flat portion across the middle frequencies and rolloff at each end. High-pass and low-pass filters produce curves with rolloff at one end only. (High-pass filters have a rolloff at the low end, and vice versa.)

7. After the initial frequency-response check, the effect of operating or adjustment controls should be checked. For example, it is possible to compare the settings of a graphic equalizer against the response curve, and then run a new curve with different equalizer settings. Generally, volume, loudness, and gain controls have the same effect all across the frequency range. Treble and bass controls may also have some effect at all frequencies. However, a treble control should have the greatest effect at the high end, whereas a bass control affects the low end most.

8. Note that generator output may vary with changes in frequency, a fact often overlooked in making a frequency-response test of any circuit (not just audio circuits). Even precision laboratory generators can vary in amplitude output with changes in frequency, resulting in considerable error. It is recommended that the generator output be monitored after each change in frequency (some audio generators have a built-in output meter). Then, if necessary, the generator output amplitude can be reset to the correct value. It is generally more important that the generator output amplitude *remain constant* rather than at some specific value when making a frequency-response check.

Voltage Gain The frequency response test just described can be used to measure voltage gain of an audio component or circuit. Voltage gain is the ratio of output voltage divided by input voltage (at any given frequency, or across the entire frequency

range). Since input voltage (audio generator output) is held constant during frequency-response measurement, the voltage-gain curve is identical to a frequency-response curve. Simply divide the output voltage by the input voltage at any given frequency to find voltage gain at that frequency.

Power Output The power output of an audio component is found by noting the output voltage across the output impedance using the equation (output voltage)^2/output impedance. In the circuit of Fig. 1.21, use load resistance R1 as the output impedance.

While on the subject of loads, here are some points to consider during both test and troubleshooting. If you do not already know, *never* operate an amplifier without a load, especially a solid-state amplifier. This is an excellent way to burn out transistors.

The most accurate measurements are made using the load with which the amplifier is normally operated (loudspeakers, the input of another component, etc.). If you must use a substitute load for measurement, use only a noninductive (carbon or composition) resistance. Do not use a wirewound resistance. Although a wirewound resistance may not result in damage, the inductive reactance of a wirewound part can result in considerable measurement error.

Input Impedance Use the circuit of Fig. 1.22 to find the input impedance of an audio circuit or component (which is the first step in finding power gain). The test conditions should be identical to those for frequency response, power output, and so on. The same audio generator, operating load, meter or scope, and frequencies should be used.

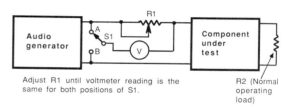

Adjust R1 until voltmeter reading is the same for both positions of S1.

R2 (Normal operating load)

Fig. 1.22. Basic test connections for input-impedance measurement.

Adjust the signal source (audio generator) to the frequency (or frequencies) at which the circuit is operated. Move switch S1 back and forth between position A and B, while adjusting resistance R1 until the voltage reading is the same in both positions of the switch.

Disconnect resistor R1 from the circuit, and measure the d-c resistance of R1 with an ohmmeter. The d-c resistance of R1 is equal to the dynamic impedance at the circuit or component input.

Keep in mind that the accuracy of the impedance measurement depends on the accuracy with which the d-c resistance is measured, not the voltmeter reading. Also, the impedance found by this method applies only to the frequency used during the test (in most solid-state audio amplifiers).

Input Sensitivity Many audio component specifications include input sensitivity, in place of power gain. Input sensitivity is based on the fact that the component or circuit must produce a given power output across a given load, with a given input voltage, all of which are easy to measure (compared to input impedance and power gain). A typical input sensitivity specification might be 50-W output with 500-mV input.

The connections for input sensitivity are the same as for frequency response (Fig. 1.21). There are two approaches to input sensitivity measurement.

With one approach, you increase the input voltage until the desired output power is obtained, and then measure the actual input voltage. For example, increase the input voltage until the output power is 50 W. Then check to make sure that the input voltage is 500 mV, or less. The other approach is to set the input to 500 mV, and check to make sure that the output power is 50 W, or more.

Load Sensitivity As you probably know, an amplifier produces maximum power when the output impedance of the amplifier circuit is the same as the load impedance.

Likewise, an audio circuit is sensitive to changes in load impedance (since the output impedance does not change). This is especially true of audio power amps, but can also be the case with voltage amps.

Figure 1.23 shows the load sensitivity of a typical audio component. With a ratio of 1.0 (load impedance same as output impedance), the output is maximum, or 100%. With the load impedance at twice the output impedance (ratio of 2.0), the output power is reduced to about 50% of maximum. (This is why you should not connect 8-Ω speakers to a 4-Ω output.) On the other hand, if the load impedance is 50% of the output impedance (ratio of 0.5), the output power is reduced to about 25%. (This is why you should not connect 4-Ω speakers to an 8-Ω output!)

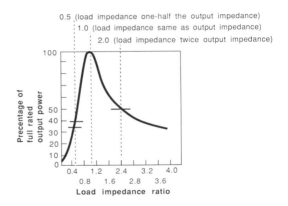

Fig. 1.23. **Load sensitivity curve of a typical audio component.**

The circuit for load-sensitivity measurement is the same as for frequency response (Fig. 1.21), except that load resistance R1 must be variable (and noninductive). If desired, you can make up a curve similar to that of Fig. 1.23 by measuring the power output at various load impedance/output impedance ratios, and at selected frequencies across the normal operating range of the component or circuit under test.

Output Impedance You can reverse the load-sensitivity test to find the actual output impedance of an audio circuit or component. The connections (Fig. 1.21) and procedure are the same, except that you vary load resistance R1 until you get maximum output power. Then *turn off the amplifier,* disconnect R1 from the circuit, and measure the d-c resistance of R1. The d-c resistance of R1 is equal to the dynamic impedance at the circuit or component output.

Again, the accuracy of the impedance measurement depends on the accuracy with which the d-c resistance is measured. Likewise, the impedance found by this method applies only to the frequency used during the test.

Power Bandwidth Some audio component specifications include a power-bandwidth factor. Such specifications require that the component deliver a given power output across a given frequency range. Generally, the power-bandwidth output is much lower than the frequency response. This is shown in Fig. 1.24 where the component produces full power output only up to 20 kHz, even though the frequency response is flat up to 100 kHz. That is, voltage (without a load) remains constant up to 100 kHz, while voltage (across a normal load, to indicate power output) remains constant up to 20 kHz.

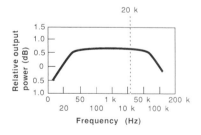

Fig. 1.24. Power-bandwidth curve of a typical audio component.

To find power bandwidth, make the power output test as described, over the frequency range given in the specifications (typically 20 Hz to 20 kHz). You can then compare this with a frequency response test, if desired.

1.4 TOOLS AND FIXTURES FOR AUDIO TROUBLESHOOTING

Most turntables, cassette decks, and CD players have special tools and fixtures recommended for field service. We describe such tools in the related chapters. Generally, tools are available from the audio component manufacturer. In some cases, complete tool kits are made available (at least to authorized factory service centers).

There are certain tools and fixtures used at the factory for both disassembly and service of the equipment. These factory tools are not available for field service (not even to factory service centers, in some cases). This is the manufacturer's subtle way of telling service technicians that they should not attempt any adjustments (electrical or mechanical) not recommended in the service instructions. The author strongly recommends that you take this subtle hint!

In addition to special tools, the mechanical sections of turntables, cassette decks, and CD players are disassembled, adjusted, and reassembled with common hand tools, such as wrenches and screwdrivers. Keep in mind that much audio equipment is manufactured to Japanese metric standards, and your tools must match. For example, you will need metric-sized Allen wrenches, and Phillips screwdrivers with the Japanese metric point.

1.5 CLEANING, LUBRICATION, AND GENERAL MAINTENANCE FOR AUDIO EQUIPMENT

There is considerable disagreement among audio equipment manufacturers concerning the need for periodic maintenance or routine checks. At one extreme, a certain manufacturer recommends replacement of a few parts after a given number of playing hours or playing times. For example, they recommend that the optical pickup of a CD player be replaced at 5000 hours of playing time, and that all motors in turntables and cassette decks be replaced after

10,000 plays. (Who counts?) At the other extreme, another manufacturer recommends no periodic replacement, cleaning, lubrication, or adjustment of any kind. "Fix it if it breaks down" is the rule. (It is fair to say that this rule will probably be observed religiously.)

Somewhere between these two extremes, other manufacturers recommend adjustment (electrical and/or mechanical) only as needed to put the equipment back in service, or when certain parts or assemblies have been replaced. However, most audio equipment manufacturers recommend a complete checkout, using the recommended test record, cassette tape, or CD disc, after any service.

The author has no recommendations in the areas of periodic maintenance except that you follow the manufacturer's recommendations. The author also realizes that the general public regards audio equipment in the same way it does TV and VCR equipment (that is, "take it in for service when it breaks down").

We describe some typical cleaning and lubrication of components in the related chapters. In addition, here are some general notes on cleaning and lubrication.

Cleaning the Outside of Components

Use a soft, clean cloth to wipe off dust and dirt accumulated on the *outside* of components. If necessary, moisten a soft cloth with diluted neutral detergent to remove heavy dirt. Never use paint thinner, benzene, or other solvents, since any of these solvents will react with the surface and cause color change (or worse).

Cleaning the Inside of Components

Never clean any part not recommended by the manufacturer. Although there are spray cans of cleaner (such as head cleaners for cassette decks), most manufacturers recommend alcohol and cleaning sticks or wands for all cleaning. Methyl alcohol does the best cleaning job, but can be a *health hazard.* Isopropyl alcohol is usually satisfactory for most cleaning. Keep in mind that both cleaning and lubrication are generally well covered in the service literature. (If only troubleshooting was so well covered!)

Lubrication of Mechanical Sections

Never lubricate any part not recommended by the manufacturer. Most turntables, cassette decks, and CD players use sealed bearings that do not require lubrication. A drop or two of oil in the wrong places can cause damage. Clean off any excess or spilled oil. In the absence of a specific recommendation, use a light machine oil such as sewing machine oil. In general, avoid spray lubricants—although they do a good job on most components that require lubrication they can also do a good job on parts that should never be lubricated!

CHAPTER 2

Troubleshooting and Repair of Amplifiers and Loudspeakers

This chapter is devoted to audio amplifiers and loudspeakers. Included here are such subjects as the general description of a typical audio amplifier and loudspeaker combination, user controls, operating procedures and installation of audio amplifier/loudspeakers, typical amplifier/loudspeaker circuit descriptions, typical test/adjustment procedures, and examples of troubleshooting based on symptoms.

2.1 GENERAL DESCRIPTION OF A TYPICAL AUDIO AMPLIFIER AND LOUDSPEAKER COMBINATION

Figures 2.1 through 2.5 show some typical audio amplifier/loudspeaker combinations.

The amplifier/loudspeaker combinations of Figs. 2.1 and 2.2 are used with an *integrated audio/video system,* including a video-monitor TV and remote control.

Fig. 2.3 shows a *complete audio system,* including an amplifier, turntable (Chapter 3), cassette deck (Chapter 4), AM/FM tuner (Chapter 5), and a CD player (Chapter 6).

Figure 2.4 shows a *single component* that includes an amplifier, turntable, cassette deck, and tuner.

Figure 2.5 shows a typical integrated amplifier as a single component.

Figure 2.6 shows a typical nonswitching stereo amplifier.

In this chapter, we consider only the nonsystem functions of a typical integrated amplifier/loudspeaker combination. Although there is no standardization, many amplifier/loudspeaker combinations are enhanced with the following features.

When the amplifier is used with a system, the signal inputs to the amplifier are selected automatically by the system remote control unit. For nonsystem configurations, the signal inputs are selected manually by means of front-panel push buttons. In the amplifier of Fig. 2.1, five push buttons select nonsystem program sources (phono, tuner, compact disc player, tape monitor, or auxiliary input).

Most modern amplifiers are provided

Fig. 2.1. RCA digital command component system.
(Courtesy RCA Corporation)

**Fig. 2.2. Quasar
model PAV5600 audio-
video system.**
(Courtesy Quasar
Company, Franklin
Park, Illinois)

Fig. 2.4. Beocenter R 2200S.
(Courtesy Bang & Olufsen)

Fig. 2.3. Sony F-V33(CD) audio system.
(Courtesy Sony Corporation of America)

with some form of *automatic output protection*. With such a feature, an accidental short circuit in the speakers or speaker leads does not damage the amplifier. The automatic protection circuit disconnects the speaker leads in the event of a short. The protection circuit usually resets automati-

cally when the amplifier is turned off (after a few seconds).

Many modern amplifiers have an *electronic volume control*. With the amplifier of Fig. 2.1, you press the up or down end of the volume control until the desired volume level is obtained. An 8-segment lighted display indicates the volume setting. The display functions when the volume is controlled remotely or manually, and shows the last volume setting before muting.

Some amplifiers have a *preset turn-on volume* feature where the volume is set to a

Fig. 2.5. Luxman model L-430 duo-beta/S dc integrated amplifier.
(Courtesy Luxman Division of Alpine Electronics of America, Inc.)

Fig. 2.6. Pioneer A-88X(BK) nonswitching stereo amplifier. (Courtesy Pioneer Electronics USA, Inc.)

preset level whenever the amplifier is turned on.

Many amplifiers have a *fluorescent display*. In the amplifier of Fig. 2.1, two 10-segment light bars constantly monitor the power output of each channel. The display also shows the program source, and flashes to indicate the automatic output protection circuit has been turned on.

Most amplifiers have some form of *muting* where the sound can be cut off without turning the volume down. This makes it possible to restore the sound to the exact level as before muting.

Virtually all amplifiers have some form of *bass, treble,* and *balance controls*. Slide-type controls are used in the amplifier of Fig. 2.1.

Many amplifiers have a *dynamic loudness compensation* circuit. This feature automatically boosts bass and treble response at low listening levels, and thus compensates for the fact that the human ear is not as sensitive to high and low frequencies when volume is low.

Most modern amplifiers include some form of *subsonic filter* to eliminate rumble. Warped records (and some malfunctioning turntables) cause rumble (very low frequency noise). The subsonic filter attenuates all signals with frequencies below about 20 Hz.

Many amplifiers have *convenience power receptacles* for components used with the amplifiers. Typically, the receptacles are unswitched (connected directly to

the power cord) and do not use the amplifier switch or fuse.

Some amplifiers can be used with *two sets of loudspeakers*, although this is not common. Most amplifiers can be used with *headphones* (connected to a front-panel headphone jack).

The following specifications are for a "typical" integrated stereo amplifier, and are included here for reference. Always check the service literature for the amplifier you are servicing. (There is no point in trying to get 50 watts per channel from a 25-watt amplifier!) The basic procedures for checking these specifications are described in Chapter 1.

Power output: 50 watts RMS per channel minimum, into 8-ohm loads which both channels drive, at frequencies from 20 Hz to 20 kHz, with no more than 0.05% total harmonic distortion (THD).

Harmonic distortion: Less than 0.05%, at frequencies from 20 Hz to 20 kHz, with power outputs from 250 mW to full rated output, load impedance 8 ohms.

Intermodulation distortion: Less than 0.09%, using frequencies of 60 Hz and 7 kHz, with power outputs from 250 mW to full rated output, load impedance 8 ohms.

Frequency response: 20 Hz to 20 kHz (± 1 dB).

Input sensitivity and impedance: 0.35 mV at 47 kΩ for phono, 21 mV at 47 kΩ for other inputs.

Output level from tape recorder jack: 280 mV.

Phono overload level: 150 mV (1 kHz).

S/N ratio: 75 dB (IHF, A network) for phono; 78 dB for other inputs.

Bass control: ±8 dB @ 100 Hz.

Treble control: ±8 dB @ 10 kHz.

Subsonic filter: 20 Hz cutoff frequency with a −6 dB per octave slope.

Power source: 120 V at 60 Hz.

Power consumption: 200 W when operated at ⅓ rated output.

The following specifications are for "typical" loudspeakers used with integrated stereo amplifiers. Again, always check the specifications for the equipment you are servicing.

Loudspeaker type: 2-way passive radiator system.

Speakers: two 4-inch woofers, one 4-inch passive radiator, one 2-inch tweeter.

Frequency range: 70 Hz to 20 kHz.

Nominal input power: 10 W.

Maximum input power: 20 W.

Impedance: 8 ohms.

Crossover frequency: 2 kHz.

Loudspeaker type: 3-way air suspension.

Speakers: 11-inch cone woofer, 4-inch mid-range, 1-inch dome tweeter.

Frequency range: 30 Hz to 20 kHz.

Nominal input power: 60 W.

Maximum input power: 120 W.

Impedance: 8 ohms.

Sound pressure level (SPL): 91 dB/W (1.0 m).

2.2 USER CONTROLS, OPERATING PROCEDURES, AND INSTALLATION

Although audio amplifiers and loudspeakers are not usually difficult to operate or install, the basic procedures may be a mystery to those totally unfamiliar with audio/stereo equipment. This section describes the basic user controls and operating procedures for a typical amplifier/loudspeaker combination. We also discuss typical installation procedures and precautions.

Keep in mind that you must study the operating controls and indicators for any amplifier/loudspeaker combination you are troubleshooting. This section describes "typical" controls and indicators, but there are subtle differences in operation you must consider. There is nothing more frustrating than troubleshooting a failure symptom when the equipment is supposed to work that way!

2.2.1 Operating Controls and Functions

Figure 2.7 shows the operating controls and indicators for a typical integrated amplifier. Compare the following sequence with the controls and indicators of the amplifier you are servicing.

To turn the amplifier on, press the

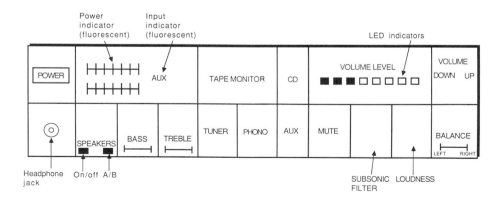

Fig. 2.7. Operating controls and indicators for a typical integrated amplifier.

POWER button. Push the POWER button again to turn the amplifier off. None of the other controls function when power is off. However, if the amplifier is used with a system, the control system usually remains active. When another system component using the amplifier is turned on, the amplifier turns on automatically (on most systems). In non-system configurations, the tape deck, CD player, turntable, or tuner/receiver must be turned on separately.

In the amplifier of Fig. 2.7, when turned on with the front-panel POWER button, the amplifier automatically switches to the input of the last device before the amplifier was turned off. This function is provided by a system-control microprocessor (discussed in Sec. 2.3).

Two rows of a 10-segment *power indicator* turn on to show the approximate power output from each channel. An *input indicator* next to the power indicator shows which input (phono, tape deck, tuner, CD player) is selected.

In manual (nonsystem) configurations, *input to the amplifier is selected* by pressing the appropriate input button (TAPE MONITOR, CD, TUNER, PHONO, AUX). The input indicator should turn on to indicate the input selected. When the amplifier is used in a system, the input is selected by remote control.

To set the volume up or down, press the UP or DOWN ends of the *volume* control rocker. The *volume level* indicator should turn on to show the relative volume (by means of an eight-segment row of lights). The eight segments turn on, from left to right, when volume is increased, as shown in Fig. 2.8.

Note that when the amplifier is muted, only one of the lights remains on. This light indicates the volume existing at the time

muting is selected, and the volume to which the amplifier will be restored when muting is removed.

In this particular amplifier, the volume setting may be decreased while the amplifier is muted (so that the amplifier can be restored at a lower level). However, increasing the volume setting during mute immediately cancels muting.

To mute the audio, press the MUTE button. This reduces the volume to minimum. Press the MUTE button again to restore the volume to the previous level.

To equalize the volume of the stereo channels, move the *balance* control *left* or *right* as necessary. When in doubt, or as an initial setting, set BALANCE to the *midpoint.*

To select the loudness function, press the LOUDNESS button. Press the LOUDNESS button again to remove or disable the loudness function. Keep in mind that the loudness compensation circuit boosts both bass and treble for low-volume listening. (Actually, as discussed in Sec. 2.3, the loudness circuit attenuates the midrange signals so that the high and low signals appear to be boosted.)

To select the low-frequency antirumble function, press the SUBSONIC FILTER button. Press the SUBSONIC FILTER button again to remove the antirumble function. Keep in mind that the *subsonic filter* is used primarily to offset problems caused by warped records. If the *subsonic filter* must be used for all records, there is probably trouble in the turntable (possibly in the platter motor drive, Chapter 3).

To increase treble response, move the *treble* control to the right. Move the *treble* control left to decrease treble response.

To increase bass response, move the *bass* control to the right. Move the *bass* control left to decrease bass response.

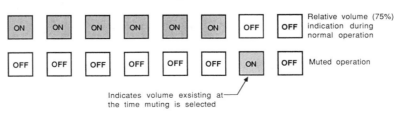

Relative volume (75%) indication during normal operation

Muted operation

Indicates volume exsisting at the time muting is selected

Fig. 2.8. Volume level indicator lights.

To select speaker operation, first set the *speakers* (A/B) control to A or B. (If only one set of speakers is used, make certain to select the correct set!) Then set the *speakers (on/off)* control to ON. Note that the *headphone jack* is connected to the amplifier output, no matter what loudspeaker configuration is used. Also, if no headphones are used, a load resistance is connected across the amplifier output. This is not always true for all amplifiers. As a general precaution, make certain that loudspeakers and/or headphones are connected to any amplifier, before turning on the power. *Solid-state amplifiers should never be operated without a load.*

To select headphone operation, insert headphones into the headphone jack. On the amplifier of Fig. 2.7, using the telephones does not turn off the speakers. However, the speakers may be turned off without affecting the headphones. This configuration is not always true for all amplifiers, so always check before you troubleshoot the circuits to solve a "no audio" trouble symptom.

To select record operation, simply connect the record output of the amplifier to the tape deck, as described in Sec. 2.2.2.

Whatever audio is heard on the loudspeakers and/or headphones is available at the record output. If you do not want to hear what is being recorded, turn the volume down, or select the mute function.

Note that this record configuration is not always true for all amplifiers. On some amplifiers, you must operate a RECORD button or switch. Also, on a few amplifiers, the volume control also affects the record level. Further, on some amplifiers, it is necessary to set a separate record level control.

2.2.2 External Connections

Figure 2.9 shows external connections for a typical integrated amplifier. Before connecting the loudspeakers, be sure to observe the precautions described in Sec. 2.2.3.

For power connections, it is usually more convenient to use the receptacles on the back of the amplifier for the other components. Make sure not to exceed the wattage rating for these receptacles (300 W in the case of the Fig. 2.9 amplifier). If the total wattage exceeds the limit, connect one or more components directly.

Standard audio cables can be used for

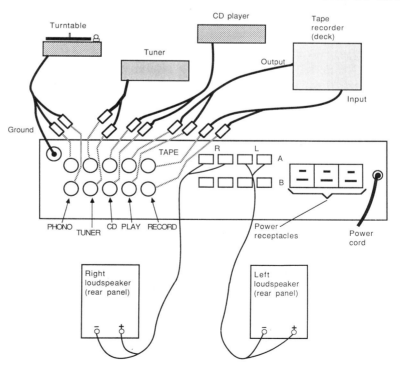

Fig. 2.9. External connections for a typical integrated amplifier.

signal connections to the stereo amplifier input jacks. Most audio components have similar jacks, but if one of the components is different, adapters or special cables may be needed. Stereo cable pairs that have the left and right connectors marked (or color coded) are more convenient than two single-channel cables.

The *phono* input is a low-level input, suitable for turntables that use a magnetic cartridge. If the turntable has a ground wire, attach the wire to the ground terminal as shown (and as discussed in Chapter 3).

The *tuner* input is a high-level input designed for an AM/FM tuner output. However, the *tuner* input can be used for some other components.

The CD input is a high-level input designed for a CD player output. However, the CD input can be used for some other components.

Note that on the amplifier of Fig. 2.9, the *tuner* and CD inputs have the same impedance, and could be interchanged. However, this is not usually the case. As described in Chapter 6, always use the CD input for a CD player. In any event, never connect a CD player to the *phono* input. This will overdrive the amplifier, and could damage the circuits.

The *tape play* input is a high-level input designed for a tape deck output. However, the *tape play* input can be used for some other components.

The *tape record* output is designed for use with a tape deck, and produces a signal level (280 mV) suitable to record on most decks. Note that the output from the *tape record* jacks depends on which input (*phono, tuner,* or CD) is selected.

2.2.3 Loudspeaker Connections

The following notes apply to the amplifier of Fig. 2.9. However, the information here can be applied when troubleshooting or repairing most amplifier/loudspeaker combinations.

It is generally best to *use the speakers designed for a particular amplifier.* This ensures a proper match of impedance, power handling capability, etc. However, using other loudspeakers does not always mean a mismatch. If you are troubleshooting an existing system, it is reasonable to assume that the system was once satisfactory (the speakers match the amplifier, and are properly connected). It is reasonable to assume this, but do not count on it.

As a general rule, the *maximum input power for a speaker is twice the nominal input power* (but always check the speaker specifications). Keep in mind that you may be able to get by with speakers of lower power-handling capability when an amplifier is operated at low volume. However, the same speakers can be damaged if the amplifier is accidentally operated at full power.

Always try to match amplifier and speaker impedances. In some cases, separate terminals are provided for different impedances. In other cases, the amplifiers can be operated with speakers of different impedances, *over a limited range.* For example, the amplifier of Fig. 2.9 can be used with speaker impedances of 6 to 16 ohms without damage or deterioration in sound. (Of course, an extreme mismatch reduces power output.)

Do not connect more than one speaker to any pair of speaker terminals. (The term speaker refers to a loudspeaker unit or enclosure that may contain one or more individual speakers, such as a woofer and a tweeter.)

Never connect or disconnect speakers when the amplifier is turned on.

Be careful to observe *polarity of the speaker leads,* as well as *left/right positioning.* No damage will result from reversed polarity, but the sound will be weird! If speakers are not connected in phase (as shown in Fig. 2.9) stereo sound has a diffused and directionless quality, and the spatial effects are lost.

If the amplifier is used with an FM/AM tuner, play a monaural source (typical AM broadcast). If the speakers are connected in phase, the sound should seem to come from a *point between the speakers* (assuming the stereo balance control is approximately at the center position). If the speakers are out of phase, the sound seems to come from a diffused source, rather than from a single point.

To correct an out-of-phase condition, make sure to reverse the connections at *only one speaker.* Many speaker wires or leads are color coded (typically red for plus and black for minus, or one wire with a stripe).

Watch out for stranded wire when working with speakers. Most speaker wire is stranded. Twist the bare ends tightly so free strands of wire cannot cause a short to adjacent terminals. Stray wire strands also find their way into finger tips or, even worse, under finger nails! Strip just enough insulation from speaker wires to allow the bare wires to seat firmly on the terminals. Note that both screw-type terminals, and plug-in terminals, are found on modern amplifier/speaker combinations.

Always use a good quality speaker wire. As a guide, do not use any wire smaller than No. 18 AWG for runs less than 30 feet, or smaller than No. 16 AWG for runs longer than 30 feet. Try to avoid long runs if possible.

Some speakers have adjustment controls, particularly to adjust the high-frequency and/or midrange levels. *Always check the setting of these controls before* you start troubleshooting any speaker problem.

Always check speaker placement when troubleshooting a speaker problem (such as a "my neighbor's stereo works better than mine" symptom!). Here are some general points to check.

You get the *best stereo sound when the speakers are upright* with the manufacturer's logo at the top, and when the cabinets are positioned so that *the tweeters are inside.* (In many cases, speakers are marked L and R.)

If speakers must be placed on their sides, position the speakers so that *the*

tweeters are toward the center of the listening area.

Place the speakers an *equal distance from each side of the sound source* (turntable, cassette deck, CD player). This is particularly true in system configurations where a video monitor is involved (it helps to center the picture in the field of sound).

Place the speakers so that the tweeters are as close as possible to the *ear level of a seated viewer/listener.* In most (but not all) cases, the tweeter is located near the top of the speaker enclosure.

If you place the speakers in corners, or with one side against a wall, you will get the strongest (but not necessarily the most accurate) bass response. If the speaker is adjustable, it may be necessary to correct this condition (lower the bass, or increase the treble).

Always keep in mind that overall sound performance of any speaker system is influenced by *variations in the speaker placement, and the acoustical qualities of the room* (even though your customer will not believe it!). That is another reason for having a set of known-good speakers in the shop.

Try to keep each speaker at the same height, or at least at the same distance from the floor, walls, furniture, etc. Unfortunately, there are some rooms where it is almost impossible to produce a good stereo sound, even though monophonic sound is no problem.

2.3 TYPICAL AMPLIFIER AND LOUDSPEAKER CIRCUIT DESCRIPTIONS

This section describes the theory of operation for a number of amplifier/loudspeaker circuits. By studying the circuits found here, you should have no difficulty in understanding the schematic and block diagram of similar amplifier/loudspeakers. This understanding is essential for logical troublelshooting and repair. No attempt has been made to duplicate the full schematics for all circuits. Such schematics are found in the service literature for audio equipment.

Instead of full schematics, the circuit descriptions are supplemented with partial schematics and block diagrams that show such important areas as signal flow paths, input/output, adjustment controls, test points, and power-source connections. These are the areas most important in troubleshooting. By reducing the schematics to these areas, you will find the circuit easier to understand, and you will be able to relate circuit operation to the corresponding circuit of the audio amplifier/loudspeaker you are troubleshooting.

2.3.1 System-Control Circuits

Figure 2.10 is the block diagram of a typical stereo amplifier. Virtually all of the amplifier functions and circuits are under control of system-control microprocessor IC01. As shown, IC01 receives the various input commands from the front-panel key-board matrix, and drives the volume-level display, D5–D12, and the function-display portion of the fluorescent display, FL1. IC01 also controls device input select IC2, volume control IC4, and relay drivers Q71/Q74.

Audio inputs are applied to the amplifier circuits through device input select IC2. Note that the phono input is applied through equalization amp IC7. The extra amplification is required since the output of the turntable is substantially less than from the CD player, tuner, or cassette deck.

IC2 selects the desired audio input source in response to signals from IC01. The selected audio input is applied to buffer amplifiers IC3 through IC2. The outputs of IC3 drive volume control IC4 which receives control signals from IC01.

The output of IC4 is applied to power amplifier IC8 through buffer and tone amplifiers IC5/IC6. B+ power to IC8 is controlled by relay RY2. In turn, RY2 is controlled by IC01 through relay drivers Q71/Q72. The

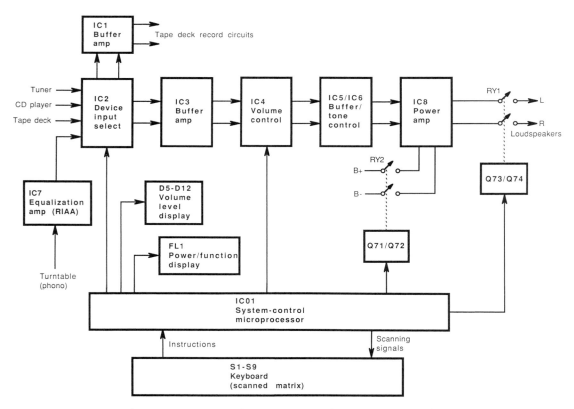

Fig. 2.10. Block diagram for typical stereo amplifier.

output of IC8 is applied to the L and R loudspeakers through relay RY1. In turn, RY1 is controlled by IC01 through relay drivers Q73/Q74.

All of these functions are selected through the front-panel buttons or switches, S1–S9. In many cases, the switches are connected to form a *scanned matrix* (often called the keyboard). In the amplifier of Fig. 2.10, IC01 provides constant scanning signals to the keyboard or switching matrix. In turn, IC01 receives signals from the keyboard to indicate the desired audio input source, and the desired audio level (volume).

2.3.2 Keyboard and Display Circuits

Figure 2.11 shows the keyboard and display circuits. As shown, the front-panel *power, volume up, volume down, mute, phono, tuner, aux, CD,* and *tape monitor* buttons are connected in a key matrix configuration. The key matrix consists of two

scan lines and six data input lines, all interconnected to the system-control microprocessor IC01.

IC01 supplies scanning pulses to the scan-A and scan-B lines from pins 15 and 16, respectively. The front-panel button switches are connected to input lines 0 through 4, pins 24 through 20 of IC01, as shown by the table in Fig. 2.11.

Pressing a front-panel button closes the corresponding momentary switch that is connected between the appropriate scan and input line. IC01 detects the button pressed (switch closure), and performs the appropriate display operation (in addition to producing the corresponding function). For example, when the CD button is pressed, the scan-A signal is applied to input-2. This causes IC01 to select the audio input from the CD player terminal, and produces a CD function indication on the front-panel fluorescent display, FL1 through IC02.

The amplifier of Fig. 2.11 front panel

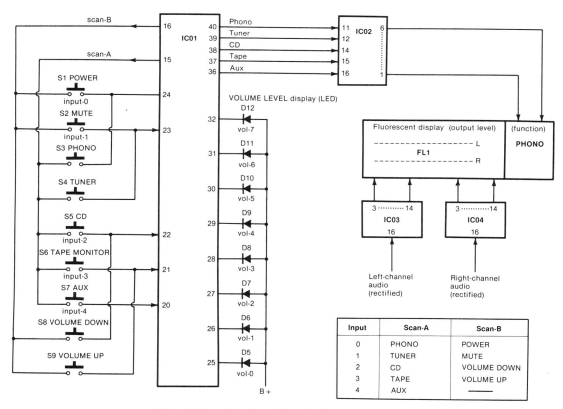

Fig. 2.11. Keyboard and display circuits.

has two display indicators: the *volume level* display consisting of an 8-LED bar display D5 through D12, and fluorescent display FL1. In turn, the fluorescent display is divided into two sections containing the *function display* and the L/R channel output level indicators.

The *volume level* display, D5 through D12, is directly controlled by eight lines from IC01. These lines consist of volume-0 to volume-7. At minimum volume, the *volume level* display is not turned on. Pressing the front-panel VOLUME UP button causes IC01 to issue the volume-0 signal at pin 25. This turns on the LED at the left end of the display.

Continuously pressing the VOLUME UP button causes IC01 to issue the volume-1 through volume-7 signals, pins 26 through 32, sequentially turning on the LED segments left to right. As volume is increased, and the next segment turns on, the previous segments remain on. Pressing the MUTE button causes the segment that is on (furthest to the right) to remain on, and all other segments to turn off. This indicates to the user where the volume level is set when muting is cancelled

The function display section of FL1 is driven by function drive IC02 at pins 1 through 6. IC01 supplies control information to IC02 as shown. Pressing a device-select button directs IC01 to issue the appropriate function control signal. For example, pressing the PHONO button causes the phono signal to appear at pin 40 of IC01. This phono signal is applied to IC02, and causes the *phono* display to appear at the right-hand side of FL1.

The L and R channel audio output level indicators of FL1 are driven by level indicator drivers IC03 and IC04. A portion of both the left and right audio outputs are rectified, and the positive portion of the audio is applied to IC03/IC04 at pin 16. IC03 and IC04 contain nine level detectors, each with its own output. As the audio output level to IC03/IC04 increases, the audio output level indicators of FL1 are turned on, in se-

quence, by the signals at pins 3 through 14 of IC03/IC04.

2.3.3 Power-Loss Protection Circuits

Figure 2.12 shows the power-loss protection circuits. The amplifier of Fig. 2.12 has a circuit that provides both long-term and short-term a-c power-loss protection. After a short-term power loss (less than 2 seconds), the amplifier returns to normal operation when power is reapplied. If an a-c power loss is longer than 2 seconds, the amplifier remains off when power is reapplied.

With a-c power applied, and the B− power supply of −14 V operating, a high is applied to D13, and about 0.7 V is applied to the base of Q01. The 0.7 V is developed by a combination of the −14 V, and about −16 V produced by D82 (which rectifies a-c from the power transformer). The 0.7 V at the base of Q01 turns Q01 on, and applies a low to pin 17 of IC01. This low is also applied to the base of Q02 through D14. The low keeps Q02 off, and pin 3 of IC01 high, during normal operation.

When the front-panel POWER button is pressed, pins 3 and 17 of IC01 will be high and low, respectively, if a-c power is present. Under these conditions, pin 34 of IC01 goes low. This low is inverted to a high by Q71, causing Q72 to turn on, and RY2 to be actuated. With RY2 actuated, power is applied to power amplifier IC8.

Approximately 4 seconds after pin 34 goes low, pin 33 goes low. This low is inverted to a high by Q73, causing Q74 to turn on, and RY1 to be actuated. With RY1 actuated, the output of power amplifier IC8 is connected to the loudspeakers.

D82, R83, R84, and C81 form a 16-V d-c supply. When a-c power is removed, the +16-V supply decays much more rapidly than the +5-V or −14-V supplies. (This is because C81 discharges rapidly through R84, while the +5-V and −14-V supply capacitors discharge slowly.)

The rapid decay of the +16-V supply reverse biases D13, and turns Q01 off. With

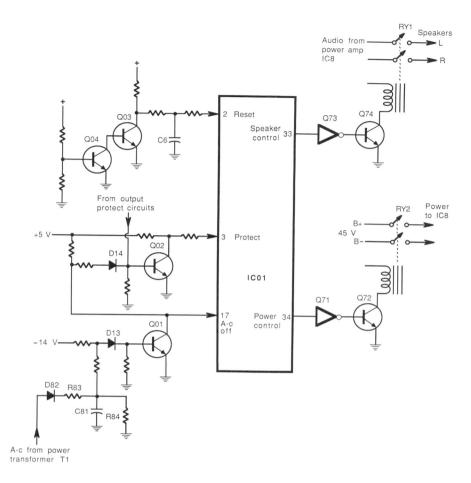

Fig. 2.12. Power-loss protection circuits.

QO1 off, pin 17 of ICO1 goes high, while pin 3 of ICO1 goes low. Under these conditions, pins 33 and 34 of ICO1 go high, opening relays RY1 and RY2. With both RY1 and RY2 open, the output of power amplifier IC8 is disconnected from the speakers, and power is removed from IC8.

If a-c power is reapplied in less than two seconds (before the +5-V and −14-V power-supply capacitors discharge), a high is reapplied to pin 3 of ICO1, as well as a low to pin 17 of ICO1. Under these conditions, both pins 33 and 34 of ICO1 are made low, and the relays are energized to reapply power and reconnect IC8 to the loudspeakers.

If a-c power is reapplied after the 2-second limit (after the +5-V and −14-V supply capacitors have discharged), system-control microprocessor ICO1 is reset by discharge in the reset circuits.

With power applied, both QO4 and QO3

are turned on, and C6 is discharged. This keeps pin 2 of ICO1 high. When power is removed and C6 discharges, pin 2 of ICO1 goes low (the reset condition), and all circuits within ICO1 are reset. ICO1 remains in this power-standby condition, as long as the power cord is connected.

2.3.4 Audio Input Select Circuits

Figure 2.13 shows the input select circuits (only the left channel is shown). As discussed in Sec. 2.1, the amplifier can be used with various audio sources including a turntable, cassette deck, tuner, CD player, and auxiliary source. The amplifier also provides for connecting these audio sources to the input of a cassette deck for tape recording.

All of these functions are controlled by input select IC2 under direction of system-control microprocessor ICO1. Commands from the front-panel switches are applied to

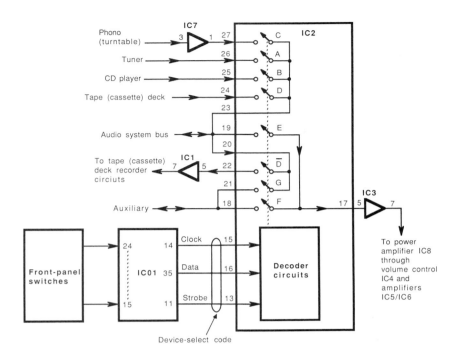

Fig. 2.13. Input select circuits.

ICO1 which generates a *device-select code* that is applied to IC2. The code includes clock, data, and strobe information at pins 15, 16, and 13 of IC2, respectively. The code is applied to decoder circuits within IC2, and causes corresponding IC2 switches to open or close.

Figure 2.14 shows a typical device-select code. IC2 receives 14 bits of serial data from ICO1. The 14 bits are transmitted at the clock rate (4 MHz), or 1-bit per clock pulse. Once the 14 bits have been transmitted, the strobe signal is transmitted and instructs

IC2 to perform the selection (close the appropriate switches).

The first 8 data bits of the code are for input switch selection. Bits 9, 10, and 11 are for channel select, while bits 12, 13, and 14 are for IC select.

As an example, if the phono (or turntable) audio is to be amplified and distributed to both channels, as well as to the input of the cassette deck for tape recording, the front-panel PHONO button is pressed. This causes bits 1, 5, 7, 9, 11, and 13 to be selected (data line goes high at those clock in-

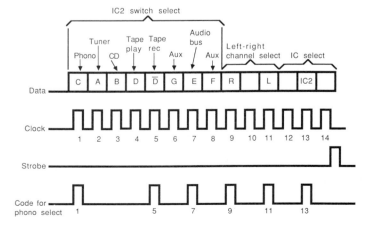

Fig. 2.14. Typical device-select code.

tervals or bits), and the corresponding IC2 switches are closed.

The phono or turntable input is amplified by IC7 (which also provides RIAA equalization). The audio at pin 27 of IC2 is distributed to pin 5 of buffer amp IC3 through switches C and E, and pins 23, 19, and 17 of IC2. The audio is also available to the cassette deck input through switch $\overline{D}$ and pins 20/21.

The amplified audio output of IC3 is applied to the power amplifier IC8 through volume control IC4, and amplifiers IC5/IC6.

2.3.5 Volume Control Circuits

Figure 2.15 shows the volume control circuits. The amplifier volume up, volume down, muting, and loudness functions are controlled by an electronic volume control or attenuator IC4. Volume is adjustable in 40 steps, including muting. Volume control IC4 is under control of system-control microprocessor IC01.

Commands from the front-panel *loudness, volume down, volume up,* and *mute* switches are applied to IC01 which generates a *volume-control code* supplied to IC4.

The code includes clock, data, and strobe information at pins 10, 11, and 12 of IC4, respectively. The code is applied to decoder circuits within IC4, and causes IC4 switches and attenuators to be selected.

Figure 2.16 shows a typical volume-control code. IC4 receives 20 bits of serial data from IC01. The 20 bits are transmitted at the clock rate (4 MHz) or 1 bit per clock pulse. Once the 20 bits have been transmitted, the strobe signal is transmitted and instructs IC4 to produce the correct amount of attenuation.

Data bits 1 and 2 are for the left and right channel selection. Bit 3 is for loudness on/off. Bits 4 through 8 are for 2-dB attenuation steps, with bit 4 for 0 dB and bit 8 for -8 dB. Bits 9 through 15 are for 10-dB attenuation steps, with bit 9 for 0 dB and bit 16 for -70 dB. Bits 17 through 20 are for an IC select code. (To select IC4, bits 17, 18, and 19 are low, with bit 20 high.)

As an example, assume that the volume is already at -10 dB, without the loudness function, and it is desired to turn the loudness function on, with a volume of -8 dB. The LOUDNESS button, S10, is pressed (once),

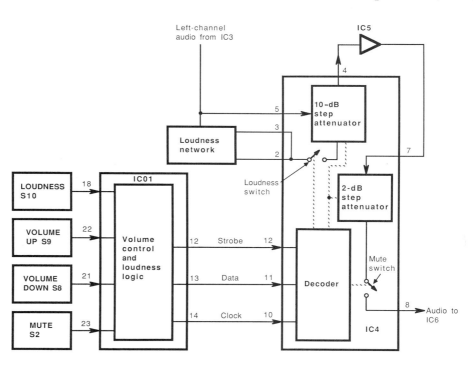

Fig. 2.15. Volume control circuits.

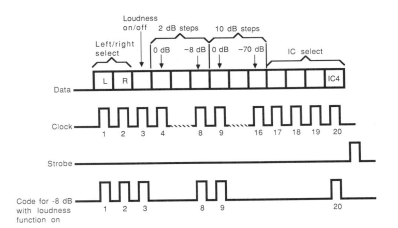

Fig. 2.16. Typical
volume-control code.

and the VOLUME UP button, S9, is held until the desired −8 dB is obtained. Under these conditions, bits 1, 2, 3, 8, 9, and 20 are selected (data line high).

As discussed in Sec. 2.3.4, the selected audio from IC3 is applied to the 10-dB attenuators of IC4 through pin 5. The output of the 10-dB attenuators is applied to the 2-dB attenuators through buffer IC5. The output of the 2-dB attenuators is applied to audio tone amplifier IC6 through the mute switch in IC4.

The 10-dB attenuator in IC4 has 8 steps, 0 dB to −70 dB, while the 2-dB attenuator has 6 steps, 0 dB to −8 dB. With the volume control setting at minimum volume (−78 dB attenuation), continuously pressing (or holding) the VOLUME UP button causes the 2-dB attenuator to step up from −8 dB to 0 dB, in 2-dB steps.

Once the 2-dB attenuator reaches 0 dB, the attenuator resets to −8 dB. At the same time, the 10-dB attenuator switches to −68 dB. This results in a 2-dB step, from −70 dB to −68 dB.

At low-volume settings, pressing the LOUDNESS button causes the loudness switch within IC4 to close, connecting a loudness network between pins 2, 3, and 5 of IC4. The circuit at pins 2 and 3 of IC4 is a Fletcher-Munson network that attenuates the mid-range audio frequencies, and passes the base/treble frequencies. This has the effect of supplying (or reinforcing) positive feed-

back to the audio at pin 5 of IC4 (at high and low frequencies).

Pressing the MUTE button opens the mute switch in IC4 to interrupt the audio. However, this does not affect the attenuators. When the MUTE button is pressed again, the audio is restored at the same level of attenuation (unless the attenuation is changed during mute).

2.3.6 Audio Output Circuits

Figure 2.17 shows the audio output circuits. The audio output power amplifiers for both channels are contained within one hybrid integrated circuit, IC8. The single IC provides for high reliability and less complex servicing. Because of the larger power rating of 50 W (RMS minimum), the IC is mounted on a heat sink.

The tone amplifiers that provide for treble and bass adjustment are also contained within a single integrated circuit, IC6. Both left and right channels use a subsonic filter consisting essentially of capacitor C18 and *subsonic filter* switch S11. The subsonic filter attenuates frequencies below 20 Hz to reduce rumble caused by warped records or defective turntables. The audio output is monitored by protection circuits, under the control of IC01, as described in Sec. 2.3.7.

Right-channel audio from volume control IC4 is applied to the noninverting input of op-amp IC6, which functions as a tone

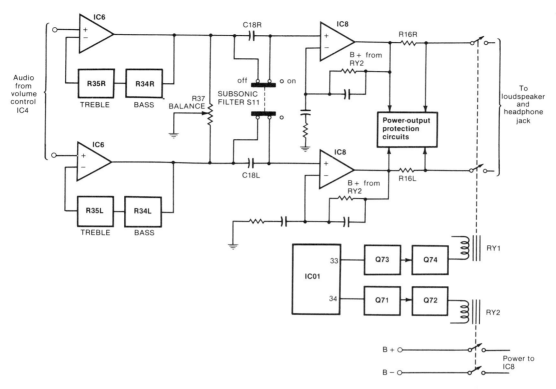

Fig. 2.17. Audio output circuits.

amplifier. Bass control R34R and treble control R35R are connected between the output and inverting input of IC6, to provide negative feedback. Decreasing the bass or treble negative feedback has the effect of boosting the bass or treble, and vice versa.

The output of tone amplifier IC6 is coupled to the balance control and subsonic filter. Balance control R37 is connected between the right and left channel audio, with the wiper connected to ground. Moving the wiper up reduces the right-channel impedance, while increasing the left-channel impedance. R37 is usually set to provide equal audio-signal levels in both channels.

With *subsonic filter* switch S11 in the OFF position, C18 is out of the circuit, and there is essentially no attenuation of low frequencies. With S11 in the ON position, C18 acts as a high-pass filter, attenuating all frequencies below 20 Hz. The output of the subsonic filter is applied to the noninverting input of power amplifier IC8.

An RC network is connected between

the output of IC8 and the inverting input of IC8. This RC network is used to prevent oscillation. The audio output from IC8 is routed through R16R which acts as the sensing resistor for the protection circuits (described in Sec. 2.3.7). The audio from R16R is applied to the speaker terminals and headphone jack as described in Sec. 2.3.1.

2.3.7 Power-Output Protection Circuits

Figure 2.18 shows the power-output protection circuits. The amplifier has three protection circuits used to prevent amplifier and loudspeaker damage or failure.

The *overload protection* circuit prevents damage to power amplifier IC8 when a low-impedance or shorted speaker is connected. The *midpoint potential protection* circuit is used to prevent damage to the loudspeaker in case of a defective IC8, and is turned on when a d-c potential (sometimes called *d-c*

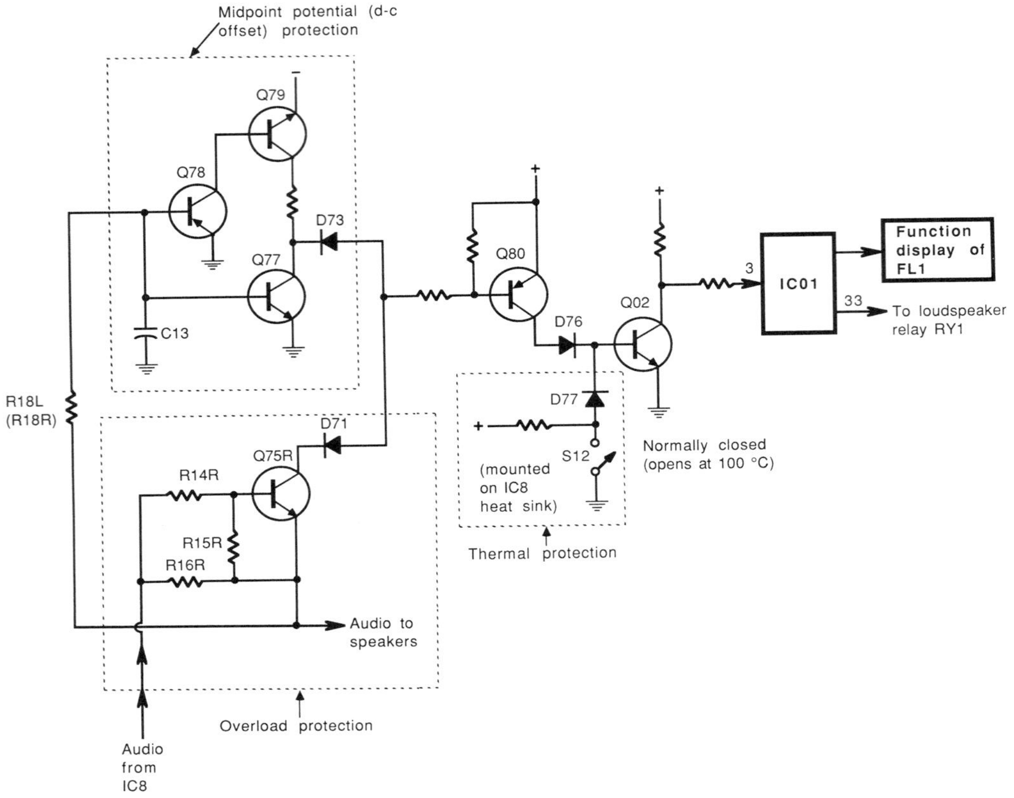

Fig. 2.18. Power-output protection circuits.

offset) is present at the output of IC8. The *thermal protection* circuit prevents damage to IC8 caused by excessive heat.

These three protection circuits are coupled to pin 3 of system-control microprocessor IC01. When any one of the circuits is turned on, pin 3 of IC01 goes low. IC01 recognizes this as a possible danger condition, and produces a high at pin 33. The high is applied to the loudspeaker relay RY1 through Q73/Q74, and causes the RY1 contacts to open, disconnecting the speakers from the IC8 output. IC01 also pulses the function display FL1 through driver IC02. The function display flashes, indicating to the user that the protection circuits are turned on.

Thermal protection switch S12 is mounted on the power amplifier IC8 heat sink, and is normally closed. This keeps D77 reverse biased, and Q02 off. With Q02 not conducting, pin 3 of IC01 is high, and

pin 33 of IC01 remains low to keep the speakers connected to the IC3 output.

If the temperature of the IC8 heat sink rises to 100 °C, S12 opens, forward biasing D77. This turns Q02 on, and produces a low at pin 3 of IC01. Under these conditions, pin 33 of IC01 goes high to disconnect the speakers from IC8. Simultaneously, pins 34 through 40 of IC01 are pulsed to flash the function display portion of FL1.

The *midpoint potential protection* circuit functions by monitoring the d-c output from IC8. In theory, there should be no d-c output from IC8 to the loudspeakers. (Excessive d-c current can damage the loudspeaker coils.) However, as a practical matter, there may be as much as ±1.7 V at the IC8 output without damage to the speaker. The midpoint potential protection circuit (called the d-c offset protection circuit on some amplifiers) is turned on if the 1.7 V value is exceeded.

If there is any d-c output from IC8 to the speakers, this potential causes C13 to charge through R18L and R18R. C13 charges to the *average value*. During normal operation, with the d-c output from IC8 less than ±1.7 V, the midpoint protection circuit is turned off.

If the average charge across C13 increases above +1.7 V, Q77 is turned on, forward biasing D73. This applies a low to the base of Q80, turning Q80 on, and forward biasing D76. This applies a high to the base of Q02, turning Q02 on, and causes pin 3 of IC01 to go low. IC01 then produces a high at pin 33 to disconnect the speakers (and to pulse the FL1 function display) as described earlier.

The overload protection circuit is the same for both channels, so only the right channel is covered here. Audio output from IC8 to the loudspeakers is applied through R16R, a 0.22-ohm resistor. This resistance is much smaller than the speaker load impedance (typically 6 to 16 ohms). During normal operation, the voltage across R16R is very small. If a shorted or very low-impedance speaker is connected, excessive output current flows through R16R, and the voltage across R16R increases sharply.

Resistors R14R and R15R are connected as a voltage divider across R16R to the base of Q75R. As the current through R16R increases (due to a short or low-impedance load), the voltage applied to Q75R increases, turning Q75R on. This forward-biases D71, turns on Q80, forward biases D76, turns on Q02, and applies a low to pin 3 of IC01 to disconnect the speakers and pulse the FL1 display.

2.4 TYPICAL TEST/ADJUSTMENT PROCEDURES

This section describes complete adjustment/test procedures for a typical amplifier/loudspeaker combination. Each procedure is accompanied by diagrams that show the electrical locations for all adjustment controls and measurement points (test points,

or TP), as well as the waveforms or signals that should appear at the test points.

Keep in mind that the procedures described here are the only procedures recommended by the manufacturer for that particular amplifier/loudspeaker combination. Other manufacturers may recommend more or less adjustment. It is your job to use the correct procedure for each amplifier you are troubleshooting.

The test/adjustment sections of most modern audio equipment service literature are good, up to a point. That is, they give you the step-by-step procedures, and show you the physical location of the adjustment controls. Unfortunately, they do not tell you what you are doing when you make the test and/or adjustments. In effect, they give you the "how" and "where," but not the "what" and "why." We bridge this information gap by describing (in boring detail) the adjustment procedures for a typical piece of equipment, but using adjustment diagrams not found in any service literature.

Also remember that some disassembly and reassembly may be required to reach test and/or adjustment points. We do not include any disassembly/reassembly here for two reasons. First, such procedures are unique and can apply to only one model of amplifier/loudspeaker. More important, disassembly and reassembly (both electrical and mechanical) are areas where service literature is generally well written and illustrated. Just make sure that you observe all the notes, cautions, and warnings found in the disassembly/reassembly sections of the service literature.

2.4.1 Basic Test Procedure

Figure 2.19 is the basic test diagram. Note that there are no internal adjustment controls for the amplifier. This is typical for many modern integrated amplifiers. Also note that the basic test diagram is essentially the same as shown in Fig. 1.21, and the procedures are similar to those described in Sec. 1.3, so we do not duplicate the procedures here.

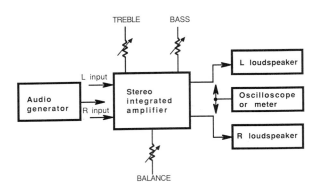

Fig. 2.19. Basic test diagram.

Generally, an integrated amplifier should be tested for proper frequency response, voltage gain, power output, input impedance, input sensitivity, load sensitivity, output impedance, distortion, and power bandwidth using the procedures of Sec. 1.3. Then the results should be checked against the specifications found in the service literature.

In addition to checking amplifier characteristics, the loudspeakers should also be checked. This brings up some problems. Although it is possible to test a loudspeaker for such characteristics as *sound pressure level* (SPL) under laboratory conditions, the most practical test is "by ear." Unfortunately, you and the customer have different ears, so the results are uncertain (at best).

To further complicate the speaker problem, some speakers are adjustable. For example, the speakers shown in Fig. 2.20 have volume pads in both the midrange and tweeters. Although these are not usually customer adjustment controls, they are often adjusted to some arbitrary setting to "match the customer's ear." From a test or troubleshooting standpoint, make sure that the speaker adjustments (if any) can control volume at the corresponding speaker, and that the controls are smooth (no abrupt changes in volume as the control is adjusted).

2.4.2 Universal Integrated Amplifier Tests

As a minimum, most integrated amplifiers have bass, treble, and balance controls. In the absence of specific test/adjustment procedures found in service literature, here are some points to consider when testing any integrated amplifier.

Operate the volume control for a midrange volume level, or as specified in the service literature.

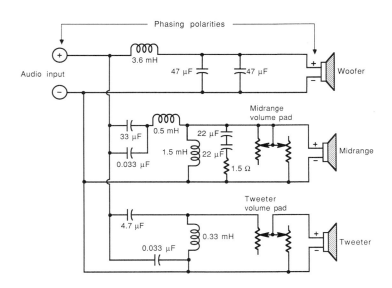

Fig. 2.20. Typical loudspeaker schematic.

Set the bass, treble, and balance controls to their midrange.

Apply a 1-kHz sine-wave signal to each of the various inputs (phono, tuner, CD, tape play, auxiliary, etc.).

Adjust the balance control until the outputs across the speakers (and/or tape record) are identical. If the amplifier has a front-panel level indicator (such as FL1 in Fig. 2.11), adjust the balance control until both channels show the same level indication.

If the balance control must be set far from midrange to get equal output (with an identical signal at both inputs), there is a severe mismatch condition. This can be the result of problems in the balance circuits, but is not limited to the balance network. For example, the problem can be a mismatch in power amp IC8 (Fig. 2.17) if the problem is evident at all inputs. In such a case, it is necessary to replace IC8 as a package even though one channel may be good.

Of course, if there is a mismatch at only one input or one output, the problem can be pinned down easily. For example, if there is a mismatch at only the *phono* input, suspect IC7 (the phono equalization amplifier, shown in Fig. 2.13). On the other hand, if the mismatch appears only at the tape record output, suspect IC1 (the tape record buffer, also shown in Fig. 2.13).

If both channels produce essentially the same signal (with an identical signal at both inputs, and with the balance control at midrange), the next step is to test the adjustment range of both the bass and treble controls.

Typically, the bass and treble controls have a ±8- to ±10-dB range, at some specific frequency. For example, the bass control of the amplifier described thus far in this chapter has a ±8-dB range at 100 Hz, while the treble control has ±10 dB at 10 kHz. 50 Hz and 20 kHz are also common base and treble test frequencies.

Set both the bass and treble controls to their midrange. Apply a 100-Hz signal to the inputs of both channels. Set the balance control until the outputs of both channels are identical.

Keep the treble and balance controls at midrange. Vary the bass control from one extreme to the other. Note that the output of each channel varies about 8 dB above and below the output existing at the bass midrange setting.

Return both the bass and treble controls to midrange, and apply a 10-kHz signal to the inputs of both channels. Leave the balance controls set so that both outputs are identical.

Keep the bass and balance controls at midrange. Vary the treble control from one extreme to the other. Note that the output of each channel varies about 8 dB above and below the output existing at the treble midrange setting.

If the amplifier passes the tests described here, it is reasonable to assume that the amplifier is functioning normally, and no troubleshooting is required. Of course, the amplifier can perform the overall functions normally, and still have a specific problem. We discuss this next.

2.5 TYPICAL TROUBLESHOOTING PROCEDURES

This section describes a series of troubleshooting procedures for a typical amplifier/loudspeaker combination. As discussed in the Preface, it is not practical to provide a specific troubleshooting procedure for every audio amplifier/loudspeaker combination. Instead, we describe a universal troubleshooting approach, using specific examples of amplifier/loudspeaker circuits. By a strange coincidence, these examples just happen to be some of the circuits described in Sec. 2.3. In this way, you can relate the theory to the troubleshooting procedures in this section. Then you can relate both to the specific amplifier/loudspeaker combination you are troubleshooting.

Most of the troubleshooting procedures discussed here are based on the symptoms produced by failure of the amplifier/loud-speaker to perform one or more operating procedures (Sec. 2.2) for failure to pass one or more test/adjustment procedures (Sec. 2.4). In most cases, the troubleshooting procedures are supplemented with troubleshooting diagrams that show all of the circuit elements involved for a particular symptom, but omit all nonessential circuit elements.

As in the case of adjustments, the troubleshooting procedures found in amplifier/loudspeaker service manuals are "limited" at best. Such manuals give you the usual troubleshooting trees with some test points to check, but no hint as to what other components are involved. We bridge that gap with the troubleshooting diagrams.

The following paragraphs are a collection of trouble symptoms that match the troubleshooting trees found in the service manual for a typical integrated amplifier. After selecting the symptom that matches the amplifier you are servicing, follow the steps in the corresponding troubleshooting procedure.

2.5.1 Power Does Not Turn On (Amplifier Dead)

Figure 2.21 is the troubleshooting diagram. If all of the power supply circuits are operating normally, there should be sound available (possibly background noise) at the loudspeakers (from at least one input), and the front-panel fluorescent display should show both power-level indications and function (or input) indications when the POWER button is pressed. If not, start by checking the power supply circuits shown in Fig. 2.21.

Note that the amplifier power supply is turned on when the power cord is connected, even if the POWER button has not been pressed. So, if power does not turn on (no display/no sound), first check the power supply voltages and make sure they are available (right after you make sure the power cord is plugged in!).

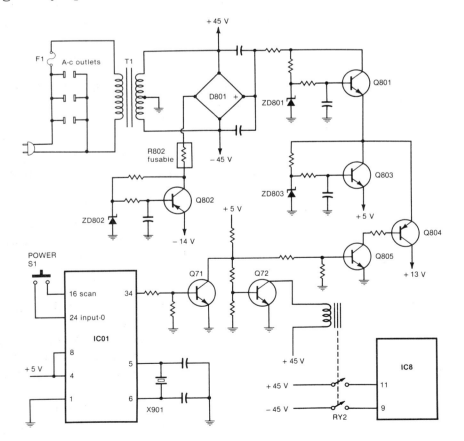

Fig. 2.21. Power circuit troubleshooting.

Check the emitter of Q801 which should be about 13 V. If not, suspect F1, D801, ZD801, and the associated circuit.

Then check the emitter of Q803 which should be about 5 V. If not, suspect Q803, ZD803 and the associated circuit.

Check the emitter of Q802 which should be about −14 V. If not, suspect Q802, ZD802, R802, and the associated circuit.

If the power-supply circuits are good, check and make sure that system-control microprocessor IC01 is receiving power (at pins 4 and 8), and is properly grounded (at pin 1). Then check for 4-MHz clock signals at pins 5 and 6. If not, suspect X901 (or possibly a defective oscillator circuit within IC01).

If IC01 is receiving power, and the clock is operating, check and make sure that pins 16 and 24 are connected when POWER switch S1 is pressed. If not, suspect S1.

With S1 closed, the scan signals from pin 16 are applied to input-0 at pin 24. This should cause pin 34 to go low (near zero volt). If the scan signals at pin 16 are available at pin 24, but pin 34 does not go low, suspect IC01.

Press POWER switch S1 again, and check to make sure that pin 34 of IC01 goes high. Press POWER switch S1 again, and check to make sure that pin 34 of IC01 goes high. Press S1 a third time so that pin 34 returns to low.

With pin 34 of IC1 low, check to make sure that the collector of Q71 is about 3 V (Q71 off). If not, suspect Q71.

If the collector of Q71 is at 3 V, check the collector of Q804 which should be about 13 V. If not, suspect Q804/Q805.

If all of the power supply voltages are available, and IC01 is good, the next step is to check for front-panel indications and sound at the loudspeakers.

If sound is available, but there are no front-panel indications, the problem is likely in the keyboard and display circuits (discussed in Sec. 2.5.2).

If the front-panel indications are present, but there is no sound from any input,

the problem is likely in the volume-control circuits (Sec. 2.5.3), or audio-output circuits (Sec. 2.5.4).

If there is no sound from a particular input, but sound from other inputs, the problem is likely in the audio-input select circuits (Sec. 2.5.5).

Of course, if the power-loss protection circuits (Sec. 2.5.6) and/or power-output protection circuits (Sec. 2.5.7) are defective, both the sound and display can be interrupted, even though the sound-processing circuits and display circuits are good. So both the power-loss and power-output protection circuits should be checked when the usual troubleshooting sequence does not reveal the fault.

Always check the reset circuits as described in Sec. 2.5.6 for a "power does not turn on" symptom.

Note that not all integrated amplifiers have the protection circuits described here. However, most modern integrated amplifiers have some form of protection circuits that can interrupt normal operation, leading you to believe that the sound-processor and/or display functions are defective. So always look for any such circuits, and find out how normal operation can be affected.

2.5.2 No Output-Power Level and/ or Function (Input) Display

Figure 2.22 is the troubleshooting diagram for a "no function (input) display" symptom. First, make sure that the power supply voltages are available, and that IC01 is apparently good, as discussed in Sec. 2.5.1.

If there is no function (input) display when the POWER button is pressed, check for about 13 V at pin 8 of IC02, and pin 35 of FL1. If missing, suspect Q804, Q805, or Q71.

If power is available to FL1, press front-panel AUX button and check to make sure that about 4.2 V appears at pin 36 of IC01. If not, suspect IC01, or the AUX S9 circuit.

If pin 36 of IC01 is at 4.2 V, check to make sure that pin 1 of IC02, and pin 33 of FL1 are at about 12.6 V, and that pin 34 of

FL1 is at about 12.1 V. If pin 1 of IC02 is not at 12.6 V, suspect IC02. If pin 34 of FL1 is not at 12.1 V, suspect D904.

If the input signals are available to FL1, but there is no function or input display, suspect FL1.

Before you remove the FL1 display from the amplifier (a tedious job), make certain that FL1 is receiving operating power. As shown in Fig. 2.22, pins 38 and 1 must receive about 1.8 V from transformer T1. If not, suspect T1 or D803.

If you do not know how a fluorescent display tube works, refer to Fig. 2.23. As shown, a fluorescent tube is similar in operation (physically and electrically) to a triode vacuum tube. The tube includes a directly heated cathode and a grid/anode segment coated with fluorescent material.

The fluorescent tube turns on when a positive voltage is applied to the grid/anode segment, with respect to the cathode. The tube turns off when a negative voltage is applied to the grid/anode segment, with respect to the cathode.

In the case of FL1, the grid/anode func-tion segment to be turned on (such as the *aux* display, *phono* display, etc.) receives about 12 V from IC02, while all other function segments are at zero volt (which is negative with respect to the cathode).

Figure 2.24 is the troubleshooting diagram for a "no output-power level display" symptom. Only the left-channel circuits are shown. The right-channel circuits are identical except that audio is applied to pin 16 of IC03 which, in turn, drives the right-channel output-power display terminals of FL1.

First, make sure that the power-supply voltages are available, and that IC01 is apparently good, as discussed in Sec. 2.5.1.

If there is no output-power level display when the POWER button is pressed, check for about 13 V at pin 15 of IC03. If missing, suspect Q804, Q805, or Q71.

If power is available to IC03, press front-panel AUX button and apply a signal to the auxiliary input jack (on the rear panel).

Check to make sure that audio is present at the loudspeaker terminals. If not, refer to Secs. 2.5.3, 2.5.4, and 2.5.5 (the audio processing circuit troubleshooting sections).

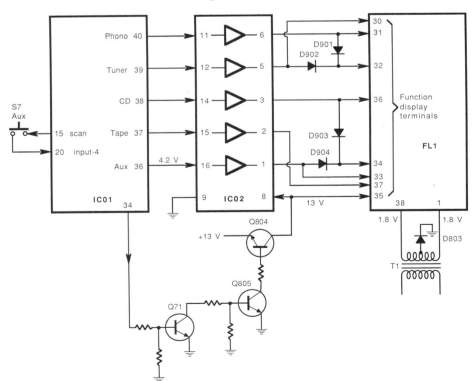

Fig. 2.22. Function display circuit troubleshooting.

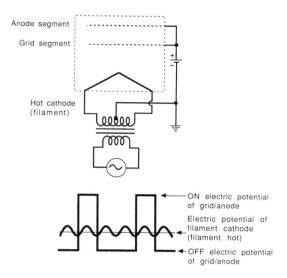

Fig. 2.23. **Basic fluorescent display.**

If audio is present at the speaker terminals, check for rectified audio at pin 16 of IC03. If not, suspect D79L and D78L. If audio is present at pin 16 of IC03, but there is no output-power level display, suspect IC03 and FL1.

Make sure FL1 is receiving about 1.8 V at pin 1. If not, suspect T1 or D803.

2.5.3 Volume Control Does Not Operate

Figure 2.25 is the troubleshooting diagram. Note that the volume-control circuits are in the audio processing path between the amplifier input and output. So, before you condemn the volume-control circuits, make certain that there is audio at pin 5 of IC4. If not, check the audio-input circuits as described in Sec. 2.5.5.

If there is audio at pin 5 of IC4, check for audio at pin 4 of IC4 while operating the VOLUME UP (S9) and VOLUME DOWN (S8) buttons. The audio volume should increase and decrease in 10-dB steps at pin 4, each time you press the corresponding VOLUME button. (If you hold the VOLUME buttons, the audio should increase or decrease steadily in 10-dB steps.)

If there is no audio at pin 4 of IC4, with audio at pin 5, suspect IC4. If there is audio at pin 4, but there is no change when the

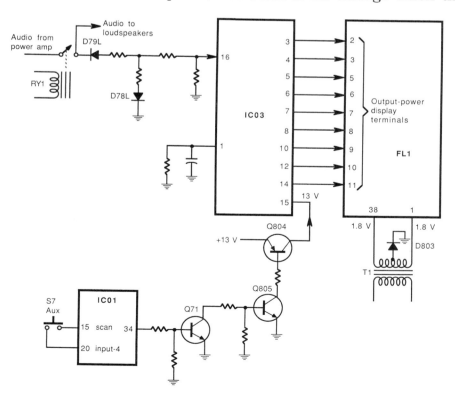

Fig. 2.24. **Output-power display circuit troubleshooting.**

VOLUME buttons are operated, use a logic probe or scope to monitor the strobe (pin 12) data (pin 13) and clock (pin 14) outputs from IC01 while holding the VOLUME buttons. Although you probably cannot decode the information on these lines, the presence of pulse activity on the lines usually indicates that IC01 is good. If any one of the lines shows no activity with the VOLUME buttons operated, suspect IC01.

If there is pulse activity on all three lines (at pins 10, 11, and 12 of IC4) but there is no change in the volume at pin 4 with the VOLUME buttons held, suspect IC4.

If there is audio at pin 4 of IC4, and the volume changes, check for audio at pin 7 of IC4. If absent, suspect IC5.

If there is audio at pin 7 of IC4, check for audio at pin 8, and make sure that the audio changes in 2-dB steps when the VOLUME buttons are operated. If there is no audio, suspect IC4. If there is audio, but there is no change with the VOLUME buttons operated, suspect IC01, or IC4. IC4 is the most likely suspect, if the audio is good at pin 7, but it is possible that IC01 is not generating the correct code to produce 2-dB changes in volume.

If there is audio at pin 8, and the audio changes in 2-dB steps when the VOLUME buttons are operated, press MUTE button S2, and make sure that the audio is cut off at pin 8. If not, suspect S2, IC01, or IC4. You can also check for pulse activity on the data code outputs from IC01 with a scope or logic probe (but you probably cannot decipher the code!). Press MUTE again, and check to make sure that audio is restored at pin 8, and at the same level (if you have not pressed the VOLUME buttons during the mute condition). If not, suspect S2, IC01, and IC4.

Note that the loudness network is part of the volume-control circuits. Also note that a failure symptom for the loudness function is usually difficult to define for any integrated amplifier. This is because the loudness function attenuates the midrange signals so that the ear hears what appears to be the same level across the audio range. (In a few amplifiers, the loudness function boosts the treble and bass.)

Unfortunately, all ears are not the same, and not all loudness networks define midrange at the same frequencies! Usually, the customer complains that "there is no differ-

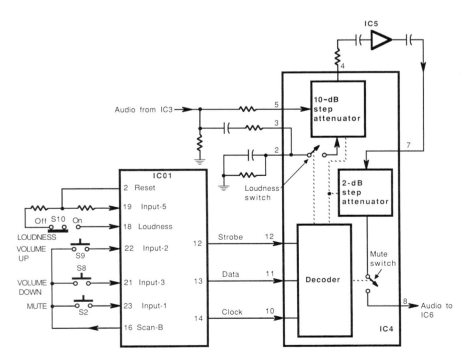

Fig. 2.25. Volume-control and loudness circuit troubleshooting.

ence when I play the same tape or record with the loudness function on or off."

To troubleshoot such a symptom, apply an audio signal (say between 7 and 10 kHz) with loudness off. Then press the LOUDNESS button (S10 in the amplifier of Fig. 2.25) and check for a drop of about 20 dB in level (at pin 4 of IC4). Repeat the test at 50 Hz and 20 kHz. There should be substantially no change in level (at pin 4 of IC4) at the low and high ends of the audio range (unless a boost circuit is used).

No matter what type of loudness circuit is used, if there is no change in audio level at any frequency when the loudness function is switched in and out, there is a problem in the loudness circuit. In the amplifier of Fig. 2.25, suspect S10, IC01, IC4, or the networks connected to pins 2 and 3 of IC4.

2.5.4 No Audio at the Loudspeakers or Headphone Jack

Figure 2.26 is the troubleshooting diagram. Note that the audio-output circuits are in the audio processing path between the amplifier input and output. So, before you troubleshoot these circuits, make certain that there is audio at pins 3 and 5 of IC6. If not, check the audio-input circuits as described in Sec. 2.5.5, as well as the volume-control circuits as described in Sec. 2.5.3.

Before you start troubleshooting the circuits, set the bass, treble, and balance controls to midrange. This simple act has been known to cure a "no audio or weak audio in one channel" symptom.

Also note that the amplifier of Fig. 2.26 has separate speaker switches (S701/S702) in each channel, and that there are two sets of outputs (A and B) for each channel. Not all amplifiers have such a configuration. However, when there is a *total loss of audio* in one or both channels, always look for speaker switches as a first step. Many "no audio" problems are solved instantly by setting a speaker switch to on!

Once you are sure that all switches and controls are properly set, check for audio at

pins 1 and 7 of IC6. If absent, but with audio at pins 3 and 5, suspect IC6. Also check the bass and treble controls since they are in the negative-feedback path of tone amplifier IC6.

If there is audio at pins 1 and 7 of IC6, check for audio (at about the same level) at pins 1 and 18 of IC8. If the audio level at pins 1 and 18 of IC8 is substantially different from the level at pins 1 and 7 of IC6, trace the audio path through the subsonic filter.

Note that the setting of *subsonic filter* switch S11 should have little or no effect on the audio level, except at very low frequencies (below about 20 Hz). If you notice a drastic change in audio level at different settings of S11, from about 1 kHz and up, look for problems in the subsonic filter circuit (such as leakage in C18).

If there is audio at pins 1 and 18 of IC8, but not at pins 10 and 13, suspect IC8. Before you pull IC8, make sure that the 45-V supply is applied to the various IC8 terminals.

As shown in Fig. 2.26, the 45-V (both plus and minus) supply is applied through relay RY2. In turn, RY2 is turned on through Q71/Q72 when pin 34 of IC01 goes low (when POWER switch S1 is pressed). Most of the other ICs receive operating power when the power cord is plugged in (whether the POWER button is pressed or not).

Because of the heavy current drain and high heat dissipation, power amplifier IC8 is turned on only during play. This is typical for most modern integrated amplifiers where the final power stage is a single IC in the 40- to 50-W range.

If the 45-V supply is absent at the IC8 terminals, suspect RY2, Q71, Q72, or IC01 (check pin 34 of IC01 for a low).

If there is audio at pins 10 and 13 of IC8, but the audio does not reach the speakers or headphones, suspect RY1, Q73, or Q74. Also check for a low at pin 33 of IC01. Pin 33 should go low at the same time as, pin 34.

Keep in mind that the power-output protection circuits discussed in Sec. 2.5.7 are designed to cut off the audio circuit in the event of an overload. Defective protection cir-

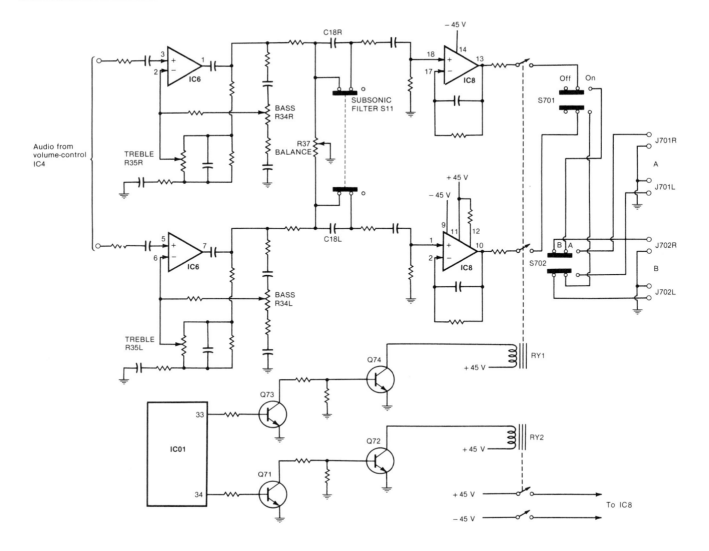

Fig. 2.26. Audio output circuit troubleshooting.

cuits can cut off the audio, even without an overload.

2.5.5 No Input-Select Operation

Figure 2.27 is the troubleshooting diagram. If you cannot select a particular input from the front panel, but other inputs are good, first make certain that the input is available from the rear-panel connectors. For example, if you cannot play the tuner, check at pin 26 of input select IC2 for tuner audio. If absent, suspect the wiring between IC2 and the rear-panel connectors. Of course, if you cannot receive audio from any input, the problem may be in the circuits

after the input-select section. Refer to Secs. 2.5.3 and 2.5.4.

If only one input cannot be selected, first check to make sure that the corresponding command is received at IC01 when the front-panel button is pressed. For example, press AUX button S7 and check to make sure that pin 15 of IC01 is connected to pin 20. If not, check the S7 wiring.

If the command is received at IC01, check to make sure that IC01 produces the corresponding command to IC2 at pins 11, 14, and 35 of IC01 and/or pins 13, 15, and 16 of IC2. Monitor these lines with a scope for the presence of clock, data, and strobe

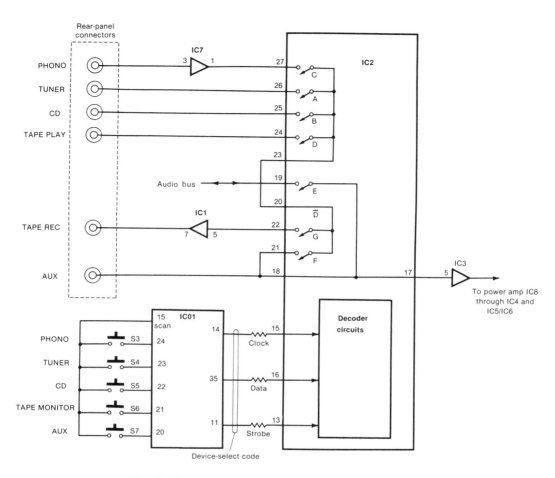

Fig. 2.27. Input-select circuit troubleshooting.

pulses. If any one of the three lines shows a complete lack of pulses, suspect IC01.

If all three lines show pulses, but the corresponding input is not selected, suspect IC2.

If only the phono input appears to be defective, suspect IC7.

If all inputs can be selected, but there is no audio to the tape recorder (Chapter 4), suspect IC1.

If there is no audio to the loudspeakers or headphones, but all input functions appear normal, suspect IC3.

2.5.6 Amplifier Does Not Turn On Automatically after a Short Power Interruption

Figure 2.12 is the troubleshooting diagram. To confirm proper power-loss opera-

tion, temporarily remove a-c power (pull the cord), while monitoring pins 3 and 17 of IC01. Check to make sure that pin 3 goes high while pin 17 goes low. Reapply power in less than 2 seconds, and check to make sure that pin 3 goes low while pin 17 goes high. If not, suspect Q01, Q02, D13, D14, D82 and the associated circuit.

Whenever there is a problem of power turn on, always check the reset circuits to make sure the system-control microprocessor has received a reset instruction. In the case of IC01 in Fig. 2.12, pin 2 should go low (to reset IC01) when power is removed, and then go high when power is reapplied. If not, suspect C6, Q03, Q04 and the associated circuit.

As a final check of the power-loss circuits, remove a-c power for more than 2 seconds. Reapply power and check to make sure that the amplifier remains off, but can be turned on when the POWER switch is pressed. If not, refer to Sec. 2.5.1.

2.5.7 Power-Output Protection Circuit Inoperative

Figure 2.18 is the troubleshooting diagram. As discussed in Sec. 2.3.7, the front-panel function display should flash on and off, and the loudspeakers should be disconnected when any one of the following occur: the final amplifier, IC8, becomes overheated (the IC8 heat sink reaches 100 °C), the constant (no audio) d-c voltage applied to the speakers exceeds ±1.7 V, or the speaker output line is shorted (or is at an impedance below that of the speakers).

Except for the low-impedance output, these conditions are difficult to simulate, making the circuits difficult to check. Also, if you do succeed in simulating any one of these conditions, and the protection circuits are not functioning properly, you can damage the equipment (burn out the speaker voice coil and/or overheat IC8, for example).

If you must check the circuits, try shorting the loudspeaker lines (either R or L, or both) to ground temporarily (very temporarily). Check to make sure that the function portion of the front-panel display flashes on and off, and that the speakers are disconnected. If not, temporarily short pin 3 of IC01 to ground, and check for a flashing display with the speakers disconnected.

If the display flashes and the speakers are cut with pin 3 of IC01 shorted, but not when the speaker lines are shorted, suspect Q75, Q77, Q78, Q79, Q80, and Q02.

If the display does not flash, and the speakers are not disconnected with pin 3 of IC01 shorted, suspect IC01.

You can also check to make sure that the anode of D77 is at ground (unless the IC8 heat sink is at 100 °C or higher). If not, suspect that S12 is open.

You can also check at the bases of Q77 and Q78. Both bases should be at 0 V (ideally), but may be at some potential less than ±1.7 V, without triggering the protection circuits. If the bases are at some value in excess of ±1.7 V, pin 3 of IC01 should go low, and the display should flash. If not, suspect Q77, Q78, Q79, Q80, or Q02.

CHAPTER 3

Troubleshooting and Repair of Linear-Tracking Turntables

This chapter is devoted to linear-tracking turntables for LP records. Included are such subjects as the general description of a typical turntable, typical turntable circuit descriptions, user-control operation procedures and installation of turntables, typical test/adjustment procedures, and examples of troubleshooting based on failure symptoms.

3.1 GENERAL DESCRIPTION OF A TYPICAL LINEAR-TRACKING TURNTABLE

Figure 3.1 shows a typical linear-tracking turntable for records, both 45 and 33⅓ rpm LPs. The major difference between linear-tracking and conventional turntables is in operation of the tonearm. On a linear-tracking turntable, the tonearm is driven by a motor, separate from the platter drive motor. The tonearm motor causes the tonearm to track the record at the *same angle from outside to inside.* This reduces distortion caused by tracking error, and reduces wear on the record. Typical linear-tracking force is 1 to 2 grams.

Although there is no standardization, many linear-tracking turntables are enhanced with such features as remote control and automatic record size detection. We describe the circuits and troubleshooting procedures for such features throughout this chapter. For now, let us concentrate on some typical features and characteristics.

On turntables with *remote control,* it is possible to control such functions as play, stop, repeat, pause, mute, and volume up/

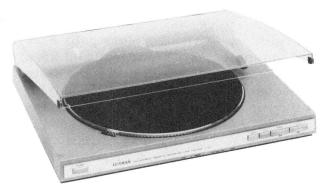

Fig. 3.1. Luxman model P-406 fully automatic, tangential tracking belt drive turntable. (Courtesy Luxman Division of Alpine Electronics of America, Inc.)

57

down from the remote unit. On some modular home-entertainment systems, the same remote unit controls the video monitor or TV, a VCR, a cassette deck, and so on. (As a practical matter, the remote may not be as useful as the manufacturers claim. You still must get up and turn the record over at regular intervals!)

With some turntables, the *record size and the turntable speed* is determined automatically when the record is set on the platter. For example, if a 12-inch record is used, the turntable speed is set automatically for 33⅓ rpm. 45 rpm is selected if a 7-inch record is used. When playing nonstandard size records (or transparent records if an optical size-detection system is used), it is necessary to select turntable speed manually.

Virtually all linear-tracking turntables use a *direct-drive* (DD) *motor* for the platter. Typically, the direct drive is done with a brushless d-c servo motor, controlled by a crystal-oscillator and phase-lock–loop (PLL) circuit. The turntable speed is monitored constantly, and maintained at the correct speed (typically within 0.003% or better). With direct drive, wow and flutter are no more than 0.025% (weighted), and signal-to-noise (S/N) ratio is in the 75- to 80-dB range.

When raising or lowering the tonearm of most linear-tracking turntables, the *output is muted.* This eliminates any noise that may be produced when the stylus touches or is lifted from the record.

Most linear-tracking turntables have a *plug-in cartridge and stylus arrangement.* Typically, the cartridge plugs into a standard mounting on the tonearm, and the stylus plugs into the cartridge. In some cases, it is necessary to adjust the cartridge/stylus in relation to the tonearm, but the trend is to make the mounting adjustment free.

A typical cartridge uses a *dual-magnet* configuration (for right and left channels), and has a *diamond stylus.* The cartridge frequency range is about 10 Hz to 25 kHz, with an output voltage of 3 to 5 mV. A typical specification is 3.5 mV at 1 kHz at 50 mm per second. The channel difference is typically 1 dB (or less) at 1 kHz, while channel separation is 20 to 25 dB at 1 kHz. Typical cartridge weight is 5 to 6 grams. The capacitance of the lead wires between the cartridge and the output connectors is typically in the 100- to 200-pF range.

3.2 USER CONTROLS, OPERATING PROCEDURES, AND INSTALLATION

Although linear-tracking turntables are no more difficult to operate than conventional turntables, there are a few differences. This section describes the basic user controls and operating procedures for a typical linear-tracking turntable. You must study the operating controls and indicators for any turntable you are troubleshooting.

Before we launch into a typical operating sequence, here are some precautions that apply to all turntables.

3.2.1 Shipping Devices

Many linear-tracking and conventional turntables have clamps or screws that hold the platter in place during shipment. Make sure such devices are removed or loosened before you apply power to the turntable. Most conventional turntables have a clamp or screw that holds the tonearm in an at-rest position when not in use. Generally, linear-tracking turntables do not have such an arrangement since the tonearm is moved along a travel guide by means of a cord and pulley. In most cases, the tonearm cannot move unless the pulley is driven by the tonearm motor. However, look for any tonearm restraints (that must be removed before use, and should be replaced before shipment).

3.2.2 External Connections

External connections between a linear-tracking turntable and the stereo amplifier are usually made from the back of the turntable. In most cases, a pin cord is supplied with the turntable for connection between the turntable's L and R stereo outputs, and the corresponding inputs on the amplifier. Although the connections are very simple, certain precautions must be observed for all turntables.

Look for any color coding on the pin cord. Typically, red is used for the right channel, while white is used for the left channel (but do not always count on it). Also look for any ground terminals or leads that are part of the pin cord. In some cases, the pin cord has a third lead (with a terminal lug) to connect the turntable chassis with the amplifier chassis.

Figure 3.2 shows typical external connections between a linear-tracking turntable and an amplifier. Note that the amplifier shown has a-c power receptacles for a number of external components (typically a turntable, cassette deck, and an AM/FM tuner, or possibly a CD player).

Do not connect the turntable to the CD, *aux,* or *tape play* inputs of an amplifier. Instead, always use the *phono* input (or whatever the turntable input is called). Generally, no damage is done if you connect the turntable to the wrong input. However, the turntable output is very low in relation to other audio components (about 5 mV for a turntable, 500 mV for a cassette deck, and 2 V for a CD player) so you must have some preamplification for a turntable output signal. Virtually all modern integrated amplifiers have such amplification, as described in Chapter 2.

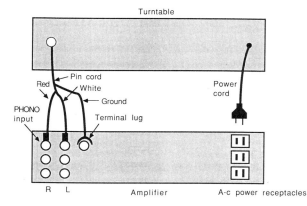

Fig. 3.2. Typical external connections between a linear-tracking turntable and an amplifier.

3.2.3 Typical Operating Sequence

Figure 3.3 shows the operating controls and indicators for a typical linear-tracking turntable. Compare the following sequence with the controls and indicators of the turntable you are servicing.

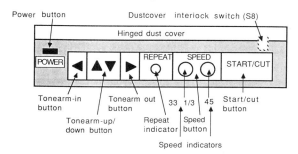

Fig. 3.3. Operating controls and indicators for a typical linear-tracking turntable.

The turntable of Fig. 3.3 has a hinged dustcover and a dustcover-interlock switch (S8). The dustcover must be closed before the platter mat will spin.

Power is applied to the turntable, and one (or both) of the two *speed* indicators turns on when you press the POWER button. When the POWER button is pressed again, power is removed and all of the indicators turn off.

With power on and the dustcover open, switch S8 is closed and the turntable is in the stop mode. With the dustcover closed, switch S8 is open and the turntable is in the standby mode.

To load the turntable, press the POWER button and note that at least one of the *speed* indicators turns on. Place the record on the platter and close the dustcover. On some turntables (such as the one shown in Fig. 3.3) it is necessary to use an adapter for 45-rpm records.

For automatic play, press the START/CUT button after the turntable is loaded. The turntable speed is selected automatically, as indicated when the corresponding *speed* indicator turns on (or remains on). When the record is finished playing, the tonearm returns automatically to the rest position, and the turntable platter stops.

Note that automatic play applies only to standard records (12 inch for 33⅓ and 7 inch for 45 rpm). Manual play must be used for all nonstandard records (such as clear discs, warped discs, etc.). Manual play is also used when you wish to start playing at some point other than the beginning of the record.

For manual play, press the POWER button and load the turntable. Press the TONEARM-IN button until the stylus is positioned over the lead-in groove of the record, or at the beginning of the part you want to play. If you overshoot, use the TONEARM-OUT button to go back to the correct position. Be careful not to position the tonearm too near the edge of the record. The stylus can be damaged if the tonearm is lowered onto the platter mat. Press the TONEARM-UP/DOWN button to lower the stylus onto the record and start playing. If necessary, press the SPEED button to select the correct speed (45 or 33⅓).

For repeat play, press the REPEAT button while the record is playing. The *repeat* indicator should turn on, and the record should

play to the end. Then the record should play from beginning to end 16 times, without further operation of the controls. *To stop the repeat function,* press the REPEAT button (during repeat play). The record should play to the end and stop. Keep in mind that the repeat mode applies only to standard records, and should not be used for any nonstandard records.

To stop play in any mode, press the START/CUT button. The record should stop playing immediately. (This also cancels the repeat function.) If you press the START/CUT button again, play will resume in automatic or manual. (If you press the START/CUT button a second time to start during the repeat mode, the record will start and continue to the end, but will not repeat.)

Use the TONEARM-UP/DOWN button to raise the tonearm for a *pause.* Press the TONEARM-UP/DOWN button again to lower the tonearm and resume play.

3.3 TYPICAL LINEAR-TRACKING TURNTABLE CIRCUIT DESCRIPTIONS

This section describes the theory of operation for a typical linear-tracking turntable. All of the notes described in Sec. 2.3 apply here. In this section, we concentrate on the circuits of a turntable similar to that shown in Fig. 3.4. Figure 3.5 is the block diagram of such a turntable.

3.3.1 System-Control Circuits

Virtually all of the turntable functions and circuits are under control of system-control microprocessor IC3. These circuits include tonearm control (both position and up/down functions), platter drive, and audio mute. IC3 receives operating commands from front-panel switches S1 through S7, as well as information signals from dustcover interlock switch S8 and tonearm rest switch S9. IC3 also receives information from the tonearm control circuits, record speed/size detectors, and platter drive.

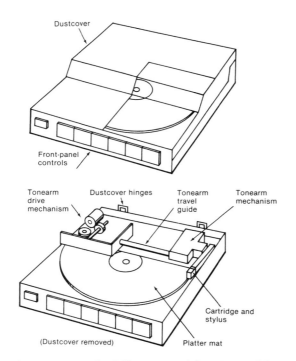

Fig. 3.4. Typical linear-tracking turntable.

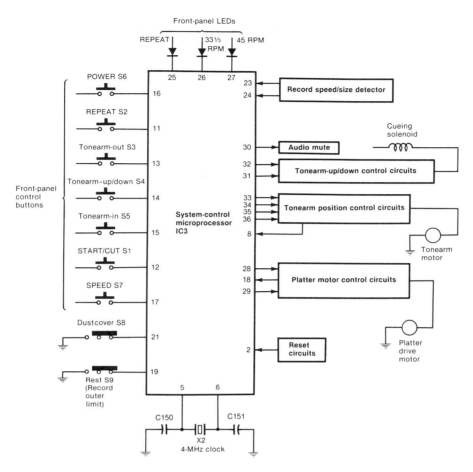

Fig. 3.5. Block diagram of typical linear-tracking turntable.

Note that IC3 is controlled by 4-MHz clock crystal X2. As a troubleshooting hint, if all functions of IC3 appear to be inoperative (with fuses good and power applied) check for 4-MHz signals at pins 5 and 6 of IC3. If the signals are absent or abnormal, it is possible that X2 or capacitors C150/C151 are defective.

3.3.2 Front-Panel Control and Indicator Circuits

Figure 3.6 shows the basic control and indicator circuits for the turntable. Note that IC3 accepts commands from the front-panel switches in the form of zero volt or ground when the corresponding switch button is pressed, and sends high or low command signals to the appropriate circuit.

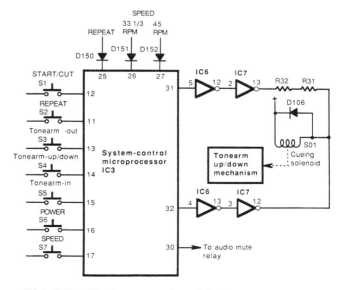

Fig. 3.6. Basic control and indicator circuits.

As an example, when the TONEARM-UP/DOWN button is pressed, switch S4 is closed and pin 14 of IC3 is grounded. This causes pins 31 and 32 of IC3 to change state. In turn, this causes cueing solenoid S01 to be energized (or deenergized) to move the tonearm up or down. Note that IC6 and IC7 invert the outputs from pins 31 and 32 twice, thus restoring the original state.

When S4 is first pressed to lower the tonearm, pins 31 and 32 both go low, causing the junction of R31 and S01 to be grounded. This lowers the tonearm. When S4 is released, pin 32 returns to high, but pin 31 remains low, grounding the junction of R32 and pin 13 of IC7. This allows enough current through S01 to hold the solenoid and tonearm down. When S4 is pressed again to raise the tonearm, pin 31 returns to high, removing current through S01, and allowing the tonearm to be raised (by the tonearm mechanism).

Note that the tonearm is also moved up and down automatically by IC3 during normal play, repeat play, and so on. This is done by changing the states at pins 31 and 32 of IC3.

As another example, when REPEAT switch S2 is pressed, pin 11 of IC3 is grounded, and IC3 produces all commands necessary to repeat play of the record 16 times. When this occurs, pin 25 of IC3 goes low, and *repeat* indicator D150 (an LED) turns on. Likewise, when SPEED switch S7 is pressed, pin 17 of IC3 is grounded, and IC3 produces all commands necessary to change speeds. When this occurs, pins 26 and 27 change states, as do the 33⅓ and 45 speed indicator LEDs, D151 and D152.

All of these functions are programmed into IC3 and cannot be changed, nor can you repair any circuit within IC3. You must replace IC3 if any one function is absent or abnormal. However, from a practical troubleshooting standpoint, you must understand and check *all results* of a particular operating command applied to IC3, before you pull IC3 from the board (a difficult and tedious job at best).

For example, if S4 is operated, pins 31 and 32 of IC3 should change state, as should pin 30. As discussed in Sec. 3.3.3, the signal at pin 30 of IC3 controls the audio mute relay that cuts off the cartridge pickup coils when the tonearm is lifted up. *So, when any command is applied to IC3, check to make sure that all commands from IC3 are made properly, and that only those commands are made.*

3.3.3 Audio Mute Circuits

Figure 3.7 shows the audio mute circuits. These circuits eliminate noise caused by the stylus making contact with the record whenever the tonearm is raised or lowered by operation of cueing solenoid S01 (in response to commands from IC3).

When the stylus (tonearm) is not down,

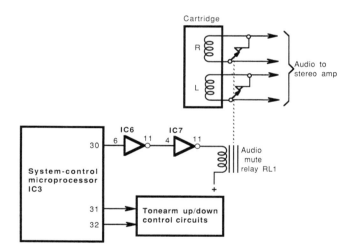

Fig. 3.7. Audio mute circuits.

pin 30 of IC3 is high (about +5 V). This high is applied to pin 6 of IC6 where the high is inverted to a low. The low is applied to pin 4 of IC7 where the low is inverted to a high. The high at pin 11 of IC7 is applied to relay RL1. This deenergizes RL1, and shorts the windings of the pickup cartridge, as well as the phonograph output connections. The output of the turntable appears as a short to the amplifier input, and the audio is muted.

When the stylus is lowered onto the record by IC3 and cueing solenoid S01, pin 30 of IC3 is low. The low is inverted twice by IC6 and IC7, and applied to RL1. This energizes RL1, removing the short from the pickup cartridge wirings and phonograph output. Whatever audio is present on the cartridge windings is applied to the amplifier.

3.3.4 Record Size Detection and Speed Selection Circuits

Figure 3.8 shows the circuits used to detect record size, and to select the appropriate playing speed (33⅓ or 45 rpm). The circuits are optical (using LEDs and phototransistors), and are in operation only when standard-size records are played.

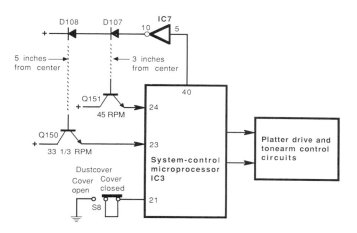

Fig. 3.8. Record size/speed selection circuits.

When the dustcover is open, interlock switch S8 is closed, grounding pin 21 of IC3. This places the turntable in the stop mode. The platter stops spinning, and the tonearm moves to the rest position (outside the record circumference).

When the dustcover is closed, S8 opens. This removes the ground from pin 21 of IC3, and causes pin 40 of IC3 to go high. The high is inverted to a low by IC7, and applied to LEDs D107/D108, causing both D107 and D108 to turn on.

The turntable platter contains slots at approximately 3 inches and 5 inches from the center of the platter. D107 and D108 are positioned over the 3-inch and 5-inch slots,

respectively. LP-detect phototransistor Q150 is positioned beneath the platter in line with D108. 45-detect phototransistor Q151 is positioned beneath D107.

With no record (or a transparent record) placed on the platter, both Q150 and Q151 conduct, and a high is applied to both pins 23 and 24 of IC3. This is detected by IC3 as a no-record-present condition. IC3 turns off power to the platter drive and tonearm control circuits. This automatically protects the stylus from possible damage caused by lowering the tonearm to the platter when there is no record present. (With nonstandard records, or transparent records, it is necessary to operate the turntable manually.)

When a standard 7-inch 45-rpm record is placed on the platter, the light from D107 to Q151 is blocked, and a low is applied to pin 24 of IC3 (but pin 23 remains high). IC3 senses this as a 45-rpm record condition, and applies appropriate commands to the platter drive and tonearm control circuits.

When a standard 12-inch LP record is placed on the platter, the light from D107 and Q151 and D108 to Q150 is blocked, and both pins 23 and 24 of IC3 go low. IC3 senses this as a 33⅓-rpm–LP record condition, and applies appropriate commands to the platter and tonearm control circuits.

When nonstandard records are placed on the platter, the playing speed must be selected by means of the front-panel *speed* switch, as described in Sec. 3.3.2.

3.3.5 Platter Motor Control Circuits

Figure 3.9 shows the circuits used to control operation of the platter motor. The circuits are essentially a phase-locked loop, or PLL, and use Hall-effect elements (which is typical for linear-tracking turntables).

The platter motor is controlled by a single PLL, IC1, that receives turntable start/stop information and speed-select information from IC3. IC1 also receives platter speed information from the Hall-effect elements.

Note that IC1 is controlled by 7.3728-

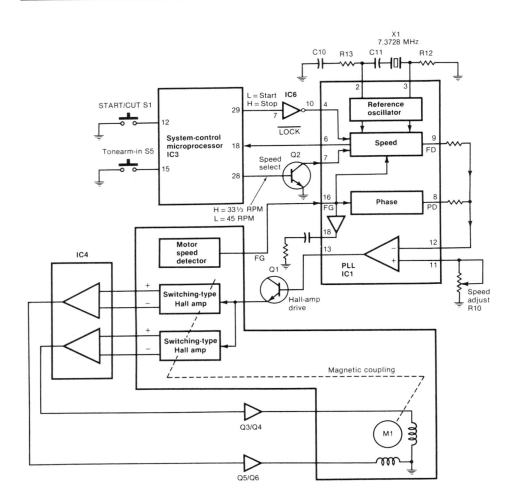

Fig. 3.9. Platter motor control circuits.

MHz clock crystal X1. As a troubleshooting hint, if all functions of IC1 appear to be absent (turntable does not turn, speed cannot be controlled), check for 7.3728-MHz signals at pins 2 and 3 of IC1. If the signals are absent or abnormal, it is possible that X1 or the associated capacitors C10/C11 or resistors R12/R13 are defective.

The signals generated by X1 are divided by a circuit within IC1, and serve as a reference for both the speed-control and phase-control portions of the PLL.

During normal operation, the motor speed detector (an integral part of the platter motor) generates frequency-generator (FG) signals. These FG signals are applied to IC1 at pin 16, and inform both the speed-control and phase-control circuits within IC1 of the actual motor speed.

The speed-control circuits of IC1 com-

pare the reference signals (from crystal X1), and the FG signals, to produce a frequency-difference (FD) signal at pin 9 of IC1. The phase-control circuits of IC1 compare the reference signals, and the FG signals, to produce a phase-difference (PD) signal at pin 8 of IC1.

The FD and PD signals are added together (in a network outside IC1) and applied to an op amp within IC1 (through pin 12) at the inverting input. The noninverting input of the op amp within IC1 is connected to speed adjust R10 through pin 11. The output of the IC1 op amp is applied to Q1 through pin 13 of IC1. If the motor speeds up, the drive signal to Q1 is altered to slow the motor down, and vice versa. The motor can be locked to the desired speed by adjustment of R10.

Transistor Q1 drives two switching-type

Hall amplifiers. Note that the Hall amplifiers are integral parts of the platter motor (as are the motor speed detect element and the rotor magnet) and are not serviceable. Each Hall amplifier supplies two inputs to differential amplifiers within IC4. In turn, the differential amplifiers of IC4 drive corresponding motor drive amplifiers Q3/Q4 and Q5/Q6, as discussed in Sec. 3.3.6.

When the turntable is in the stop mode, pressing either the START/CUT or TONEARM-IN buttons causes IC3 to produce a low or start signal at pin 29 of IC3. This low is inverted to a high by IC6, and applied through pin 4 of IC1 to the speed-control circuits within IC1. The speed-control circuits recognize this start command, and cause pins 8 and 9 of IC1 to go low for an initial start period. During this period, pin 13 of IC1 goes high, turning Q1 and the Hall amplifiers on to start the platter motor. Once the platter motor approaches the desired operating speed, the platter motor drive circuits take over to control motor speed, as described in Sec. 3.3.6.

3.3.6 Platter Motor Drive Circuits

Figure 3.10 shows the circuits used to drive platter motor M1.

As discussed in Sec. 3.3.5, Q1 receives input drive from PLL IC1. In turn, Q1 supplies drive bias to both Hall amplifiers (within the platter motor).

The Hall amplifiers are magnetic-sensi-

tive devices coupled to the platter motor rotor (an 8-pole magnet). Each Hall amplifier has two outputs of opposite polarity. As the magnetic fields of the rotor pass over the Hall amplifiers, the outputs change polarity. The outputs of the Hall amplifiers are applied to the inputs of two differential amplifiers within IC4.

A positive-going signal is applied at pin 3 of IC4. At the same time, a negative-going signal is applied to pin 2 of IC4. The resulting output at pin 1 of IC4 is positive going, and applied to the bases of Q5/Q6. A positive signal on the base of Q6 (PNP) turns Q6 off. A positive signal on the base of Q5 (NPN) turns Q5 on to conduct through the motor winding.

The current through Q5 and the motor winding causes the rotor to turn. As the motor rotates, the output polarities of the Hall amplifiers reverse, and are applied to pins 2 and 3 of IC4. The result is a negative output signal at pin 1 of IC4. This negative signal turns Q5 off and Q6 on, reversing the current flow through the motor winding. In effect, this action produces an a-c motor drive signal. The a-c frequency is 2.2 Hz at 33⅓ rpm, and 3 Hz at 45 rpm.

Note that the two windings of the platter motor are positioned such that the respective drive signals are approximately 90° out of phase. This sustains continuous rotation of the platter motor (in one direction) in the conventional manner.

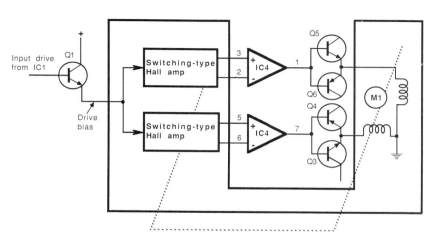

Fig. 3.10. Platter motor drive circuits.

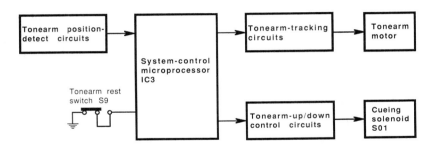

Fig. 3.11. Tonearm control circuits.

3.3.7 Tonearm Control Circuits

Figure 3.11 is a block diagram of the circuits used to move the tonearm across the record, as well as to raise and lower the tonearm. As discussed earlier, the tonearm is linear tracking. That is, the stylus tracks the record groove at the same angle from the outside to the inside of the record.

System-control microprocessor IC3 receives tonearm-position information from the tonearm position-detect circuits (Sec. 3.3.8) and the tonearm rest switch S9. IC3 evaluates this information to keep track of exactly where the tonearm is in relation to

the start and end of a record. IC3 controls movement of the tonearm communication with the tonearm tracking circuits (Sec. 3.3.9) that drive the tonearm motor. As discussed in Sec. 3.3.2, the tonearm is raised and lowered by cueing solenoid S01.

3.3.8 Tonearm Position-Detect Circuits

Figure 3.12 shows the circuits used by IC3 to detect the position of the tonearm in relation to the record start and end. Again, an optical system (LED and phototransistor) is used. However, in this case, the LED and

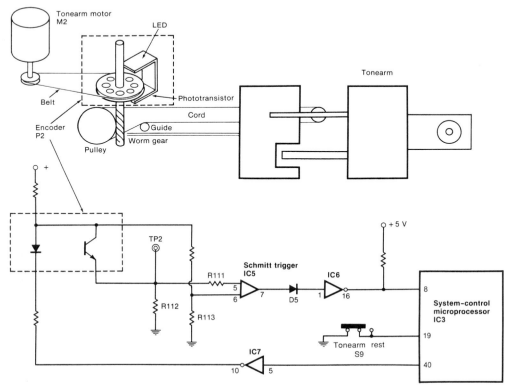

Fig. 3.12. Tonearm position-detect circuits.

phototransistor are part of an encoder, P2. A slit disc is positioned between the LED and phototransistor of P2. When the tonearm is driven across the record by the tonearm motor, the slit disc rotates and interrupts the light from the LED to the phototransistor, causing the phototransistor to produce pulses of current. These pulses are applied to pin 8 of IC3 through a Schmitt trigger, IC5, diode D5, and an inverter within IC6.

When the tonearm is at the "rest" position (past the outside of the record), tonearm rest switch S9 is closed, grounding pin 19 of IC3. Pressing either the START/CUT or TONEARM-IN buttons causes IC3 to turn on the tonearm drive motor (as described in Sec. 3.3.9). As the tonearm motor rotates, the tonearm is pulled across the record (along a guide) toward the center of the record by a belt-gear-and-pulley mechanism shown in Fig. 3.13.

When the tonearm moves to a distance of 147.5 mm (about 5.8 inches) from the center of the record, tonearm rest switch S9 opens, and IC3 senses that the tonearm is at the start position for a standard 12-inch LP record. From that point, IC3 uses the pulses from encoder P2 to determine the position of the tonearm.

The pulses from encoder P2 are applied to Schmitt trigger IC5 through R111 (Fig. 3.12). The output of IC5 is rectified by D5 to produce a positive pulse, and applied to pin 8 of IC3 through the inverter of IC6. The number of pulses from P2 is directly proportional to the movement of the tonearm. One pulse is equal to 0.081255 mm (about

0.0032 inch) of tonearm movement. IC3 counts the pulses, setting the pulse count to zero when rest switch S9 opens.

A tonearm auto-in-position count and an auto-return-position count are programmed into IC3. The auto-in start count for a 12-inch LP record is zero, while the auto-return count is 1138 pulses. For a 7-inch 45-rpm record, the tonearm auto-in start count is 770 pulses, while the auto-return count is 1196 pulses. Again, keep in mind that these pulse counts are programmed into IC3 and cannot be altered (or even checked). If IC3 does not respond properly to a particular pulse count, IC3 must be replaced.

3.3.9 Tonearm Tracking Circuits

Figure 3.14 shows the circuits used by IC3 to control drive of the tonearm across the record in response to commands. The circuits are a form of tracking servo, and function to keep the tonearm stylus properly tracking in the record groove from start to end.

The tonearm is gimbal mounted and pivots from side to side as well as up and down. This tonearm motion opens and closes a shutter positioned between an LED and phototransistor assembly P1 that is part of the tonearm. As the tonearm pivots in the record groove, the LED light to the phototransistor is interrupted, or passed, causing the phototransistor to turn on or off as required.

When IC3 receives commands to stop the tonearm, pins 33, 34, and 35 of IC3 are low, while pin 36 is high. The high at pin 36 of IC3 is applied to the base of Q103, turning

Fig. 3.13. Tonearm travel mechanism.

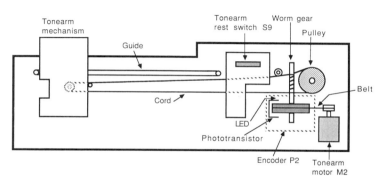

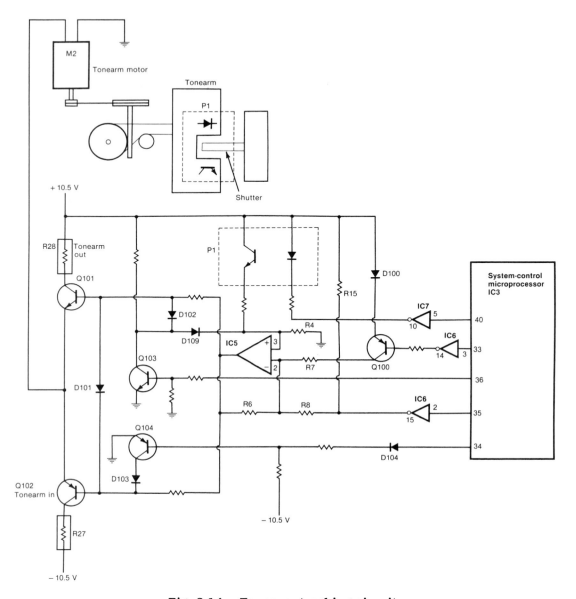

Fig. 3.14. Tonearm tracking circuits.

Q103 on. This forward biases D102 and turns Q101 off. The low at pin 34 of IC3 is applied to the base of Q104, turning Q104 on. This forward biases D103 and turns Q102 off. With both Q101 and Q102 off, tonearm motor M2 does not turn.

When IC3 receives commands to start the play mode, pins 33 and 35 of IC3 are low, while pins 34, 35, and 40 are high. The high at pin 40 is inverted to a low by IC7, turning on the LED within P1. This activates the tonearm shutter control function. Note

that pin 40 of IC3 goes high only when the dustcover is closed, and play is selected.

The high on pin 34 of IC3 is applied to the base of Q104, turning Q104 off and reverse biasing D103. The high on pin 36 of IC3 is applied to the base of Q103, turning Q103 on. This forward biases D102 and turns Q101 off. The low at pin 33 of IC3 is inverted by IC6 and applied to the base of Q100, turning Q100 off. The low at pin 35 of IC3 is inverted by IC6 at the junction of R8 and R15. This places a high at the inverting input of IC5 (pin 2). The noninverting input of IC5 (pin 3) is set by the output from the phototransistor within P1.

With the tonearm shutter open, the voltage levels at pins 2 and 3 of IC5 are equal, and the output at pin 1 of IC5 is zero volt. This keeps Q102 off, and keeps tonearm motor M2 stopped.

As the stylus tracks the record groove, and the tonearm starts to pivot, the shutter is closed. The level applied to pin 3 of IC5 goes low, as does the output of IC5 at pin 1 (to about −9 V).

The low from pin 1 of IC5 is applied to the base of Q102, turning Q102 on. Current flows to tonearm motor M2 through Q102 and fuse resistor R27. This turns M2 on, and causes the tonearm to move in relation to the record groove. Once the tonearm is moved far enough that the shutter opens, the output at pin 1 of IC5 returns to zero volt, and the tonearm stops.

When the TONEARM-IN button is pressed (or when the turntable is started automatically from the rest position, as described in Sec. 3.3.4, pins 33, 34, 35, and 36 of IC3 are all made high (and the tonearm is raised as described in Sec. 3.3.2). Raising of the tonearm opens the tonearm shutter.

When the TONEARM-OUT button is pressed (or during the automatic tonearm-return operation that occurs during stop as described in Sec. 3.3.4), pins 33, 34, and 36 of IC3 are made low, while pin 35 is high. The tonearm is raised as described in Sec. 3.3.2. Raising of the tonearm opens the tonearm shutter.

The low at pin 34 of IC3 turns Q104 on. This connects the base of Q102 to ground through D103, and prevents the output of IC5 from turning Q102 on. The low at pin 36 of IC3 turns Q103 off. This disconnects the base of Q101 from ground through D102, and permits the output of IC5 to control Q101.

The low at pin 33 of IC3 is inverted by IC6 and turns Q100 off. The low at pin 35 of IC3 is inverted by IC6, placing pin 2 of IC5 at

about 3.5 V. With Q103 off, D109 is forward biased, and about 9 V is applied to pin 3 of IC5. With 3.5 V at pin 2, and 9 V at pin 3, the output of IC5 (pin 1) goes high (about +9 V). This high turns Q101 and motor M2 on, causing the tonearm to move out.

The tonearm continues to move out as long as the TONEARM-OUT button is pressed, or until the tonearm reaches rest switch S9 and closes S9 (grounding pin 19 of IC3), as described in Sec. 3.3.8.

The high at pin 36 of IC3 turns Q103 on. This connects the base of Q101 to ground through D102, and prevents the output of IC5 from turning Q101 on. The high at pin 34 of IC3 turns Q104 off. This disconnects the base of Q102 from ground through D103, and permits the output of IC5 to control Q102.

The high at pin 33 of IC3 is inverted by IC6 and turns Q100 on. The high at pin 35 of IC3 is inverted by IC6, grounding the junction of R8 and R15 (in effect). Under these conditions, and with the shutter open, the voltage at pin 3 of IC5 is about 5 V lower than the voltage at pin 2 of IC5. This causes the output of IC5 to go low (about −9 V). The low turns Q102 and motor M2 on, causing the tonearm to move in.

During manual operation or when the TONEARM-IN button is used, the tonearm continues to move in as long as the TONEARM-IN button is pressed. During automatic start operation, the tonearm continues to move in from the rest position until the start of a 7-inch or 12-inch record is reached, as described in Sec. 3.3.4.

3.4 TYPICAL TEST/ADJUSTMENT PROCEDURES

This section describes the test/adjustment procedures for a typical linear-tracking turntable. All of the notes described in Sec. 2.4 apply here. In this section, we concentrate on the procedures for a turntable similar to that shown in Fig. 3.4.

3.4.1 Platter Speed Adjustment

Figure 3.15 is the adjustment diagram. Virtually all turntables have some form of adjustment for rotational speed. Typically, the turntable is operated at 33⅓ and/or 45 rpm, and the speed is checked with a strobe light. Some turntables have separate adjustments for 33⅓- and 45-rpm speeds. In the turntable of Fig. 3.15, the speed-control circuits are adjusted only at 33⅓ rpm. Actually, the phase-control circuits are adjusted to make sure that the turntable speed is phase locked by the PLL at 33⅓ rpm. The speed-control circuits are locked at the correct speed by crystal X1 that controls the PLL.

As shown in Fig. 3.15, the phase-control circuits are adjusted by R10 connected to one input of a summing network within the PLL, IC1. The other input of the summing network receives FG signals from the phase-control circuits of IC1. In turn, the phase-control circuits receive feedback FG signals from the platter motor M1 speed detector.

In basic terms, the turntable is operated at 33⅓ rpm. Potentiometer R10 is then adjusted until the platter speed is phase locked at 33⅓ rpm, as indicated by the strobe light. The speed can then be changed to check for proper phase lock at 45 rpm. However, there is no adjustment at the 45-rpm speed.

The service literature for the turntable of Fig. 3.15 recommends an alternate procedure for speed adjustment *without a strobe*. Again, the turntable is operated at 33⅓ rpm, and the d-c voltage is monitored at pin 8 of PLL IC1. (Note that this is the FG output of IC1.) If the d-c voltage is 1.4 V ±0.1 V, it can be assumed that the turntable is properly phase locked at 33⅓ rpm.

Keep in mind that this procedure applies to only one particular turntable. It is recommended that turntable speed always be checked with a strobe, if available.

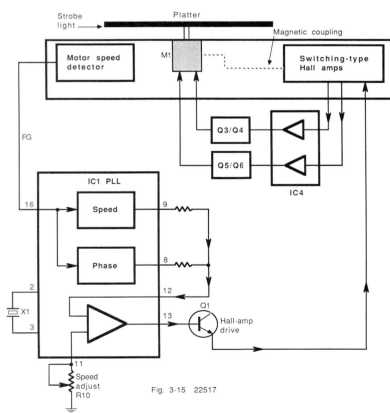

Fig. 3.15. Platter speed adjustment diagram.

3.4.2 Linear Tracking Sensor Adjustment

Figure 3.16 is the adjustment diagram. The purpose of this adjustment is to make sure that the linear tracking sensor shutter opens and closes properly. This is a mechanical adjustment, although the results are measured electrically.

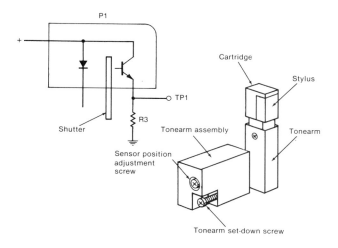

Fig. 3.16. Linear tracking sensor and stylus set-down position adjustment diagram.

As shown in Fig. 3.16, when the tracking sensor shutter opens, light from the LED in P1 is applied to the phototransistor. This turns the P1 phototransistor on, drawing more current through R3 and changing the voltage across R3 (at TP1). The voltage at TP1 is restored to the previous value when the shutter is closed.

With the tonearm in the raised position, adjust the sensor position adjustment screw for an indication of 6 V ±0.5 V at TP1. Then turn the adjustment screw 180° clockwise. This should produce a reading of about 9 V at TP1.

Note that on this particular turntable, if the tonearm assembly cannot be adjusted, the entire tonearm must be replaced. However, the stylus and cartridge can be replaced as separate components, as discussed in Sec. 3.5.

3.4.3 Stylus Set-Down Position Adjustment

Figure 3.16, used for tracking adjustment (Sec. 3.4.2), also shows the screw used in this adjustment. The purpose of the adjustment is to make sure that the stylus sets down at the proper point on the record when the tonearm is lowered. Again, the adjustment is mechanical, but there are no electrical indications. Instead, a test record is required.

During this adjustment, the turntable is operated at 45 rpm with a test record installed. (The test record indicated in the service literature must be used.) The tonearm set-down screw is then adjusted until the stylus sets down onto the record at the correct point (at count 14 on the test record in this case). Of course, this adjustment applies only to a particular turntable. However, many linear-tracking turntables have similar adjustments.

3.5 TYPICAL TROUBLESHOOTING PROCEDURES

This section describes the troubleshooting procedures for a typical linear-tracking turntable. All of the notes described in Sec. 2.5 apply here. In this section, we concentrate on the circuits of a turntable similar to that shown in Fig. 3.4.

The following paragraphs are a collection of trouble symptoms that match the troubleshooting trees found in the service manual for a typical linear-tracking turntable. After selecting the symptom that matches the turntable you are servicing, follow the steps in the corresponding troubleshooting procedure.

3.5.1 Speed Indicator LEDs Do Not Turn On When Power Button Is Pressed

Figure 3.17 is the troubleshooting diagram. The *speed* indicator LEDs, D151/D152, should turn on when the POWER button is pressed. If not, there are several possible causes.

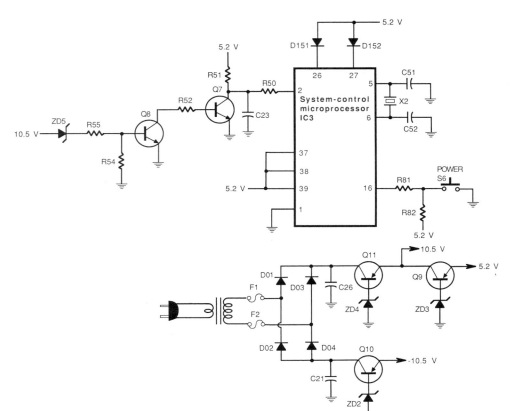

Fig. 3.17. Power circuit troubleshooting.

First, check fuses F1 and F2 (just after you have made sure that the power cord is plugged in). As an alternate, check for proper voltages from the power supply circuits shown in Fig. 3.17. There should be 10.5 V, 5.2 V, and −10.5 V available. If not, check the corresponding components.

For example, if 10.5 V is available from Q11, but there is no −10.5 V, suspect Q10 and/or ZD2. If 10.5 V and −10.5 V are available, but there is no 5.2 V, suspect Q9 and/or ZD3.

Next, check to make sure that pin 2 of IC3 is at 5.2 V. If not, suspect reset circuit Q7, Q8, and ZD5. Note that this circuit resets IC3 each time power is removed and applied.

Check for a 4-MHz signal at pins 5 and 6 of IC3. If not, suspect crystal X2 or C51/C52.

Finally, make sure that pin 16 of IC3 is at 5.2 V when POWER switch S6 is not pressed, but drops to near zero when S6 is pressed.

Finally, check to make sure that pins 26 and/or 27 are low (zero volt). If both pins are high (with a good crystal, X2, and all power available), suspect IC3. If either pin 26 or 27 is low, but the corresponding LED does not turn on, suspect D151/D152.

3.5.2 No Phono Output from the Turntable

Figure 3.18 is the troubleshooting diagram. If the turntable appears to operate normally (platter spins and tonearm moves across the record), but there is no phono output from the turntable to the amplifiers, the cartridge is the most likely suspect. You can try replacing the cartridge as the first step, but there are some other simple checks to make if a cartridge is not readily available.

Start by measuring both the left and right phono outputs with a known-good record playing. Typically, the output is in the 3- to 5-mV range for a dual-magnet cartridge. The actual output should be substantially the same for both channels. If not, this indi-

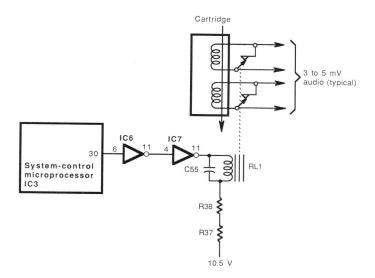

Fig. 3.18. Audio circuit troubleshooting.

cates a failure of one cartridge coil (unless the record happens to be recorded that way!).

Next, check the audio mute circuits (if any). In the circuit of Fig. 3.18, RL1 must be energized for audio to pass from the cartridge to the phono output connectors. RL1 is energized when pin 30 of IC3 is made low during normal play. This low is inverted twice by IC6 and IC7, and applied to the open end of RL1. If pin 30 is not low, suspect IC3. If pin 30 is low, check for a high from IC6, and a low from IC7, to RL1. If the open end of RL1 is low, but RL1 is not energized, suspect RL1, C55 (a possible short), R37, R38, or that the 10.5 V is not available at R37.

We will not go into cartridge replacement here, since each turntable has a different cartridge assembly. However, most linear-tracking turntables have cartridge assemblies that can be plugged in. Often, the stylus can be replaced without removing the cartridge. Because it is so simple, many technicians prefer to replace the cartridge first for a "no phono output" symptom.

3.5.3 Turntable Does Not Rotate

Figure 3.19 is the troubleshooting diagram. If the platter does not spin when power is applied, the dustcover is closed, and the START/CUT button is pressed, check for a low at pin 12 of IC3 with START/CUT

switch S1 pressed. If pin 12 of IC3 is not low, suspect *start/cut* switch S1.

Next try pressing the TONEARM-IN button, S5. If this starts the turntable, but pressing START/CUT switch S1 does not (pin 12 of IC3 low), IC3 is most likely at fault.

If the platter does not spin with either S1 or S5 pressed, check to make sure that pin 21 of IC3 is low. If not, and the dustcover is definitely closed, suspect S8.

Check to make sure that pin 29 of IC3 is low. If not, suspect IC3. This low is inverted to a high by IC6 and applied to pin 4 of IC1. If not, suspect IC6.

With a high at pin 4 of IC1 (and crystal X1 operating normally), check to make sure that pins 8 and 9 of IC1 are near 0 V initially and rise to about 2.4 V when S1 or S5 are actuated. If not, suspect IC1.

Check to make sure that pin 13 of IC1 is about 6 V. If not, suspect R6 through R10 and C6/C7 or IC1.

Check to make sure that the base of Q1 is about 3.5 V. If not, suspect R4/R5, R69/R70, or Q1.

Finally, check for motor drive signals from Q1 through the motor circuits as shown in Fig. 3.19, keeping the following points in mind.

When tracing the platter motor drive signals, the outputs of the two switching amplifiers in M1 should have substantially the

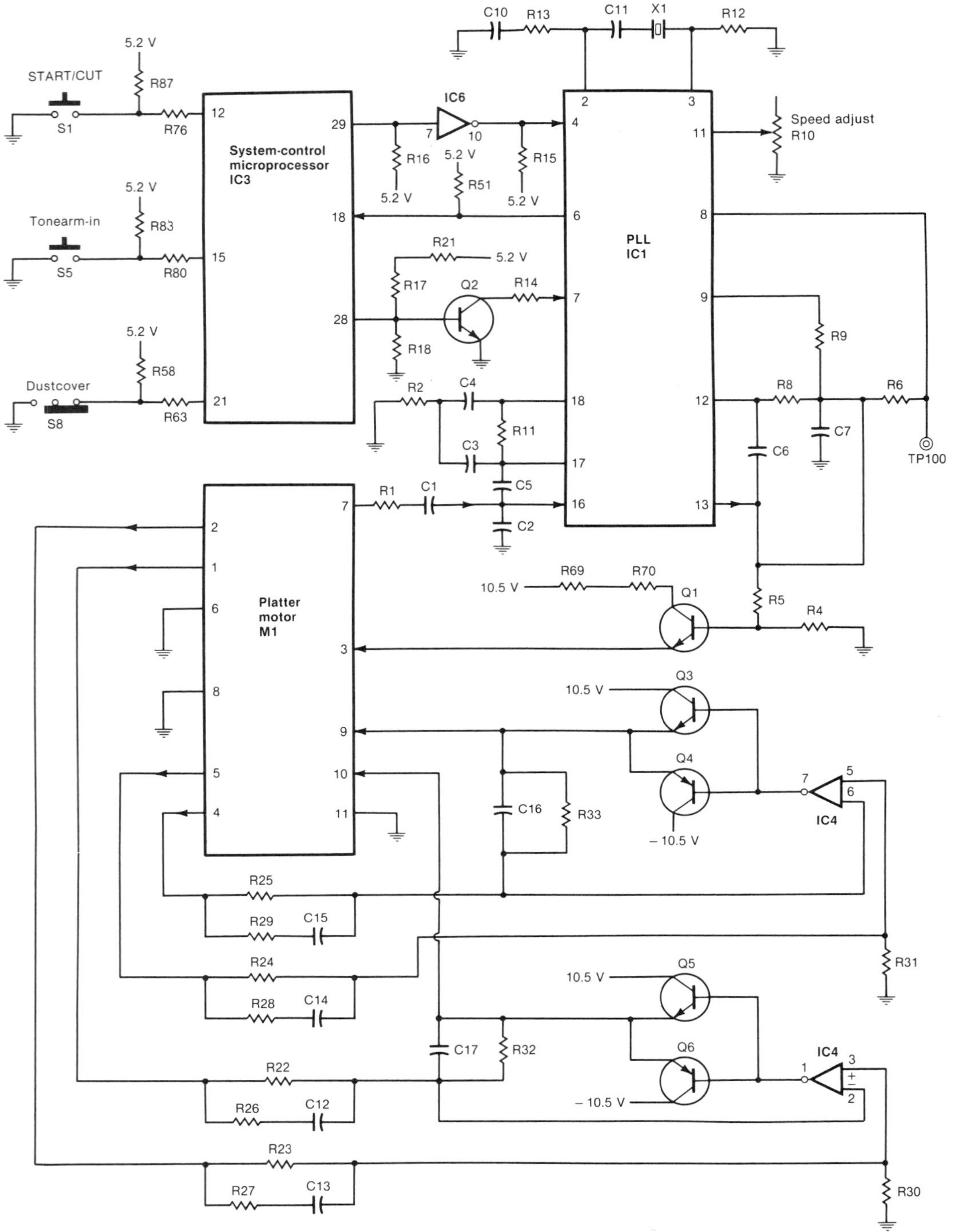

Fig. 3.19. Turntable drive circuit troubleshooting.

same output. If not, suspect M1. Note that on most turntables, the entire platter motor assembly must be replaced as a package.

The outputs of IC4 should also be the same. If not, suspect IC4. Likewise, the outputs from Q3/Q4 and Q5/Q6 should be the

same in amplitude (although shifted in phase by 90°). So, if there are outputs to both motor windings, and the outputs are substantially equal in amplitude, but the motor does not operate, suspect M1.

Note that if the platter should be locked

mechanically, pin 6 of IC1 goes low, as does pin 18 of IC3. This causes IC3 to turn the platter drive off (pin 4 of IC1 goes low). So always look for anything that might jam the platter or prevent the motor from turning. Check the service literature for any lubrication instructions. In some cases, the platter motor requires lubrication (such as a drop or two of silicone oil on the drive shaft). Do not lubricate unless the literature so recommends.

The status at pin 7 of IC1 determines the speed of the platter motor. When pin 28 of IC3 goes low, Q2 is cut off, causing pin 7 of IC1 to go high. This selects the 45-rpm speed. However, the platter motor should run no matter what the status at pin 7 of IC1. The motor also runs with or without speed feedback (FG) signals at pin 16 of IC1. Of course, motor speed will probably be abnormal, as discussed next.

3.5.4 Turntable Rotates at Abnormally High or Low Speed

Figure 3.20 is the troubleshooting diagram. If the turntable rotates at a very high or low speed, no matter which speed is selected, disconnect the power cord, short the

base of Q1 to ground, and then reconnect the power cord. Turn the platter by hand and check for an a-c output (FG signals) at pin 18 of IC1.

If there is no output at pin 18 of IC1 with the platter being rotated, suspect the speed detector in platter motor M1, or the summing amplifier in IC1. You may be able to pin down which of the two components is at fault if you monitor the signal at pin 16 of IC1.

If there is an a-c signal from the speed detector to pin 16 of IC1, but not at pin 18 of IC1, it is reasonable to assume that IC1 is at fault. However, the output from the speed detector is very low (even when the motor is being driven normally) and can be difficult to monitor.

If you get an output at pin 18 of IC1, check to make sure that the output at pins 8 and 9 of IC1 start at zero volt when the platter is rotated slowly, and then increase to about 2.4 V when the platter is rotated fast (by hand). If not, suspect IC1.

If you get correct outputs at pins 8 and 9 of IC1, check to make sure that the output at pin 13 of IC1 is about 6 V when the platter is rotated slowly, then drops to about 0 V when

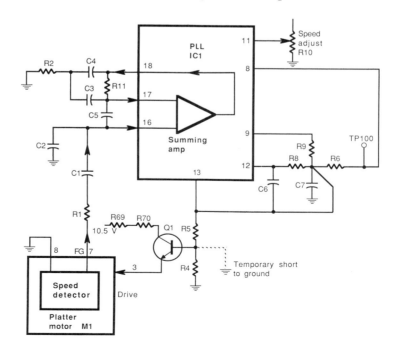

Fig. 3.20. Turntable speed circuit troubleshooting.

the platter is rotated fast. If not, suspect IC1 or R4 through R10 and C6/C7.

3.5.5 Turntable Rotates at the Wrong Speed

Figure 3.21 is the troubleshooting diagram. If the speed is set at 33⅓-rpm when a 45-rpm record is used, or vice versa, the fault is probably in the record size-detect circuits, Q150/Q151 and/or D107/D108, although the problem can be in IC3.

First, with no record installed, check to make sure that both D107 and D108 are turned on by a high at pin 40 of IC3. This high is inverted to a low by IC7. Then check to make sure that both pins 23 and 24 are high. If either pin 23 or 24 is low, check the corresponding size-detect circuit (Q150/D108 for pin 23, Q151/D107 for pin 24).

Next, check to make sure that both the 33⅓-rpm and 45-rpm speed indicator LEDs (D151 and D152) are on (with both pins 23 and 24 of IC3 high). If not, check for a low at pins 26 and 27. If pins 26 and 27 are low, but the corresponding LED is now on, suspect the LED. If pins 26 and 27 are not low, with pins 23 and 24 high, suspect IC3.

Next, check to make sure that pin 28 is high when 33⅓ rpm is selected (pin 23 high, pin 24 low), and goes low when 45 rpm is selected (pin 24 high/pin 23 low). If not, suspect IC3.

If pin 28 of IC3 goes to the correct state when pins 23 and 24 are made high or low, but the correct speed is not selected, suspect Q2 or IC1. When 33⅓ rpm is selected, pin 28 of IC3 goes high. This turns Q2 on and makes pin 7 of IC1 low.

Also, check to make sure that *speed* switch S7 controls the status at pin 28 of IC3. First, check to make sure that pin 17 of IC3 goes low when S7 is pressed, and returns to high when S7 is released. If not, suspect S7. Pin 28 of IC3 should change to the opposite state each time S7 is pressed. If not, suspect IC3.

After making any change in the record size-detect circuit, or replacement of IC3 or IC1, always check for correct platter speed/phase adjustment as described in Sec. 3.4.1.

3.5.6 Tonearm Does Not Move In from the Rest Position

Figure 3.22 is the troubleshooting diagram. If the tonearm does not move from the rest position when the START/CUT button is pressed (from the stop condition), or during repeat mode, or when the TONEARM-IN button is pressed, the problem is probably electrical, but can be mechanical.

As shown in Fig. 3.13, the tonearm is driven by motor M2 through a mechanical assembly. The belt that couples motor M2 and the worm gear is the most vulnerable

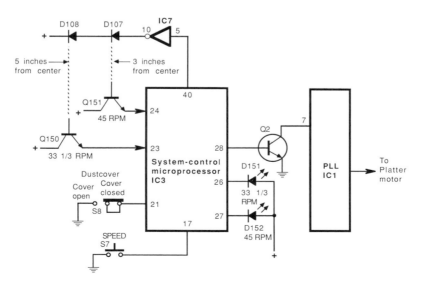

Fig. 3.21. Turntable size/speed detect circuit troubleshooting.

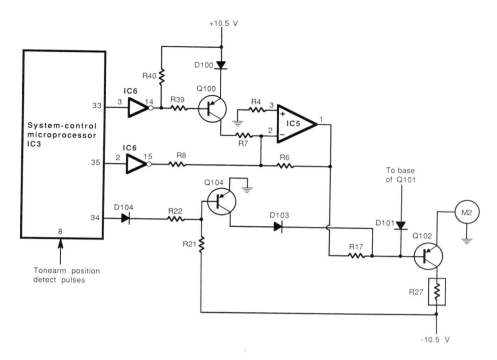

Fig. 3.22. Tonearm-in circuit troubleshooting.

part of the assembly. So always look for a defective belt before troubleshooting the circuit. Also look for anything that might jam or bind the tonearm or mechanical assembly.

Once you are sure the mechanical assembly is good, check to make sure that the platter is spinning. This indicates that power is applied and that IC3 is performing some of the normal functions. If not, refer to Sec. 3.5.3.

If the platter is spinning, check to make sure that both pins 33 and 35 (Fig. 3.22) are high when the tonearm is supposed to be moving in. If not, suspect IC3.

Next, check to make sure that both pins 14 and 15 of IC6 are low. If not, suspect IC6.

With pin 14 of IC6 low, the base of Q100 should be about 9 V. If not, suspect Q100, R39, or R40.

Check for a negative output at terminal 1 of IC5. If not, suspect IC5 or the associated components.

Check for about 8 V at the base of Q104. If not, suspect Q104 or the associated com-

ponents. Pay particular attention to D103/D104 and R21/R22.

With Q104 off, check to make sure that Q102 is turned on, and about −8 V appears at the Q102 emitter. If not, suspect Q102, or the associated components. Pay particular attention to D101/D103 and R17/R27.

With about −8 V at the emitter of Q102, tonearm motor M2 should operate and drive the tonearm in from the rest position. If not, suspect M2. Keep in mind that M2 is not supposed to continue rotating when the tonearm reaches the inner limit of the record (as determined by the correct number of pulses applied to pin 8 of IC3. Refer to Sec. 3.5.10).

If motor M2 is definitely turning in the right direction, but the tonearm is not moving normally, again look for any mechanical problem that might cause the tonearm not to move (broken or slipping belt, slipping worm gear or gear pulley, broken cord or tension spring, tonearm binding on the travel guide, etc.). Check the service literature for any lubrication recommendations, particu-

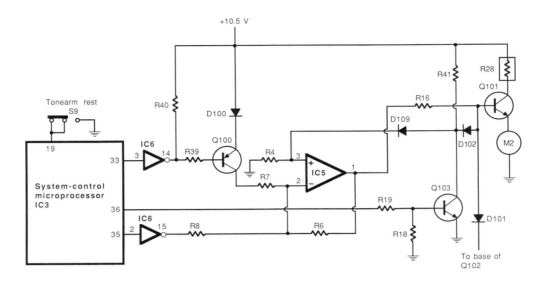

Fig. 3.23. Tonearm-out circuit troubleshooting.

larly for the worm gear, gear pulley, and any gear bearings.

3.5.7 Tonearm Does Not Move Out toward the Rest Position

Figure 3.23 is the troubleshooting diagram. First, make sure that the tonearm is capable of moving as described in Sec. 3.5.6. If not, clear any mechanical problems before you attack the circuits.

Once you are sure that the tonearm is capable of moving, check to make sure that pins 33, 34, and 36 of IC3 are low, while pin 35 is high when the tonearm is supposed to be moving out. If not, suspect IC3.

Check to make sure that pin 15 of IC6 is low, while pin 14 of IC6 is high. If not, suspect IC6.

Check for about 10 V at the base of Q100. If not, suspect Q100 or the associated components. Pay particular attention to D100 and R7/R39/R40.

Check for a positive output at pin 1 of IC5. If not, suspect IC5 or the associated components.

Check for about 9 V at the collector of Q103. If not, suspect Q103 or the associated components. Pay particular attention to D101/D102 and R18/R19/R41.

With Q103 off, check to make sure that

Q101 is turned on, and about 8 V appears at the Q101 emitter. If not, suspect Q101 or the associated components. Pay particular attention to D101/D102 and R16/R28.

With about 8 V at the emitter of Q101, tonearm motor M2 should operate and drive the tonearm out toward the rest position. If not, suspect M2. Of course, M2 is not supposed to continue rotating past the point where the tonearm actuates rest switch S9.

Again, if M2 is definitely turning in the right direction, but the tonearm does not move, look for mechanical problems (Fig. 3.13).

3.5.8 Tonearm Does Not Move Up or Down

Figure 3.24 is the troubleshooting diagram. First, check to make sure that pin 14 of IC3 goes low when TONEARM-UP/DOWN switch S4 is pressed. If not, suspect S4.

Next, check to make sure that pins 31 and 32 of IC3 are about 3.5 V (initially, with the tonearm up). If not, suspect IC3.

Check to make sure that pins 12 and 13 of IC6 are inverted from pins 4 and 5. If not, suspect IC6.

Check to make sure that pins 12 and 13 of IC7 are inverted from pins 2 and 3. If not, suspect IC7.

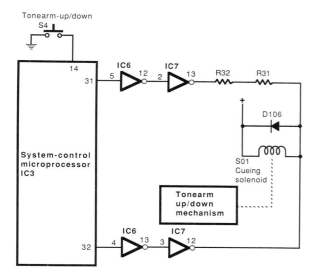

Fig. 3.24. **Tonearm-up/down circuit troubleshooting.**

Check to make sure that pins 12 and 13 of IC7 (pins 31 and 32 of IC3) both go low when S4 is pressed (pin 14 of IC3 low), and that pin 12 of IC7 goes high (but pin 13 of IC7 remains low when S4 is released). Then check to make sure that both pins 12 and 13 of IC7 return to high when S4 is pressed again. If not suspect IC3 or IC6/IC7.

If pin 12 of IC7 is low, but the tonearm does not lower onto the record, suspect S01 or D106. If pin 13 of IC7 is low, but the tonearm does not stay lowered, suspect R31/R32 or possibly S01 and/or D106.

Generally, solenoid S01 cannot be replaced as an individual component on most

linear-tracking turntables. The entire tonearm assembly must be replaced as a package. However, always check the parts list in the service literature for the turntable you are servicing.

3.5.9 Tonearm Does Not Move In During Play

Figure 3.25 is the troubleshooting diagram. First, make sure that the tonearm moves in from the rest position. If not, refer to Sec. 3.5.6. If the tonearm moves in from rest, but does not continue in play when the start of the record is reached, check to make sure that pins 33 and 36 of IC3 are high, and pins 34 and 35 are low. If not, suspect IC3.

Next, try the tracking adjustment described in Sec. 3.4.2.

If the tracking adjustment does not correct the problem, suspect P1. Before you replace P1, make sure the P1 LED is receiving power. Pin 10 of IC7 goes low and connects the P1 LED to ground through R2 when pin 40 of IC3 goes high. If not, suspect IC3, IC7, or R2.

3.5.10 Tonearm Does Not Stop

Figure 3.26 is the troubleshooting diagram. If the tonearm does not stop when the rest position is reached, check rest switch S9 and pin 19 of IC3. S9 should actuate and ground pin 19 of IC3 when the tonearm reaches the rest position. If S9 does not actuate, suspect S9. If S9 actuates and pin 19

Fig. 3.25. **Tonearm tracking circuit troubleshooting.**

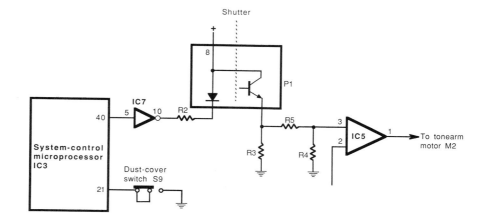

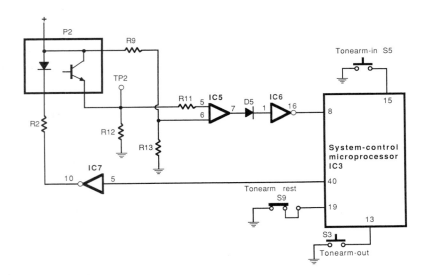

Fig. 3.26. Tonearm stop circuit troubleshooting.

of IC3 goes low, but the tonearm does not stop, suspect IC3.

If the tonearm does not stop when the TONEARM-IN or TONEARM-OUT buttons are released, check the output of P2 across R12. The pulse output from P2 should go from about 3 V to 5 V. If not, suspect P2.

Before you replace P2, make sure the P2 LED is receiving power. Pin 10 of IC7 goes low and connects the P1 LED to ground through R2 when pin 40 of IC5 goes high. If not, suspect IC3, IC7, or R2.

Next, check to make sure that the pulse output from pin 7 of IC5 goes from zero to about 8 V. If not, suspect IC5. Trace the pulses through D5 and IC6 to pin 8 of IC3.

There is no practical way to check the actual number of pulses to IC3. However, if pulses are present at pin 8 of IC3, but the tonearm does not stop at the correct point (or does not return when the inner limit of the record is reached), suspect IC3.

3.5.11 The Repeat Function Cannot Be Selected

Figure 3.27 is the troubleshooting diagram. First, check to make sure that pin 11 of IC3 goes low when REPEAT switch S2 is pressed. If not, suspect S2 and the associated wiring.

Next, check to make sure that pin 25 goes low, and that *repeat* LED D150 turns on, when REPEAT switch S2 is pressed. If pin 25 does not go low, suspect IC3. If pin 25 goes low, but D150 does not turn on, suspect D150. Make certain D150 is receiving power (5.2 V).

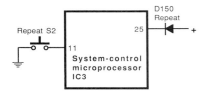

Fig. 3.27. Repeat circuit troubleshooting.

Keep in mind that IC5 should issue the same commands during repeat as during play. The platter should spin and the tonearm should move from the rest position across the record to the automatic-return position, and then return to rest. So do not pull IC3 to correct a "no repeat" symptom until you are sure that normal play is available.

If (when repeat is selected) the tonearm moves from rest position to the automatic-return position across the record, but does not return to rest, refer to Sec. 3.5.7. If the tonearm does not move from rest during repeat, refer to Sec. 3.5.6.

Troubleshooting and Repair of Audio Cassette Decks

This chapter is devoted to audio cassette decks. Included are such subjects as the general description of a typical cassette deck, typical deck circuit descriptions, user-control operation procedures and installation of decks, typical test/adjustment procedures, and examples of troubleshooting based on failure symptoms.

4.1 GENERAL DESCRIPTION OF A TYPICAL AUDIO CASSETTE DECK

Figure 4.1 shows a typical audio cassette deck. The deck described here incorporates a number of modern features not found in all decks, as well as the "typical features" found in most decks. By studying all of these features, you should have no trouble in understanding any modern audio cassette deck.

Our deck is a *4-track, 2-channel stereo* model that requires an amplifier/loudspeaker combination (Chapter 2) to play and record audio cassettes. The deck uses standard size audio cassettes.

Three types of tape can be used: stan-

Fig. 4.1. Sony TC-FX520R stereo cassette deck.
(Courtesy Sony Corporation of America)

dard or normal, chromium-oxide (CrO₂), and metal. (Actually, CrO₂ is chromium-dioxide, although it is usually called chromium-oxide, chrome, chromium, or possibly "CRO.")

As is the case with most modern cassette decks, our model includes Dolby® Noise Reduction (NR), both the B and C systems.

Like all of the audio components described in this book, our cassette deck is *under control of a microprocessor* (actually two microprocessors). The microprocessor circuits monitor and control all functions via

---

®"Dolby" is a trademark of Dolby Laboratories Licensing Corporation

soft-touch buttons or controls on the front panel.

In contrast to some older-type decks, there is no mechanical linkage between the front-panel controls and the cassette drive mechanism in our deck. Each control addresses the microprocessor circuits. In turn, the microprocessor controls the mechanical functions (as well as the electrical functions).

Our deck includes a *scan/play system,* making it possible to scan a tape and play only the first 10 seconds of each program. This permits the listener to sample tape segments as an aid in program selection. Up to 15 of the scanned programs can be selected for playback (in the order the programs were recorded) by entering an assigned number in memory.

The deck also includes a *random access memory* function. This feature holds up to 15 programmed selections for *playback in any order.*

A *record-mute* control adds a 4-second quiet interval to tapes during record.

Two 20-segment light bars are used to indicate peak levels of each channel. These light bars are similar to the fluorescent audio-level indicators described for the integrated amplifier in Chapter 2.

An automatic tape cueing feature permits the deck tape-transport to automatically cue the beginning of the tape (just past the leader). This makes it possible to access blank tape quickly. For partially recorded tape, the deck "finds" the end of the previous recording and cues the starting point for the next recording.

In a typical playback sequence, the transport automatically cues the beginning of the tape, just past the leader. This occurs immediately before playback. In a typical recording sequence, the deck finds the end of the last recording (or just past the leader in the case of a completely blank tape), and then cues the starting point for new segments.

Our deck includes an *auto-reverse tape transport* system. This means that both sides of the tape can be played or recorded *without turning over the cassette tape.* Less sophisticated cassette decks require the user to remove, and turn over, the cassette to play or record the opposite side. The auto-reverse system automatically reverses tape direction (to play or record the opposite side) when the first side is finished.

Two opposing arrows in the lower-left corner of the fluorescent display on our deck indicate which direction the tape transport is playing or recording. The arrow pointing to the right indicates side-1 operation, while the arrow pointing left indicates side-2 operation.

The use of arrows, rather than names, is quite common on modern cassette decks. This is because the functions performed vary with the side that is being played (or recorded), and can lead to some obvious confusion.

To keep confusion to the minimum, we use the following terms to designate tape-transport control buttons.

Play designates either of the buttons that have a single arrow.

Fast forward (FF) designates the button with a double arrow pointing in the same direction as the lighted arrow in the display.

Rewind designates the button with double arrows pointing in the opposite direction from the lighted arrow in the display.

Reverse play is for side 2 of the cassette. The beginning of the program material of side 2, and the end of the program material of side 1 are at the same end of the tape.

The specifications in Chart 4.1 are for a "typical" audio cassette deck, and are included here for reference. Always check the service literature for the deck you are servicing. The basic procedures for checking these specifications are described in Chapter 1.

4.2 USER CONTROLS, OPERATING PROCEDURES, AND INSTALLATION

Although the controls for most audio cassette decks are standardized, there are differences. This section describes the basic

Chart 4.1. Typical Audio Cassette Deck Specifications

Track system:	4-track, 2-channel stereo	
Tape:	Cassette tape	
Tape speed:	4.75 cm/s	
Recording system and bias frequency:	A-c bias, 85 kHz	
Erasing system:	A-c erase	
Erase ratio:	60 dB (at 1 kHz) or more	
Frequency response:	NORM-I:	20 Hz to 16 kHz
		40 Hz to 16 kHz (±3 dB)
	CrO_2-II:	20 Hz to 18 kHz
		40 Hz to 17 kHz (±3 dB)
	Metal-IV:	20 Hz to 19 kHz
		40 Hz to 18 kHz (±3 dB)
S/N ratio (A-weighted reference, 3% THD, metal):	Dolby NR off: 59 dB	
	Dolby NR B on: 68 dB	
	Dolby NR C on: 74 dB	
Wow and flutter:	0.06% (WRMS)	
Input sensitivity and impedance:	Microphone:	0.4 mV (with impedance of 0.5 to 5 kΩ)
	Line in:	55 mV (with impedance of 200 kΩ or more)
Output level and load impedance:	Line out:	500 mV (with load impedance of 50 kΩ or more)
	Headphone:	80 mV (with load impedance of 8 Ω to 2 kΩ)
Distortion:	Less than 1% (1 kHz)	
Crosstalk:	60 dB (at 1 kHz) or more	
Power source:	120 V, 60 Hz	
Power consumption:	25 W	

user controls and operating procedures for a typical deck. You must study the operating controls and indicators for any cassette deck you are troubleshooting.

4.2.1 External Connections

External connections between an audio cassette deck and the stereo amplifier are usually made from the back of the deck. In many cases, two pin cords are supplied with the deck (or amplifier) for connection between the deck's L and R stereo inputs/outputs, and the corresponding inputs/outputs on the amplifier. (The deck outputs are connected to the amplifier inputs, for playback, while the deck inputs are connected to the amplifier outputs, for recording.) Although the connections are very simple, certain precautions must be observed for all decks.

Look for any color coding on the pin cords. Typically, red is used for the right channel, while white is used for the left channel (but do not always count on it). Also look for any ground terminals or leads that are part of the pin cord. (Ground terminals are quite common for phono turntables, but usually not for cassette decks.)

Figure 4.2 shows typical external connections between an audio cassette deck and an amplifier. Note that the amplifier shown has a-c power receptacles for a number of external components (turntable, cassette deck, tuner, and/or CD player). Use a standard polarized wall outlet if necessary.

Do not connect the deck to the CD, *aux*, or *phono* inputs of an amplifier. Instead, always use the *tape play* input (or whatever the deck input is called on the amplifier). Generally, there is no damage done if you connect the deck to the wrong input. However, the deck output does not match the other audio components.

For example, the typical 500 mV output of a cassette deck is too high for the typical 5 mV of a turntable, and too low for the typical

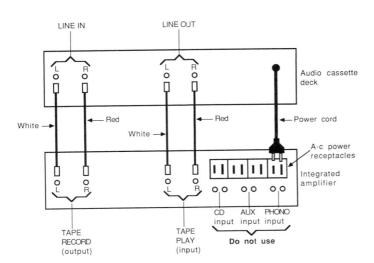

Fig. 4.2. Typical external connections.

2 V of a CD player. Generally, the *tape record* output of an integrated amplifier is applied through a buffer to the deck, as described in Chapter 2.

Do not connect the output of a cassette deck to the output of the amplifier, or the input of the deck to the input of the ampli-

fier! Damage may result, and the connections will not work.

4.2.2 Typical Operating Controls

Figure 4.3 shows the operating controls and indicators for a typical audio cassette deck. Figure 4.4 shows the details of the front-panel display. Compare the following with the controls and indicators of the deck you are servicing.

Pushing the POWER switch or button turns the deck on; pushing POWER again turns the deck off. None of the other controls function when power is off. There is a 4-second delay from turn on until the deck starts playing.

The *timer* button permits operation of the deck with an external timer.

The *eject* button opens the cassette door for inserting and removing cassettes.

When STOP is pressed, tape motion stops, but power stays on. Cassettes may be removed or inserted after STOP is pressed, without turning off the power. *Stop* is also used while pro-

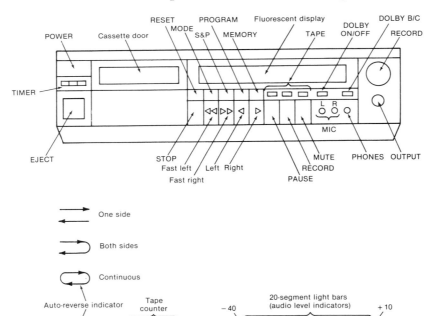

Fig. 4.3. Operating controls and indicators.

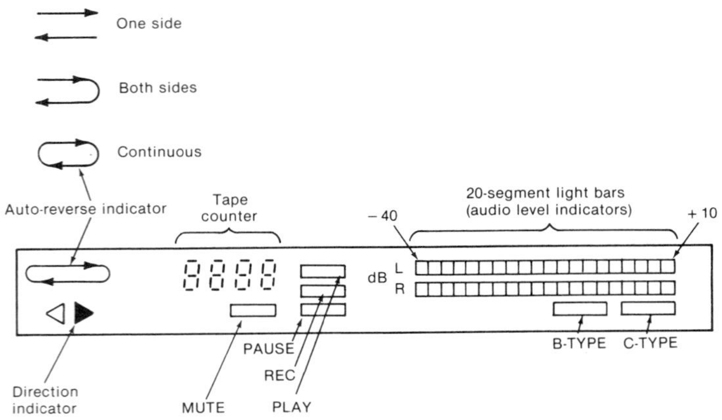

Fig. 4.4. Details of front-panel fluorescent display.

gramming the memory to erase entries. The last entry is erased if STOP is pressed momentarily. The entire memory is erased if STOP is pressed for more than 1 second.

The button with *double arrows pointing left* moves the tape rapidly to the left—on side 1, this is rewind; on side 2, the function is fast forward.

The button with *double arrows pointing right* moves the tape rapidly to the right—on side 1, this is fast forward; on side 2, the function is rewind.

The button with a *single arrow pointing left* plays side 2 (tape moves from right to left), and is also used in conjunction with *record* to start recording on side 2.

The button with a *single arrow pointing right* plays side 1 (tape moves from left to right), and is also used in conjunction with *record* to start recording on side 1.

Pause is used to interrupt recording or playback. The tape stops moving and remains stopped until the pause is ended by pressing PLAY. The *pause* indicator (Fig. 4.4) turns on during *pause,* and the record (recording) indicator stays on if there is a pause during record.

If PAUSE is pressed while the deck is searching for a program, the search continues until the program is found and the tape pauses at the beginning of the program.

Record switches the tape deck into the recording mode, but does not start the tape moving. *Record* is used in conjunction with one of the play buttons (single arrow) to begin recording.

Mute is used *only during record.* When MUTE is pressed momentarily, a 4-second quiet interval is recorded on the tape for automatic cueing. The interval may be extended by holding the button. The cassette deck automatically switches to the recording-pause mode at the end of the muted interval. Press PLAY or PAUSE to continue recording.

The recording input is automatically switched from the input jacks to the MIC (microphone) jack when a microphone is plugged into the L or R (or both) jacks. Make

certain to unplug the microphones to record from any other source.

Use of the *phones* (headphones) jack does not affect any other function of the tape deck. So headphones can be plugged in or out during both record and play. (This is not true in all decks.)

The *output* control sets the level of audio at both the *phones* jack and the rear-panel output jacks (to the speakers through the amplifier), but does not affect record level.

The two *record* controls (one behind the other) set the level of audio during record. Note that the outer knob is for the L (left) channel.

Dolby NR B/C selects either Dolby B or Dolby C for both recording and playback. Most tape deck manufacturers recommend that Dolby C be used for recording because of improved noise reduction. However, make certain to play prerecorded tapes with the Dolby type used during record.

Dolby NR on/off should be set to ON *only for tapes recorded with Dolby noise reduction,* during play. During record, use Dolby as desired, but make certain to play back any Dolby-recorded tape with the correct Dolby type. Commercial tapes recorded with Dolby noise reduction are supposed to be so designated on the label.

The three *tape* type switches are mechanically interlocked so that pressing one of the switches releases the other two switches. Make certain to press the button corresponding to the type of tape in use. (This can cure many "poor sound quality" trouble symptoms.)

Table 4.1 lists some typical tapes available for use with cassette tape decks.

Memory enters the program selections into memory. *Program* is used to select the program number (which increases one increment each time PROGRAM is pressed).

When S&P (scan and play) is pressed, the tape rewinds and begins playing the first 10 seconds of each recording on one side of the tape. The tape counter (Fig. 4.4) indicates the numerical order of the programs on the tape as they are played (A-01, A-02, A-03, etc.).

Table 4.1. Some Typical Tapes for Use with
Cassette Tape Decks

NORM I	CrO₂ II	METAL IV
BASF (PRO I)	BASF (PRO II)	BASF (METAL IV)
FUJI (FXI, FL)	FUJI (FX II)	FUJI (METAL)
Maxell (UD, XL1)	Maxell (XL II)	Maxell (MX)
Scotch (Master I)	Scotch (Master II)	Scotch (Metafine)
Sony (SHF)	Sony (EHF)	Sony (Metallic)
TDK (AD, OD)	TDK (SA, SAX)	TDK (MA)

The reversing mode changes each time MODE is pressed. The mode is indicated in the upper-left corner of the display unit (Fig. 4.4). Three modes are available: one-side mode, both-sides mode, and continuous mode.

With the *one-side mode*, you may record or play in one direction or the other, and the tape stops at the end. You must manually select the reverse mode to record or play the other side of the tape.

With the *both-sides mode*, recording or playing begins with side 1 (tape moving from left to right). At the end of side 1, the tape reverses and plays (or records) side 2 (right to left) and stops. The tape deck does not reverse at the end of side 2.

With the *continuous mode*, the tape automatically reverses at the end of each side, and continues playing until the tape is stopped (up to a maximum of 16 "round-trips"). If you record in the continuous mode, the tape stops after both sides have been recorded.

The *reset* control resets the tape counter (Fig. 4.4) to 0000. The counter resets automatically when the tape is rewound to the beginning.

When the tape has been rewound to the beginning, or when RESET is pressed, the fluorescent display (Fig. 4.4) tape counter reads 0000. The counter advances as the tape plays, and reads *end* when the tape reaches the end.

During programming, when the PROGRAM button is pressed the first time, the counter reads 01. Each time PROGRAM is pressed, the number increases (up to 15).

During scan and play, the selection number that is being played (for audition) is displayed. A-01 designates the first selection on the tape, A-02 is the next selection, etc. Note that the number is preceded by A.

As the tape deck starts playing each selection from memory, the display shows which program is being played, according to the order in memory. For example, P-03 indicates that the third selection entered into memory is playing. The number is preceded by P to indicate programmed playback.

The *play* indicator turns on to indicate that tape is playing or recording. The *rec* indicator turns on to indicate that the deck is recording (or is in the pause mode) during record. The *pause* indicator turns on to indicate that the tape deck is in the pause mode. The *mute* indicator turns on to indicate that the tape deck is recording with the input muted.

The L and R level meters (two 20-segment light bars) shows the instantaneous level of the signal during recording or playback. Note that the range is −40 dB to +10 dB.

One of the two *direction indicator* arrows turns on whenever power is on. The arrow pointing to the right indicates that the tape deck is set to record or play side 1 (left to right). The arrow pointing right indicates that the deck is to play or record side 2 (tape travel right to left).

The B-type or C-type indicators turn on to indicate the corresponding Dolby noise reduction system selected.

4.2.3 Initial Setup

The following paragraphs describe the initial setup procedure for the tape deck shown in Figs. 4.3 and 4.4. Keep in mind that not all cassette decks have the sophisticated operating controls and indicators found here. However, most modern cassette decks have similar control and indicator functions.

Press POWER to turn on the power *before* you insert the first cassette. The tape drive or transport may have moved during shipment (bouncing in the customer's car on the way to the shop). Turning on the power resets the tape transport to the normal rest position (on most decks).

Normally, you can insert and remove cassettes with the power on or off (unless the transport is moving!). However, if the transport has been jarred or moves, it is safer to turn on the power before installing the first cassette.

Press EJECT to open the cassette door. The power may be on or off, but the transport must be *stopped before* you try to insert a cassette.

With the cassette door open, insert the cassette with side 1 toward the front of the tape deck, and with the opening in the cassette facing down. Make sure to close the cassette door before starting any play or record mode.

Press the corresponding TAPE selector switch for the type of tape to be used.

If a prerecorded tape is used, check the label to determine if the recording was made with Dolby noise reduction. If not, make sure that Dolby NR on/off is set to OFF. If Dolby was used, set Dolby NR on/off to ON, and Dolby NR B/C to B or C as appropriate.

If you are going to record a tape with Dolby, Type C is recommended (by most deck manufacturers) for best S/N ratio and dynamic range. A possible exception is where the tape may likely be played without Dolby or with Type B only.

The tape deck selects the both-sides mode when first turned on. You can select a different reversing mode by pressing MODE. The mode selected is indicated by the lines and arrowheads on the upper-left side of the fluorescent display (Fig. 4.4). The deck must be turned on to select a different mode.

Unless a recording is to be made with microphones, make certain to unplug microphones from the L and R MIC jacks. (This can sometimes cure a "no audio" trouble symptom.) Signals from all other sources are disabled when microphones are plugged in.

Note that the *output* control sets the level of audio to the *phones* jack, and to the integrated stereo amplifier, but not to the record heads (as discussed in Sec. 4.2.7). Gen-

erally, the *output* control is set so that the volume for the speakers is the same as for other components (turntable, tuner, CD player, etc.).

Use the fast-forward or fast-reverse (buttons with double arrows) switch to wind tape. It is generally good practice to wind the tape to one end before removing the cassette from the tape deck. In this way, if the counter shows 0000 or *end,* all the tape is wound onto one cassette hub.

If you (or the customer) runs a tape part way in either direction, remove the tape, and then reset the counter to 0000 or *end,* the results can be a "sometimes I can't play or record the whole tape" trouble symptom.

Press EJECT to open the cassette door, and remove the cassette. Turn off power, unless you are going to play another cassette.

4.2.4 Normal Playback Operation

The following paragraphs describe the basic playback sequence for the tape deck shown in Figs. 4.3 and 4.4. The basic playback sequence is generally quite simple for most modern cassette decks. You turn the power on, insert a cassette, and press a PLAY button. In our deck, you must also set the tape-type, noise-reduction, and reverse-mode controls as required.

Keep the following points in mind when operating any deck with controls similar to ours.

Remember, there are two play buttons, one for each direction of travel.

For side 1, press the button with a single arrow, pointing right. Play is from left to right.

For side 2, press the button with a single arrow, pointing left. Play is from right to left.

The buttons for fast forward and rewind are interchanged when the playing direction is changed. This is shown as follows:

	Side-1	Side-2
Rewind	← ←	→ →
Fast Forward	→ →	← ←

To play the tape, press the PLAY button (single arrow) for the side of the tape you want to play. To pause during playback, press PAUSE. To resume playback, press PAUSE again (or press the PLAY button for the side you are playing).

To reverse direction while the tape is playing (to play the other side) press the PLAY button whose arrow points in the opposite direction from current tape travel.

To advance the tape rapidly (fast-forward), press the button with double arrows pointing in the same direction that the tape is presently moving. The tape should advance until the end of the tape leader is reached, or until you press STOP.

To rewind to an earlier point on the tape, press the button with double arrows pointing in the direction opposite to tape travel. The tape should rewind to the beginning of the leader, unless you press STOP to interrupt rewinding.

To rewind to the beginning of the tape, just past the leader (automatic tape cueing), press both buttons with double arrows at the same time. This should also cause the *pause* indicator to flash.

You can skip to the beginning of the next selection on the tape by pressing both buttons (simultaneously) that have arrows pointing in the direction of tape travel. For example, on side 1, press both buttons (single and double arrow) pointing right. For side 2, press both buttons pointing left.

To return to the beginning of a selection that is playing, press the SINGLE-ARROW button in the direction of tape travel, and the DOUBLE-ARROW button in the opposite direction. For example, on side 1, press the SINGLE-ARROW button pointing right, and the DOUBLE-ARROW button pointing left (simultaneously). For side 2 press the SINGLE-ARROW button pointing left, and the DOUBLE-ARROW button pointing right (simultaneously).

4.2.5 Scan-and-Play Operation

The following paragraphs describe the scan-and-play sequences for the tape deck shown in Figs. 4.3 and 4.4. Scan and play provides a very convenient method for finding and playing one or more selections on a tape, without having to refer to the cassette label.

Our tape deck starts from the beginning of the side you have selected, and plays the first 10 seconds of each selection or program. Each time you hear a selection you want to play, press the MEMORY button. When this scanning process is complete, or when you have made 15 selections, the tape deck automatically rewinds to the first selection and begins playing.

Many of the automatic functions for our deck (and on most audio cassette decks) operate by sensing the blank intervals between programs. On our deck, the tape must have been recorded with at least 3 seconds of blank tape between programs so the system can identify the programs as separate selections. This brings up an obvious problem. Recordings of conversations that have quiet intervals lasting longer than 3 seconds may be recognized as multiple selections.

Once the initial setup has been made as described in Sec. 4.2.3, and the side has been selected by pressing the appropriate PLAY button (single arrow), scan and play is selected by pressing STOP and then S&P.

The tape automatically rewinds to the first selection and starts playing. The counter shows a flashing A, followed by the number of the selection. The indication during rewind to the first selection is A-00. This changes to A-01 when the first selection begins playing.

After 10 seconds, the tape deck skips to the next selection and plays 10 seconds; then skips again until all selections on one side of the tape have been auditioned, or until 15 selections have been entered into memory. The sequence of display is A (flashing), A-00, A-01, A-02, A-03, . . . , A-0n.

Press MEMORY each time you hear a selection you want to play. The tape deck should skip immediately to the next selection.

You may skip the next selection before the 10-second audition is over by pressing the button with double arrows pointing in the direction of tape motion (fast forward).

At the end of the tape, the deck automatically rewinds and begins playing the first selection. If you have made 15 entries in memory before you reach the end of the tape, the deck automatically rewinds the tape and begins playing.

If you wish to start playing selections before the tape finishes scanning, press the button with double arrows pointing opposite the tape motion. If you want to play just one selection, press MEMORY and REWIND (double arrow) when you hear the selection during scan.

The tape deck stops at the end of the tape if you have made no entries in memory.

When the first selection begins playing, the counter displays P-01, indicating that this is the first program selection.

When the second program selection begins, the display changes to P-02. When the last selection is finished, the deck stops and the display shows a 4-digit number indicating the position of the tape. Memory is erased when all selections have been played.

4.2.6 Random Memory Play Operation

The scan-and-play feature (Sec. 4.2.5) plays selections in the order recorded on the tape. With random search (or random access), you can play selections in random order, regardless of the selection sequence on the tape. However, the memory capacity remains at 15 selections.

Before you can program the memory for random play, you need to know the number of the selections on the tape. If the selections are not listed on the cassette label, audition the tape with scan and play and make a list.

Assume that you want to play selection numbers 8, 3, and 7, in that order; assume that the cassette has been inserted, and power is on. If you make a mistake in the following steps, you can erase the last entry you made by pressing STOP momentarily. If

you hold STOP down more than 1 second, the entire memory is erased.

Press and release PROGRAM until 08 appears.

Now press MEMORY. The display should change to P-01, indicating the first selection, and then to 08, designating the selection number.

Press PROGRAM again until 03 appears.

Press MEMORY and the display should change to P-02, indicating the second entry in memory, and then to 03, designating the selection number.

Repeat the process for selection number 7, and any more selections you wish to enter (up to a total of 15). After you have selected 15 programs, P *end* appears in the display.

You can repeat the same selection by calling up the selection number with *program* and pressing MEMORY more than once. A single selection can be repeated up to 15 times, or three selections can be repeated five times each. The same selection can be played at different places in the program.

When you have completed program selection, press the button with two arrows pointing opposite to the direction indicator in the display (rewind). The tape deck finds the first selection entered in memory, and begins playing the entire program. As each selection begins playing, the counter displays the program number.

4.2.7 Recording Operation

The first step in recording is to set up the deck as described in Sec. 4.2.3, and turn on the selected audio source (tuner, turntable, CD player, etc.). Then start recording by pressing RECORD and PLAY (single arrow button) simultaneously. The deck will then record whatever audio has been selected, without further operation of controls. Stop recording by pressing STOP. However, there are several points to be considered before you record anything (and before you check out the record function during and/or after troubleshooting). The following notes apply specifically to the deck shown in Figs. 4.3

and 4.4, but are also useful for most modern audio cassette decks.

If you intend to record a "live" source, make the initial setup *well beforehand.* Of course, once you become familiar with the controls of a particular deck, setup should require less than a minute. Here are the basic steps.

Turn on the deck (but do not press RE-CORD or PLAY), insert the cassette, select the type of tape, and the type of noise reduction.

Select either the one-side mode or the both-sides mode (if the deck has both modes). If you choose the both-sides mode, start recording on side 1. (This can eliminate confusion if you make a practice of starting all recordings on side 1.)

Observe the tape-direction arrow in the display. If the arrow points to the right, recording is on side 1; if the arrow points to the left, recording is on side 2. To reverse sides, press PLAY for the opposite side, and then press STOP.

Select the position on the tape where you want to begin the recording.

To begin recording at the beginning of the tape, press the REWIND button (double arrow to the left for side 1, double arrow to the right for side 2), then press RECORD.

If the cassette has program material previously recorded, you can find the end of the last recorded segment by pressing RECORD and the appropriate FAST-FORWARD button (double arrow pointing right for side 1; double arrow pointing left for side 2).

The cassette deck is now ready for setting the recording levels.

Turn on the audio source device, and prepare to play the material you want to record. In a typical audio system the steps are as follows:

1. Turn on the source device.
2. Turn on the stereo amplifier.
3. Select the source device for recording.

If microphones are involved, plug the microphones into the jacks on the tape deck. On most decks, the microphones must be unplugged before recording from any other source.

The recording inputs from the audio components of one manufacturer are usually designed for approximately equal levels. This means that the customer need not readjust the recording levels frequently, once properly set. This is not necessarily true when troubleshooting, where a component is often checked out with components from other systems (or with shop standard components). Here are some thoughts on setting recording levels.

There are two *record* level controls (on one shaft) of the deck shown in Fig. 4.3. The L and R indicators (Fig. 4.4) show the levels for corresponding channels. Always watch the level indicators while adjusting the *record* level controls.

Make the initial record level adjustment with a *monophonic source,* such as an AM broadcast. This ensures that the levels to the right and left input jacks are equal.

The levels can be adjusted in the recording monitor mode (by pressing RECORD alone, without pressing PLAY), or while you are recording (pressing RECORD and PLAY simultaneously), whichever is convenient.

When recording with microphones, sound coming from a point midway between the two microphones should produce the same indication on both input indicators. There are many variables in live recording, so you should make test recordings beforehand to determine the optimum recording levels and microphone placement.

In any recording, the indicators should show approximately the *same average levels.* The following are typical levels for a cassette deck.

For Tape Types I and II (Normal and CrO_2), the +3-dB lights of the level indicators should light occasionally.

For Tape Type IC (Metal), the +6-dB lights of the level indicators should light occasionally.

Keep in mind that these levels are for

reference only. Always check the specifications for any deck you are troubleshooting.

On the deck of Figs. 4.3 and 4.4, you may pause during a recording by pressing PAUSE, and resume by pressing PAUSE again (or by pressing PLAY for the direction in which you have been recording). The pause feature is convenient for editing out unwanted parts of the material you are recording.

The deck of Fig. 4.3 does not determine that the material recorded before and after the pause are different selections, unless a 3-second (minimum) quiet interval separates the selections. If you want the material to be two separate selections or programs, insert a 4-second quiet interval between the selections.

A 3-second quiet interval must be recorded between selections for the automatic search system of the Fig. 4.3 deck to operate properly. You may record this interval when you end a selection, or before you begin recording the next selection. There are several ways of doing this, depending on the equipment used with the deck.

Press MUTE before you press STOP. The tape will run 4 seconds and stop, at which time the tape deck goes into the recording-pause mode. From the recording-pause mode, you may start another recording by pressing PAUSE or the appropriate PLAY button.

If the audio source component has a pause feature, press the source component PAUSE button, when the material you are recording is finished. Wait about 4 seconds, and then stop the deck (press STOP).

When recording from a component with no pause feature, turn off the component about 4 seconds before stopping the deck.

To insert the muted interval before you begin a recording, start the deck about 4 seconds before you turn on the audio source component.

On most audio cassette decks, tapes are automatically erased each time you make a recording. (Keep this in mind if you find a cassette in a deck brought in for service!)

If you want to erase an entire tape without using the deck, use a *bulk tape eraser* (being careful not to use the bulk eraser near a customer's tape!).

You can erase part of a tape without recording new material (on most decks). To erase a long passage, begin recording in the usual way, but turn the input levels to minimum. To erase a short passage, begin recording in the usual way, and hold down MUTE until the unwanted material has had time to pass across the recording head.

Do not erase a tape using either of these methods until you first play the tape to *find the exact part to be erased.*

4.3 TYPICAL AUDIO CASSETTE DECK CIRCUIT DESCRIPTIONS

This section describes the theory of operation for a typical audio cassette deck. All of the notes described in Sec. 2.3 apply here. In this section, we concentrate on the circuits of a deck similar to that shown in Figs. 4.3 and 4.4. Figure 4.5 is the block diagram of such a deck.

4.3.1 Circuit Overview

As shown in Fig. 4.5, the *record/playback heads* serve a dual purpose: recovery of the signal from the tape during playback, and recording of the audio signal on the tape during record mode. The *record/playback switching circuits* (Sec. 4.3.2) are responsible for determining whether the heads are in playback or record.

The *tape-transport or mechanism microprocessor* IC500 provides the necessary switching signals to the record/playback switching circuits, and also outputs control signals to the main *signal-processing circuits*, as described in Sec. 4.3.2. The main purpose of IC500 is to monitor and control the tape-transport mechanism (Sec. 4.3.8).

The microphone (MIC) input is applied directly to the signal processing circuits, as is the line in/out jack input. This line in/out is a bidirectional audio bus used with audio systems. A separate line out is provided for

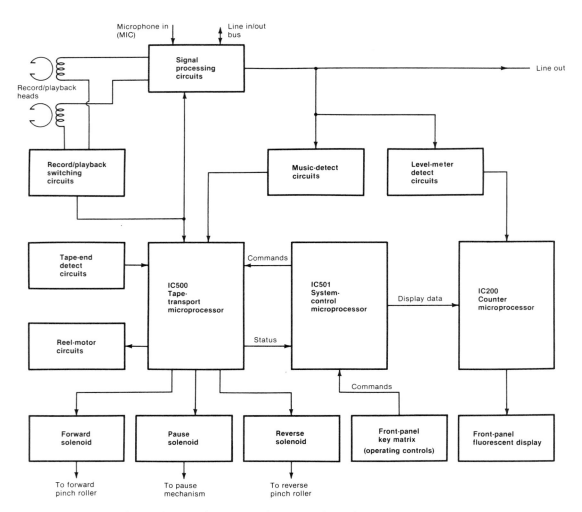

Fig. 4.5. Basic block diagram of audio cassette deck.

normal "stand alone" operation. The line out is also used to supply signals to the *music-detect circuits* (Sec. 4.3.3), and to the *level-meter detect circuits* (Sec. 4.3.6).

The *music-detect circuit* provides the scan-and-play operation and the random-memory-play function. The music-detect circuit is responsible for detecting the music (or other program material) recorded on tape, and causes the tape to go from search to play for 10 seconds, and then back to search, during scan and play. During random memory play, the music-detect circuit causes the deck mechanism to go to the play mode, and remain there until the end of the passage. The mechanism then goes to search until the next programmed selection.

The *level-meter detect circuit* rectifies the audio signal from the signal-processing circuits, and generates a d-c control voltage applied to counter microprocessor IC200. This d-c voltage represents the audio level, and is used to generate the L and R bar graph (20-segment light bars) on the front-panel fluorescent display.

The output from the *tape-end detect circuit* (Sec. 4.3.5) is applied to IC500. Tape-transport microprocessor IC500 is also responsible for driving the *reel-motor circuits* (Sec. 4.3.9) and operating the three tape-transport solenoids (Sec. 4.3.10).

IC500 issues status signals to system-control microprocessor IC501, and receives command signals from IC501. The status signals inform IC501 as to the mechanical and functional status of the deck. Commands from IC501 inform IC500 as to what function is selected via the front-panel key matrix (Sec. 4.3.7).

IC501 also issues display-data signals to IC200. These data signals cause IC200 to generate front-panel indications on the fluorescent display as described in Sec. 4.3.6.

4.3.2 Record/Playback Circuits

Figure 4.6 shows the overall record/playback circuits (for one channel) in block form. The record/playback heads are placed in the playback mode, or record mode, by the record/playback switching circuit. This switching circuit is controlled by an output from pin 24 of IC500.

During the playback mode (IC500 pin 24 low), the head recovers the recorded audio signal from tape, and applies the signal to a playback amplifier. Both the amplifier

and record/playback switching are shown in Fig. 4.7.

With pin 24 of IC500 low, both Q62 and Q63 are turned on (grounding the record input to the head), while Q61 is turned off (permitting the recovered audio to pass to IC60).

Note that the equalization network connected to IC60 is the standard equalization circuit for most audio cassette tapes, with 3180 μs (R69/C62), 120 μs (R64/C62), and 70 μs (R61/C61) time constants. The voltage gain of IC60 is about 49 dB at 400 Hz.

The output of the playback amplifier is applied to the playback portion of the Dolby processing circuits in IC300 through playback-gain control RT60. After processing by the Dolby circuits as described in Sec. 4.3.4, the audio is applied to the headphone amplifier, and to the music detect circuits (Sec. 4.3.3).

Figure 4.8 shows the headphone amplifier circuit. Note that *output* level control

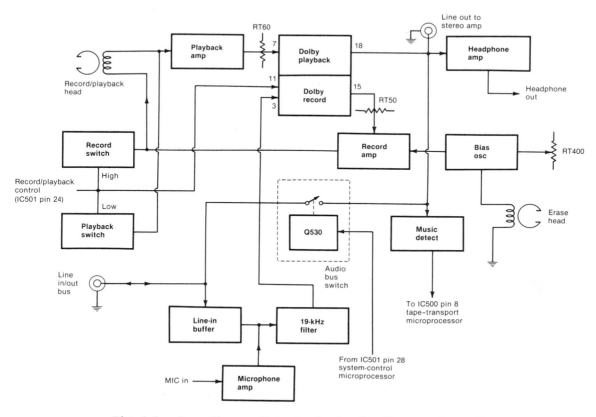

Fig. 4.6. Overall record/playback circuits (for one channel).

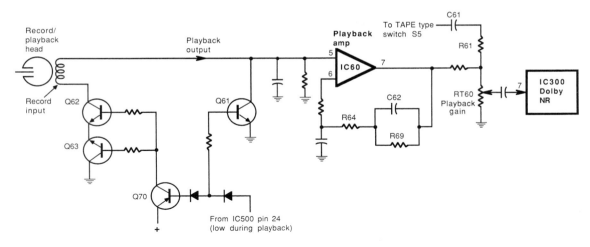

Fig. 4.7. Playback amplifier and record/playback switching.

RV40 controls audio to both the headphones and line (stereo amplifier). The output of the headphone amplifier is typically 80 mV into 8 Ω impedance when a Dolby calibration tape is used.

Audio-bus switch Q530 permits the line in/out jack to be used as a bidirectional audio bus connection during system operation. Audio-bus switch IC01 is controlled by Q530 which, in turn, is controlled by the signal at pin 28 of IC501 (high for audio bus).

During nonsystem operation (audio-bus switch IC01 open), the line in/out jack acts as a line-in function only. During system operation, the line in/out jack may be used as both an in and out connection (in, switch open, during record; out, switch closed, during playback).

During the record mode (IC500 pin 24 high) both Q62 and Q63 are turned off (re-

moving the ground from the record input to the head), while Q61 is turned on (disabling the audio to IC60). This places the record/playback heads in the record mode.

The audio at the line in/out jack is applied to the line-in buffer circuits. Figure 4.9 shows the line-in buffer, microphone amplifier, and Dolby filter (19 kHz filter) circuits.

The buffer keeps the line input at an impedance of about 200 Ω. The audio exits the buffer and is applied to a 19-kHz filter. This filter removes any 19-kHz pilot signals from an FM multiplex broadcast (Chapter 5), and/or a-c bias leakage. Either of these signals can trigger the Dolby NR circuits, thus upsetting the proper response characteristics of the Dolby NR function.

Audio from the filter is applied to the record portion of IC300. Figure 4.10 shows the frequency-response characteristics of

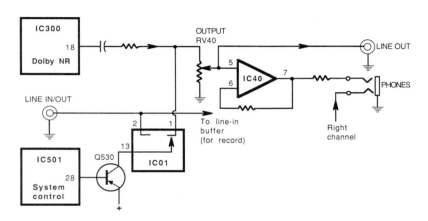

Fig. 4.8. Headphone and line-out circuit.

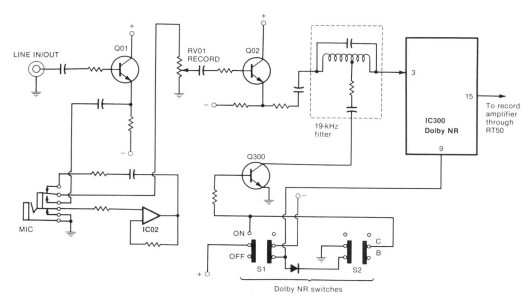

Fig. 4.9. Line-in buffer, microphone amplifier, and Dolby filter circuits.

the circuit from line in to IC300. We discuss Dolby further in Sec. 4.3.4.

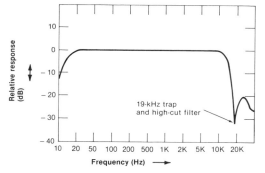

Fig. 4.10. Frequency-response characteristics from line in to IC300.

During microphone operation, the signal flow is identical to line in, except that audio from the microphones is applied to the microphone amplifier, and then to the 19-kHz Dolby filter. This bypasses the line-in filter.

Audio from IC300 is applied to the record amplifier through recording/playback level adjustment RT50, together with signals from the bias oscillator. After processing by the record amplifier, the audio is applied to the record input of the record/playback head, and is recorded onto tape.

Figure 4.11 shows the record amplifier and bias oscillator circuits. Note that a fixed amount of bias current is applied to the erase head. However, the record head receives higher or lower bias current, depending on the position of *tape* select switch S5. Bias current is also adjusted by RT400.

The record amplifier consists of IC50, with the associated components to compensate for record-current requirements. These components boost both high and low ends of the frequency range. (This is commonly called *equalization*.) *Tape* select switch S5 cuts in the components as necessary to provide the correct compensation for the three basic types of tape (normal, CrO_2, and metal).

4.3.3 Music-Detect Circuits

Figure 4.12 is a simplified diagram of the music-detect circuits. These circuits locate music passages on the cassette tape. This function is necessary for the scan-and-play capability, as well as random-access operation.

Figure 4.12 is a simplified diagram of the music-detect circuits. These circuits locate music passages on the cassette tape. This function is necessary for the scan-and-

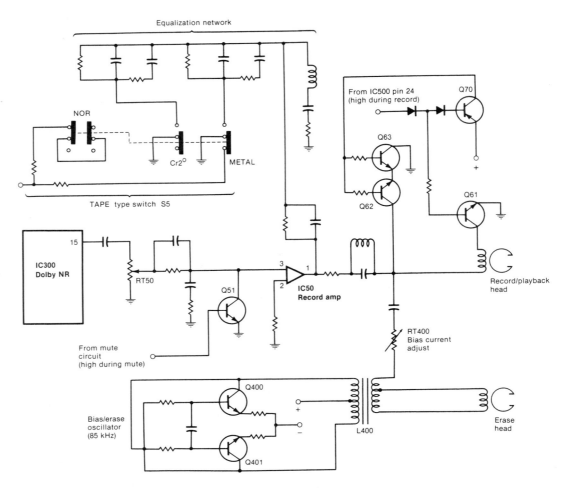

Fig. 4.11. Record amplifier and bias oscillator circuits.

play capability, as well as random-access operation.

The left and right audio signals are summed together through R30L/R30R. The summed signals are applied to the music-detect circuits within IC500 through a filter and amplifier, IC30. The frequency-response characteristics of the filter are determined by the status of Q30.

During high-speed search, Q30 is turned on by a high on the line-mute output from pin 27 of IC500. This grounds R33/R34, and increases attenuation provided by the filter. More attenuation is necessary

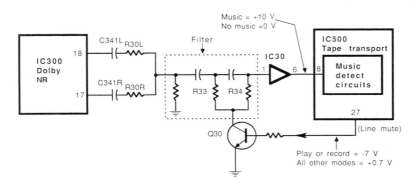

Fig. 4.12. Basic music-detect circuits.

since signal amplitude is increased when tape is moved across the head at search speed. Such an increase in signal amplitude can be mistaken for the presence of music.

During normal play, the line-mute output at pin 27 of IC500 goes low, turning Q30 off, and restoring the filter attenuation to normal.

The output of IC30 is either about +10 V when there is music, or 0 V when there is no music. This output is applied to pin 8 of IC500, and causes IC500 to take the appropriate action (supply signals to the tape-transport mechanism to produce scan-and-play and/or random-access operation).

Although the function is called "music-detect," the circuits operate on signals of any kind (voice, tone, etc.) as long as the signals are substantially above the background level.

4.3.4 Dolby Record/Playback Circuits

The audio cassette deck shown in Figs. 4.3 and 4.4 is capable of providing either Dolby B or Dolby C processing during both playback and record. The Dolby functions are incorporated into a single module (IC300), commonly known as an MD300 Dolby noise reduction module. The use of a single module for Dolby operation is quite common for modern audio cassette decks.

We will not go into the internal circuits of the Dolby module here. If any of the internal circuits fail to work properly, you must replace the entire module (as is the case with any IC). However, you should have some knowledge of what is done by the internal circuits to properly troubleshoot the circuits that are external to the Dolby module.

Figure 4.13 shows the basic block diagram of a tape recorder with Dolby noise reduction. Note that Dolby processing occurs both in recording and playback. The input audio to be recorded is processed before the audio is applied to the record amplifier. The audio taken from the tape is processed after

amplification by the playback amplifier. This is typical for most audio cassette decks.

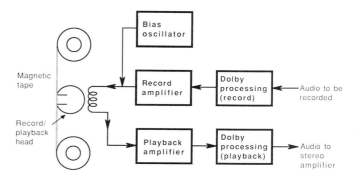

Fig. 4.13.   Basic circuits for tape recorder with Dolby noise reduction.

"Hiss" noise (made up of predominantly high frequency) is introduced into the system at various points (typically at the tape, record/playback head, playback amplifier, or bias circuit). This annoying noise can be reduced by passing the signal through a circuit with the characteristics shown in Fig. 4.14.

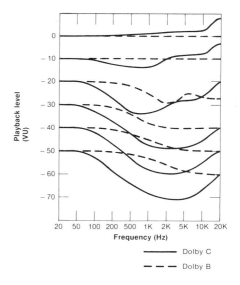

Fig. 4.14.   Dolby B/C record/playback curves.

As shown in Fig. 4.14 (Dolby B/C record/playback curves), high-level and/or low frequencies (below about 1000 Hz) are not affected by the Dolby NR circuits. However, low-level signals (where the noise is most objectionable and noticeable), and high-frequency signals (where the noise components are present), are suppressed by about 10 dB with Dolby B or by about 20 dB with Dolby C. This results in an improvement in signal-to-noise ratio (as well as improved dynamic range).

However, any original signal (music, voice, etc.) is also modified by such a circuit during record. High-frequency and low-level signals are suppressed along with the hiss or other noise components. So the original signal must be modified to the same extent, but in the opposite direction, during playback. In effect, the low levels and high frequencies are boosted by the same amount during playback that they were suppressed during record. This leaves the output signal an exact reproduction of the input signal, but with the noise components suppressed.

Figure 4.15 is a simplified block diagram of the Dolby processing module (IC300). Note that the module is controlled by mode-select signals at pin 9, and record/playback signals at pin 11.

During the record mode, pin 11 of IC300 is set to about 6 V by IC500. This causes the Dolby record circuits within IC300 to turn on, and the playback circuits to turn off.

Audio signals to be recorded from the line or microphones are applied through amplifiers and the 19-kHz filter to pins 3 and 4 of IC300 (as discussed in Sec. 4.3.2). These signals can be processed for either Dolby B or Dolby C, or can be recorded without any Dolby processing, depending on the voltage at pin 9 of IC300. In turn, the pin-9 voltage is set by Dolby NR switches S1 (ON/OFF) and S2 (B/C).

During the record Dolby-off mode (−7 V at pin 9 of IC300), the audio is routed through IC300 with no processing, and exits IC300 at pins 14 and 15 for application to the head through the record amplifier.

During the record Dolby-B mode (0.6 V at pin 9 of IC300), the audio is processed (suppressed by about 10 dB), and is applied to the head through the record amplifier.

During the record Dolby-C mode (6.3 V at pin 9 of IC300), the audio is processed (suppressed by about 20 dB), and is applied to the head through the record amplifier.

During the playback mode, pin 11 of IC300 is set to about −7 V by IC500. This causes the Dolby playback circuits within IC300 to turn on, and the record circuits to turn off.

Audio signals taken from the tape by the head are amplified and applied to pins 7 and 8 of IC300 (as discussed in Sec. 4.3.2). These signals can be processed for either Dolby B or Dolby C, or can be played back without any Dolby processing, depending on the voltage at pin 9 of IC300 (as set by Dolby NR switches S1/S2).

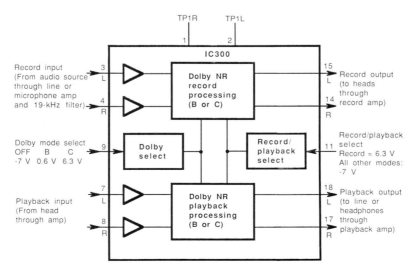

Fig. 4.15. Typical Dolby processing module.

During the playback Dolby-off mode (−7 V at pin 9 of IC300), the playback audio is routed through IC300 with no processing, and exits IC300 at pins 17 and 18 for application to the line or headphones through the playback amplifier.

During the playback Dolby-B mode (0.6 V at pin 9 of IC300) the audio is processed (boosted by about 10 dB), and is applied to the line or headphones.

During the playback Dolby-C mode (6.3 V at pin 9 of IC300), the audio is processed (boosted by about 20 dB), and is applied to the line or headphones.

4.3.5 Tape-End-Detect Circuits

Figure 4.16 shows the tape-end-detect circuits used to sense the leader at both ends of the cassette tape. Most audio cassette decks have some similar circuit to stop the tape transport automatically when the tape reaches either end. In our deck, the function also permits the tape to reverse directions, and keeps the gap in program material to a minimum (during reversal).

Input to the circuit is from an LED/phototransistor sensor. The LED produces a light source that is applied to the tape surface, while the phototransistor receives light reflected from the tape. The output of the sensor is applied to pin 9 of IC500 through two amplifiers within IC100. The amount of current through the LED (and thus the amount of light generated) can be adjusted by RT100.

The reflected light remains constant as long as oxide-coated tape passes by the sensor. When the leader is reached (at either end), there is a drastic change in reflected light. This changes the output to pin 9 of IC500, indicating that the tape is near the end. IC500 then causes the tape transport to reverse direction, or stop, depending on the operating mode.

One benefit of the reflective system is that it works equally well on any type of leader (metal, clear, or translucent). Also, the automatic-reverse feature occurs even if no leader is present on the tape. When the tape moves to the end of the reel, the reel hub stops rotating. This is sensed by IC500 which reverses or stops the tape.

During normal operation, a fixed amount of light is reflected onto the phototransistor, producing a fixed voltage across R100. This allows C100 and C101 to charge to the same voltage. The voltage remains constant as long as the reflected light is constant (oxide coating). When the leader moves under the phototransistor, there is a drastic change in reflected light, changing the voltage across R100.

If the leader is metal, the reflectivity goes up, causing the drop across R100 to increase rapidly. In turn, this causes C100/C101 to charge to a higher level, producing a positive "pulse" at pin 5 of IC100.

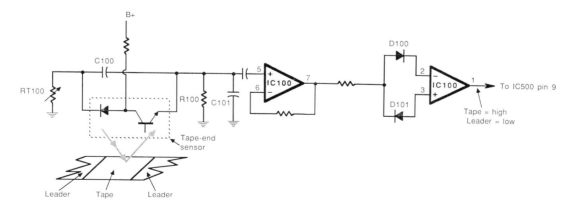

Fig. 4.16. Tape-end-detect circuits.

If the leader is clear or translucent, the reflectivity goes down, causing the drop across R100 to decrease, producing a negative "pulse" at pin 5 of IC100.

No matter what type of leader is involved, a pulse appears at pin 7 of IC100 when the leader is reached. The positive or negative pulse is applied through D100 or D101 to pins 2 or 3 of IC100. In turn, this produces a pulse at pin 1 of IC100. The pulse (applied to pin 9 of IC500) is high when the oxide-coated tape is passing the sensor, and goes low when the leader is reached.

4.3.6 Front-Panel Display Drive Circuits

Figure 4.17 shows the front-panel display drive circuits in simplified form. As shown, counter microprocessor IC200 is responsible for generating the necessary grid and segment drive signals applied to front-panel fluorescent display FL200.

Note that operation of FL200 is very similar to the operation fluorescent display FL1 used on the integrated amplifier described in Chapter 2 (Secs. 2.3.2 and 2.5.2). So we will not duplicate these descriptions here. Instead, we concentrate on drive signals to FL200.

There are essentially two drive sources

or inputs to IC200: one from the audio-level detect circuits, and one from the tape-transport control, IC500.

The audio-level detect circuits receive both left- and right-channel audio (samples from either playback or record circuits) through RT200L and RT200R. These controls are provided for adjusting the left and right audio channels to the same level (as discussed in Sec. 4.4). The audio-level detect circuits generate left and right d-c control signals applied to pins 6 and 7 of IC200. The circuits also generate a reference voltage applied to pin 5.

The control signals and reference signals are applied to level-detect logic within IC200. The output of the level-detect logic is applied to the decoder and display-drive logic. The drive logic produces the necessary signals to both the grids and segments of FL200. These signals activate the 20-segment light bars (bar graph) to indicate audio level of both channels.

Tape-transport microprocessor IC500 transmits status signals to pin 13 of IC200. These status signals are a combination of data and sync information from pins 15 and 14 of IC500, respectively. The input to pin 13 of IC500 is applied to the decoder and display drive logic. In turn, the logic generates four grid-drive signals and 18 segment-

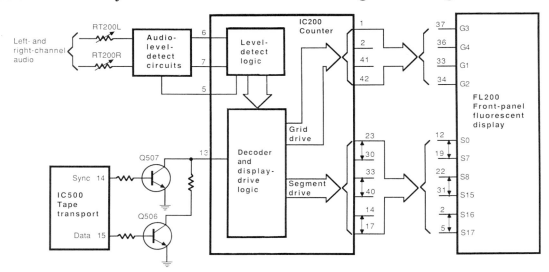

Fig. 4.17. Front-panel display drive circuits.

drive signals. These signals activate various function indicators on FL200 (such as *play, record, pause, mute, tape counter,* etc., shown in Fig. 4.4).

4.3.7 Key-Scan Matrix and Function-Command Circuits

Figure 4.18 shows the key-scan matrix circuits in simplified form. Note that these circuits are similar (but not identical) to those for the integrated amplifiers (as described in Sec. 2.3.2). Note that most modern audio cassette decks have some similar circuits for converting front-panel commands (pushing a key, button, or switch) into electri-

cal signals that operate the tape transport and corresponding front-panel display.

In the circuit of Fig. 4.18, key-scan pulses are produced in sequence from pins 9, 10, 11, and 12 of IC501, and applied to the key-scan matrix (front-panel operating key switches). These four scan signals, S0 through S3, are coupled back into IC501 through four input ports, K0 through K3, at pins 13, 14, 15, and 16 of IC501, when the appropriate button is pressed.

For example, if the STOP button is pressed, the S1 output is applied to the K0 input. This causes IC500 to stop the tape transport, in both playback and record.

Note that all of the function-command

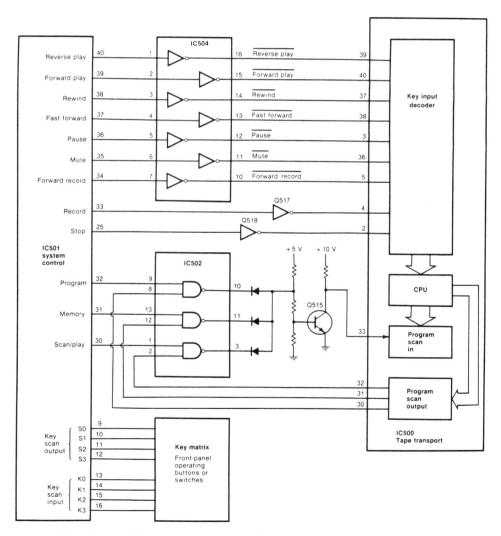

Fig. 4.18. Key-scan matrix and function-command circuits.

outputs from IC501 are single control signals, except for *program, memory,* and *S&P* (scan and play). For example, a *mute* command requires only a single signal at pin 35. All of these single control signals are inverted (by IC504 or Q517/Q518) before application to IC500. For example, the *mute* command high at pin 35 of IC501 appears as a low at pin 36 of IC500.

The *program, memory,* and *S&P* functions use a separate scan-out/scan-in matrix. This is necessary to synchronize system-control microprocessor IC501 with tape-transport microprocessor IC500 during such complex functions as memory and scan and play.

For example, when s&p is pressed, the high at pin 30 of IC501 is applied to a NAND gate within IC502. The other input of the NAND gate receives continuous scan pulses from pin 32 of IC500. These scan pulses are produced by IC500, and are synchronized with the IC500 clock.

The combination of two highs at the NAND-gate input produces a low at the base of Q515, and causes pin 33 of IC500 to go high (each time pin 32 of IC500 goes high). With

these two signals synchronized, IC500 causes the tape-transport (and play) circuits to perform the scan-and-play function.

4.3.8 Tape-Transport Components and Functions

Figures 4.19 through 4.21 show the major tape-transport components of a typical audio cassette deck. Note that this cassette deck contains all of the mechanical components found in most decks, plus the components for automatic reversal (which is not typical). So we will describe both the typical and nontypical tape-transport components here.

Our deck uses a *single pair of record/ playback heads.* These heads are physically rotated 180°, depending on the direction of play or record. This requires a *dual set of capstans,* but only one capstan motor. Note that the capstan motor is always rotating whenever power is applied (unlike the reel motor).

A *single reel motor* provides drive to both the takeup and supply reels through gears. The direction of reel rotation is determined by the tape transport, IC500, as discussed in Sec. 4.3.9.

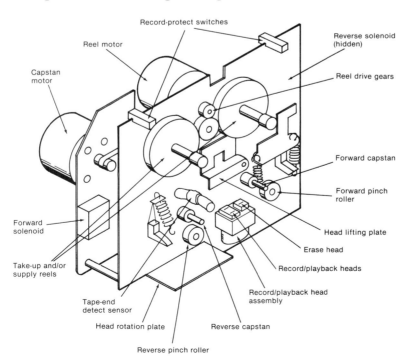

Fig. 4.19. Major tape-transport components (cassette side).

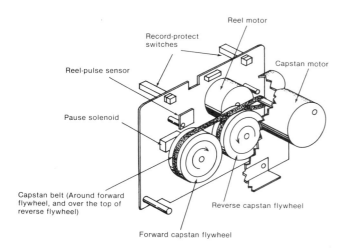

Fig. 4.20. Major tape-transport components (motor side).

As shown in Fig. 4.20, the *capstan flywheels* are belt driven by the capstan motor. The forward capstan flywheel rotates clockwise, while the reverse capstan flywheel rotates counterclockwise. This is possible because the belt is wound "around" the forward flywheel, but "over the top" of the reverse flywheel. As a result, the single capstan motor is required to turn in only one direction.

Microprocessor-controlled *solenoids* lift the proper *pinch roller* against the corresponding capstan to move the tape in the desired direction. The forward solenoid activates the linkage that places the transport into the forward mode. The reverse solenoid is used for reverse play or record. The pause solenoid initiates the pause mode. Selection and control of the solenoids are discussed in Sec. 4.3.10.

The *head-rotation plate* and *head-lifting plate* (both of which are not found on typical decks) rotate the *record/playback head assembly* to the correct position. Both plates are linked mechanically to the solenoids. The head-rotation plate moves left or right, depending on which solenoid (forward or reverse) is activated. The head-lifting plate lifts the record/playback head assembly after the head has been rotated.

Figure 4.21 shows details of the head rotate/lift functions. When the head-rotation plate moves either right or left, the small metal tabs attached to the rotation plate move the head-rotation gear-rack assembly.

For example, in forward (play or record), the head-rotation plate moves to the left. This causes the record/playback head assembly to move to the position shown in Fig. 4.21. The head pull-in spring keeps tension on the head, holding the head against mechanical stops to eliminate any mechanical play.

When reverse is selected, the head-rotation plate and gear-rack assembly move to the right, rotating the record/playback head assembly counterclockwise. After about 180° of rotation, the head pull-in spring takes over, causing the head to flip to the full-reverse direction.

The *tape-end detect sensor* (shown just above and to the left of the head assembly in Fig. 4.19) detects the leader at either end of the cassette tape, as described in Sec. 4.3.5.

The *reel-pulse sensor* (just above the forward capstan flywheel, Fig. 4.20) detects reel rotation by means of pulses generated when the reel rotates past a Hall-effect generator, as described in Sec. 4.3.9.

Fig. 4.21. Details of head rotate/lift function.

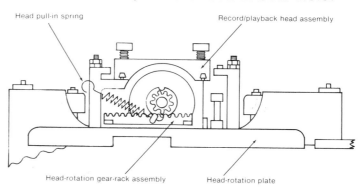

Two *record-protect switches* are located along the top edge of the transport mechanism, next to the installed cassette. These switches provide a safety feature to prevent accidental erasure of a prerecorded tape. This is done by removing the small tabs on the edge of the cassette. With the tabs removed, the switches are open, preventing system-control microprocessor IC501 from placing the deck in record, as discussed in Sec. 4.3.11.

Always check the cassette tabs when troubleshooting a "no record operation" trouble symptom. If one or both tabs are removed, do not expect the deck to record! Try another cassette with the tabs intact, or put some heavy scotch tape over the tab areas.

4.3.9 Reel-Motor Control Circuits

Figure 4.22 shows the reel-motor control circuits. As discussed in Sec. 4.3.8, the two reels (supply and takeup) are geared to a single motor. (Each reel assumes the supply or takeup function, depending on the operating mode, forward or reverse). The reel motor can be driven in either direction, and at two different speeds, through operation of the reel-motor drive, IC650. In turn, IC650 receives control signals and voltages from tape-transport IC500. The direction of reel rotation (forward/reverse), as well as the reel speed (fast/normal) depends on the signals applied to IC650 from IC500.

The logic at pins 18 and 19 of IC500

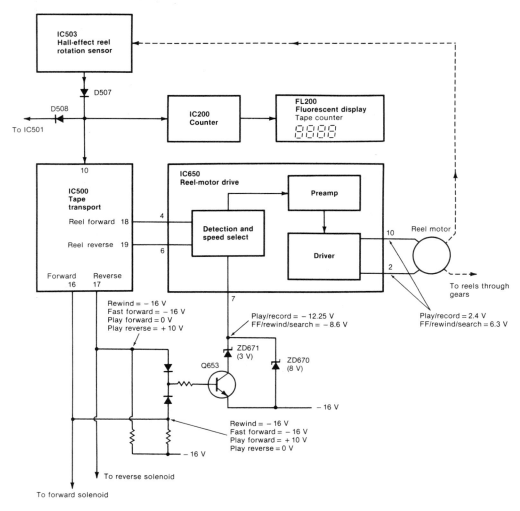

Fig. 4.22. Reel-motor control circuits.

determines the direction of reel-motor rotation. With pin 18 high, the motor rotates forward. With pin 19 high, the reel motor reverses direction. These signals are applied to the reel motor through logic and amplifiers within IC650. With both pins 18 and 19 of IC500 low, the reel-motor voltage at pins 2 and 10 of IC650 drops to zero, and the reel motor stops.

The logic at pins 16 and 17 of IC500 (which is also applied to the forward and reverse solenoids, as discussed in Sec. 4.3.10) determines the reel-motor speed. This logic is *tristate*. That is, pins 16 and 17 can be high (+10 V), low (0 V or ground), or "floating" (where the output of IC500 can be pulled in either direction). For example, a −16-V supply is coupled to pins 16 and 17 through resistors. When the two pins are floating, both pins go to −16 V. When one pin is floating, that pin goes to −16 V, but the other pins go to 0 V or +10 V, as determined by the command within IC500.

For example, during fast forward where high speed is required, both pins 16 and 17 float, and thus go to −16 V. This turns Q653 off, removing the 3-V zener ZD671 from the circuits. With ZD651 out, −8.6-V zener ZD670 applies about −8.6 V to pin 7 of IC650. This causes the reel-motor drive voltage at pins 2 and 10 of IC650 to go to about 6.3 V, driving the reel motor at fast speed (about three times normal).

During forward play where normal speed is required, the output at pin 17 of IC500 goes to 0 V or ground. Since this is well above the Q653 emitter bias of −16 V, Q653 turns on, producing about −12.25 V at pin 7 of IC650. This causes the reel-motor drive voltage at pins 2 and 10 of IC650 to go to about 2.4 V, driving the reel motor at normal speed.

As the reel rotates in either direction, Hall-effect generator IC503 produces pulses. These pulses are applied to the front-panel fluorescent tape-counter display, FL200 through IC200, producing the 4-digit tape count (Fig. 4.4).

The same IC503 pulses are applied to

IC500 through D507, and to IC501 through D508. If the reel stops because of some mechanical problem (jammed reel, stuck tape, etc.), the pulses stop. This causes IC500 to remove drive to the reel motor and IC501 to shut the system down.

4.3.10 Tape-Transport Solenoid-Control Circuits

Figure 4.23 shows the circuits used for control of the three tape-transport solenoids. As discussed in Sec. 4.3.8, the forward and reverse solenoids operate the pinch rollers that hold the tape against the corresponding capstans. These solenoids also operate the head-rotation and head-lifting plates. The pause solenoid stops tape drive (even though the capstan motor continues to rotate).

The three solenoid-control circuits are essentially the same. When pins 16, 17, or 22 are high, the corresponding transistors Q652, Q651, and Q650 are turned on, the solenoids are energized, and the functions (forward, reverse, or pause) are activated. Note that signals at pins 16 and 17 are also applied to the reel-motor control circuits (Sec. 4.3.9).

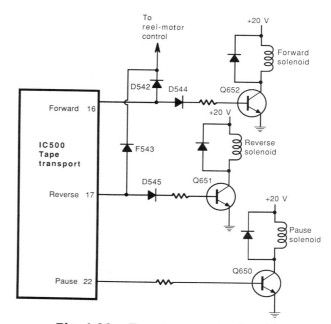

Fig. 4.23. Tape-transport solenoid-control circuits.

4.3.11 Record-Protect Circuits

Figure 4.24 shows the record-protect circuits. As discussed in Sec. 4.3.8, the record-protect switches prevent IC501 from placing the deck in the record mode when a prerecorded cassette (with protect tabs removed) is installed.

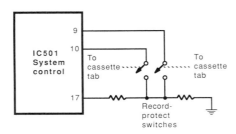

Fig. 4.24. Record-protect circuits.

When a cassette with the tabs intact is installed, the record-protect switches are closed. Scan signals from pins 9 and 10 of IC501 are applied to pin 17, permitting normal control by IC501.

When a cassette with tabs removed is installed, the record-protect switches are open. This prevents scan signals from being applied to pin 17, thus preventing record operation, no matter what logic or commands are present in IC501.

Note that there is a separate record-protect switch for forward and reverse. Keep this in mind when troubleshooting a "no record in one direction" trouble symptom. Check to make sure that *both tabs* are in place on the cassette. Try another cassette or put heavy scotch tape over the missing tab area.

4.4 TYPICAL TEST/ADJUSTMENT PROCEDURES

This section describes the electrical test/adjustment procedures for a typical audio cassette deck. All of the notes described in Sec. 2.4 apply here. In this section, we concentrate on the procedures for a deck similar to that shown in Figs. 4.3 and 4.4.

4.4.1 Mechanical Adjustments

We do not describe mechanical adjustments for a cassette deck. There are several reasons for this.

First, the procedures can often be complex and consume considerable space. More important, the adjustments can apply to only one specific deck. For example, most of the mechanical adjustments described for the deck of Figs. 4.3 and 4.4 are concerned with the head-reversal mechanism (which is not typical for most decks).

Another reason for omitting mechanical adjustments is that you must follow the exact procedures outlined in the service literature. For example, the deck of Figs. 4.3 and 4.4 has a *mirror tape* available to check for tape curling, as well as specific adjustment points to correct such curling.

Further, the service literature for the deck of Figs. 4.3 and 4.4 also recommends use of a *torque cassette* to measure tape drive and reel torque. Although use of a torque cassette is typical, the remedy for correcting problems is somewhat unique. In this case, if the drive and torque are not correct, and you cannot cure the problem by replacement of pinch-roller springs or by cleaning, you must replace the entire assembly.

To sum up, there are virtually no "universal" or "typical" mechanical adjustments. This is in contrast to electrical test/adjustments. Most audio cassette decks require one or more of the electrical test/adjustment procedures described here, even though the adjustment points may be different.

4.4.2 Test Tapes or Cassettes

As discussed in Chapter 1, you will need test tapes to properly test and adjust a cassette deck. Our deck requires four special test tapes or cassettes, in addition to three blank cassettes (standard or normal, chrome, and metal).

The four special test tapes include the following:

1. A mirror-tape for tape-travel checks
2. An 8000-Hz tape for azimuth adjustment
3. A 3000-Hz tape for motor speed adjustment
4. A Dolby tape for Dolby NR checks

4.4.3 Test Equipment

The following equipment is required to properly test and adjust our cassette deck, as well as virtually all modern decks.

1. Audio generator with attenuator (calibrated in dB)
2. Electronic voltmeter (EVM)
3. Frequency counter
4. Oscilloscope

4.4.4 Preliminary Setup

Make the following checks and control settings before any tests and/or adjustments.

1. Clean the heads, pinch rollers, tape guide, and capstan using alcohol, as discussed in Sec. 4.5.
2. Set the *record* level and *output* level controls to maximum.
3. Set the *Dolby NR* switch to OFF. (Always make all tests and adjustments with Dolby off, unless you are checking a Dolby function.)
4. Set the *tape* type switch as follows:
   - When a test tape, standard tape, or no tape is installed, set the *tape* type switch to NOR 1.
   - When a chrome tape is used, set *tape* to CRO2.
   - When a metal tape is used, set *tape* to METAL IV.

4.4.5 Tape Speed Test/Adjustment

The purpose of this test/adjustment is to make certain that the tape motor is rotating at the correct speed. Some decks have adjustment controls for drive circuits to the

motor. Our deck has a semifixed variable resistor located inside the motor. Generally, adjustment is not required unless the motor is replaced. However, the speed should be checked every time it is serviced.

Connect a frequency counter to the *line* output terminals (or at any convenient point where playback audio can be measured).

Load a 3000-Hz test tape, and play the tape in the normal forward mode (do not record!).

After a warmup of about 20 minutes, check the frequency reading on the frequency counter.

The ideal frequency reading is 3000 Hz, indicating that motor speed is right on. A typical speed (frequency) tolerance is ±1% (30 Hz), so any reading between 2970 and 3030 Hz is satisfactory (but check this against the service literature).

If necessary, adjust the motor speed resistance until the motor speed is within tolerance (preferably with a frequency reading of exactly 3000 Hz). Always allow sufficient time for the motor speed to stabilize as you make this adjustment.

Make the initial test and/or adjustment at some point near the middle of the tape. Then check to see if there is any difference in frequency reading at points near the beginning and end of the tape. Any differences in frequency reading indicate *tape speed fluctuations.*

If you notice any tape speed fluctuations (almost all decks have some speed fluctuations), find the percentage of fluctuation using the following equation.

$$\text{Tape speed fluctuation} = \frac{f1 - f2}{3000} \times 100(\%)$$

where
   $f1$ is maximum frequency reading,
   $f2$ is minimum frequency reading.

A typical speed fluctuation tolerance is ±1%. This means that the difference between the maximum and minimum frequency readings should be 30 Hz or less.

If the motor speed cannot be brought

within tolerance, or if the speed fluctuations are greater than 1%, this usually means that the motor must be replaced.

4.4.6 Azimuth Test/Adjustment

The purpose of this test is to make certain that the heads are properly adjusted in relation to tape travel. Ideally, the heads should be centered so that the output (amplitude and phase) is the same from each head, in both forward and reverse modes. Typically, if the heads are not centered, one head produces more output when the tape moves in one direction, and less output when the tape reverses direction. (Keep this in mind when troubleshooting such a symptom. Of course, if there is severe unbalance, the problem is most likely a defective head, rather than azimuth adjustment.)

Most decks have some form of azimuth adjustment. Figure 4.25 shows the head assembly (and adjustment screws) for our deck. Note that there are two azimuth screws and two W-nuts. The W-nuts are for adjusting the tape guides so that tape travel is straight and true, *in relation to the assembly*. The azimuth screws are for adjusting the tape *in relation to the tape path*.

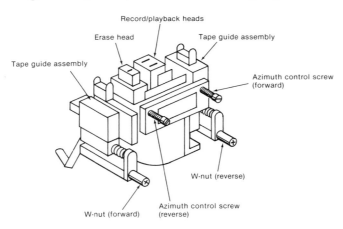

Fig. 4.25. Head assembly adjustment points.

A word of caution before going on. *Never* make any mechanical adjustments to the heads or head assembly until you are certain that such adjustment is required! The heads do not often "go out of alignment"

with normal use, particularly if the head adjustment screws are sealed with "screw lock" at the factory, or at the last service station. However, the heads should be tested for proper azimuth at each service.

Connect an EVM and scope to the *line out* terminals. A dual-channel scope is convenient in that you can monitor both channels simultaneously. Likewise, you can use a dual-channel meter such as shown in Fig. 1.7.

Load an 8000-Hz test tape.

First play the tape forward, and note the reading on both channels. Then play the tape in reverse, and note both channel readings.

In our deck, the maximum deviation in amplitude between the L and R channels, and/or between the forward and reverse operation, is 2 dB (which is much easier to read on a meter than a scope). If the difference is 2 dB or less, *leave the heads alone.*

If you must adjust the azimuth, here are some tips to make it easier.

Use one channel as a reference point for both voltage amplitude measurement and phasing comparisons.

Adjust the azimuth screws (Fig. 4.25) for maximum voltage output. In our deck, the right-side azimuth screw is adjusted in the forward mode, while the left-side screw is for reverse mode. Keep in mind that there is interaction between these adjustments (another good reason for not tampering with head adjustments).

Once both heads are adjusted for maximum output, compare the phase of the two output signals on the dual-channel scope. If the phase is within 90° (between the left and right channels), quit while you are ahead. If not, make *a slight adjustment of one channel* (but not both) to bring the phase difference within 90°.

Keep in mind that if there is a severe unbalance condition in the audio circuits, do not try to correct the problem by head adjustment! Find the problem!

After the azimuth adjustments are complete, remove the 8000-Hz test tape. Load a mirror tape and play it in the forward direc-

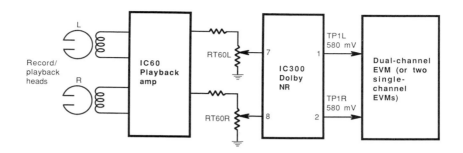

Fig. 4.26. Playback gain adjustment.

tion. Check tape travel across the heads. The tape travel should be straight and true. There should be no "tape curl." If necessary, adjust the tape guides (with the W-nuts, in our deck) so that the mirror tape reflects straight and true tape travel.

Always recheck the azimuth adjustments after making the tape path adjustments (or any other adjustments your particular head assembly requires). As a general rule, *all head adjustments interact.*

On our particular deck, where the heads are physically rotated in forward and reverse, check to make sure that the azimuth screws are not loosened when the heads are rotated.

When you are certain that the heads are properly adjusted, apply "screw lock" to all adjustment screws.

4.4.7 Playback Gain Adjustment

Figure 4.26 is the adjustment diagram.

The purpose of this test is to set the playback gain for both channels.

Connect a dual-channel EVM (or two EVMs) to TP1L and TP1R of Dolby noise-reduction IC300.

Load a Dolby calibration tape.

Play the tape in the forward direction, and adjust RT60L and/or RT60R to get 580 mV (rms) at each test point.

4.4.8 Fluorescent Meter Adjustment for 0 dB

Figure 4.27 is the adjustment diagram. The purpose of this test is to set the front-panel 20-segment light bars (Fig. 4.4) to produce the correct indication for a given audio level (0 dB).

After playback gain has been adjusted, connect an audio generator to the *line in* terminals, and inject a 400-Hz signal.

Adjust the output level of the audio generator to produce the same reading at TP1L

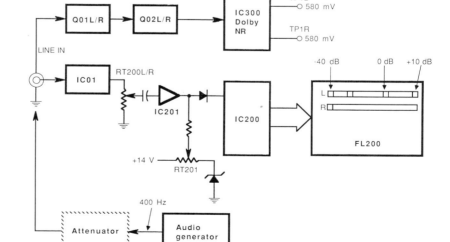

Fig. 4.27. Fluorescent meter adjustments.

and TP1R of Dolby IC300 as is produced by the Dolby calibration tape during playback-gain adjustment (580 mV rms).

Adjust RT200L and/or RT200R until the 0-dB segment or lamp *just begins to turn on.*

4.4.9 Fluorescent Meter Adjustment for −40 dB

Figure 4.27 is again the adjustment diagram. The purpose of this test is to set the front-panel 20-segment light bars (Fig. 4.4) to produce the correct indications for a given audio level (−40 dB).

Leave the audio generator at 400 Hz, but connect an attenuator between the generator and the *line in* terminals. Attenuate the generator output signal by −37 dB.

Adjust RT201 until the −40 dB lamp *just turns off.*

4.4.10 Bias-Current and Record/Playback Output Level Adjustments

Figure 4.28 is the adjustment diagram. Both the bias-current and record/playback output level should be adjusted together (on our deck). The two functions are usually interactive on most decks.

Note that on some decks, the actual head current (bias or erase) is measured and adjusted. This is done by inserting a resistor (typically 1 kΩ so that the readings are in mV) at a test point in the head circuit, and measuring the voltage drop across the resistor. The head current is then adjusted to a given value.

A different procedure is used on our deck (and a few other decks). The audio is recorded and played back at a low frequency, and then at a high frequency. Head current is adjusted until the playback level is the same (within a given tolerance) at both low and high frequencies.

For bias-current adjustment, connect an audio generator to the *line in* terminals, and adjust the generator for 1.2 kHz with an output level of 0 dB. Adjust the attenuator for −23 dB. Place the deck in record.

Using normal (NOR) tape, record at 1.2 kHz for about a minute. Readjust the generator frequency to 12 kHz, and continue recording for another minute.

Play back the recordings. The output difference between 1.2 and 12 kHz should not exceed +2 or −1 dB. If the difference is greater, adjust RT400L and/or RT400R until the 12-kHz playback is no greater than +1 dB more than the 1.2 kHz playback.

For recording/playback level adjustment, leave the audio generator connected to *line in,* but reset the generator frequency to 400 Hz with an output of 0 dB. Then set the attenuator to −3 dB.

Record the 400-Hz signal. Play back the

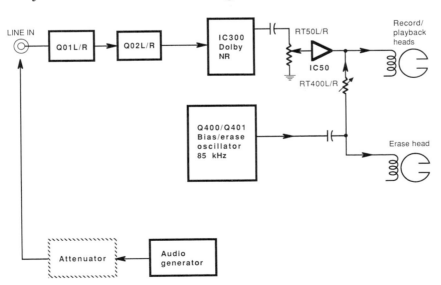

Fig. 4.28. Bias-current and record/playback output adjustments.

tape and note the playback level. The output difference between record and playback should not exceed ±0.5 dB. If the difference is greater, adjust RT50L and/or RT50R for the correct level.

With the record/playback level properly set, recheck the bias current adjustment for each of the three different types of tape. Set the *tape* select switch to each position (NOR, CrO₂, and METAL) as required.

The following shows the playback level to be expected of each tape type:

Normal (NOR) +2.5 dB, −1.5 dB

Chrome (CrO₂) +4 dB, −3 dB

Metal (METAL) +4 dB, −3 dB

4.4.11 Tape Leader Adjustment

Figure 4.29 is the adjustment diagram. The purpose of this adjustment is to make sure that the tape-end detect circuits reverse (or stop) the tape when the leader is reached at either end.

Before starting this adjustment, make sure that the tape guides (Fig. 4.25) are clean. On our deck, the top of the flat surface on the right-hand guide must be clean to ensure good light-reflecting qualities. The light must pass from the sensor LED through the leader to the reflective surface, and then back to the phototransistor, when the leader is over the flat surface.

Connect a d-c voltmeter across R100.

Press and *hold down* the FORWARD PLAY button to prevent the tape-end detector from being activated.

Adjust RT100 for 5.5 V as measured across R100.

Load any standard tape and play forward to the tape end. When the deck automatically reverses, press STOP immediately, and check to make sure that the tape reversal takes place as soon as the leader crosses the tape guide.

4.4.12 Dolby NR Operation Checks

The purpose of these tests is to check operation of the circuits within Dolby NR IC300. Both Dolby-B and Dolby-C functions must be checked (if the deck has both functions).

Connect the audio generator to *line in*. Adjust the generator to 5 kHz, attenuated to −40 dB.

Make a recording on metal tape for about 1 minute with Dolby NR *off*, and for a similar time with Dolby B *on*.

Play the tape back with Dolby NR *off*. The output difference between the Dolby-off and Dolby-B recordings should be about 10 dB.

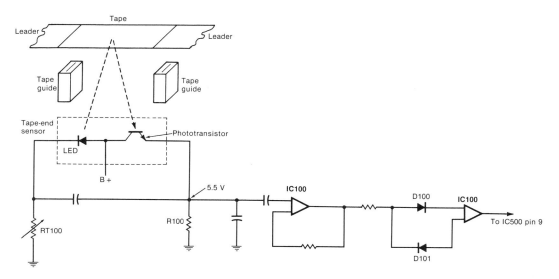

Fig. 4.29. Tape leader adjustment.

Leave the audio generator connected to *line in.* Adjust the generator to 1 kHz, attenuated to −40 dB.

Make a recording on metal tape for about 1 minute with Dolby NR *off,* and for a similar time with Dolby C *on.*

Play the tape deck with Dolby NR *off.* The output difference between the Dolby-off and Dolby-C recording should be about 16 dB.

4.5 CLEANING, LUBRICATION, AND HEAD DEGAUSSING

Follow the service literature instructions!

4.5.1 Cleaning

After about 10 hours of operation (actually, when the customer brings in the deck for service), clean the heads, capstans, and pinch rollers with a head-cleaning bar or wand and alcohol.

Although there are spray cans of head cleaner or solvent, most manufacturers recommend alcohol and cleaning sticks (or Q-tips, cotton swabs, etc.) for all cleaning. Methyl alcohol does the best cleaning job, but can be a health hazard (especially if you drink it!). Isopropyl alcohol is usually satisfactory for most cleaning (don't drink that either).

4.5.2 Lubrication

Never clean or lubricate any part not recommended in the service literature. Most audio cassette decks use many sealed bearings that do not require either cleaning or lubrication. A drop or two of oil in the wrong places can cause problems, even possible damage. Clean off any excess or spilled oil using gauze soaked in alcohol.

In the absence of specific recommendations, use a light machine oil (such as sewing-machine oil) and a medium grease or lubricating paste.

Lubricate the *rotary portion* of the cassette mechanism (tape transport) with one or two drops of oil. Apply grease to the *sliding portions* of the mechanism.

Be very careful to keep oil or grease from getting on the belt, flywheels, or pinch rollers. Oil or grease on these surfaces can cause slippage (resulting in erratic tape drive and poor audio).

Perform lubrication once a year, or after each 1000 hours of operation (sure you will!).

4.5.3 Head Degaussing

Some technicians never degauss the heads, while others degauss at each service (using a commercial *head eraser*). In between these extremes, some technicians degauss only when certain symptoms occur.

The two most common symptoms are background noise that increases with time, or a decrease in output at high frequencies (treble) with time.

The author has no recommendations on head degaussing, except: *NEVER degauss the heads with a cassette in place* (particularly a customer's favorite tape, or an expensive shop test tape).

4.6 TYPICAL TROUBLESHOOTING PROCEDURES

This section describes the troubleshooting procedures for a typical audio cassette deck. All of the notes described in Sec. 2.5 apply here. In this section, we concentrate on the circuits of a deck similar to that shown in Figs. 4.3 and 4.4.

The following paragraphs are a collection of trouble symptoms that match the troubleshooting trees found in the service manual for a typical audio cassette deck. After selecting the symptom that matches the deck you are servicing, follow the steps in the corresponding troubleshooting procedure.

4.6.1 Preliminary Checks

Always make a few preliminary checks before launching into a full troubleshooting routine.

It is assumed that if you have such obvious symptoms as "none of the front-panel LEDs turn on when POWER is pressed," you will check the fuses (right after checking to make sure that the power cord is plugged in).

It is also assumed that you will check for bad solder connections, broken copper bands, loose or unseated boards, and the like (cleaning the module and board contacts with a pencil eraser, as necessary).

Before you get too far into troubleshooting, you should check the various power supply voltages if entire sections (or functions) appear to be inoperative. This means that you must be able to locate the power-supply circuits on the schematic and/or block diagrams, and measure the voltages. (If you cannot do either of these, you are in trouble!).

If all power supply voltages are good, make certain that all ICs (microprocessors, amplifiers, inverters, etc.) are receiving power, and that the ICs are properly grounded at the correct pins.

In the case of microprocessor ICs, check to make sure that the *clock* and *reset* circuits are functioning. If not, the microprocessors will not operate properly, and some or all of the deck functions will be missing or abnormal, even if all other circuits (including the microprocessors) are good.

This means that you must be able to locate the clock pins on the microprocessor using the schematic diagram, and monitor the clock signal with a scope or counter. (Generally, clocks do not go off frequency, but sometimes the circuit oscillates at an overtone, beyond the microprocessor frequency limit.)

In the case of the reset circuit, microprocessors usually have a reset input that must be held low (or high, check the schematic) for normal operation. All microprocessor functions are reset (to zero or start) when power is removed and reapplied.

4.6.2 Tape Transport Inoperative During Playback

Figure 4.30 is the troubleshooting diagram. From a troubleshooting standpoint,

the tape transport consists essentially of the reel motor, capstan motor, and solenoids (pinch roller and pause), all of which function to drive the tape across the heads in both forward and reverse directions.

On our deck, the capstan motor should start rotating when power is first applied, and should continue regardless of the operating mode. If not, check the power wiring to the capstan motor. If power is available, but the capstan motor and belt are not turning, suspect the motor.

On most decks, the forward or reverse solenoids actuate and pull the pinch roller against the tape and capstan when forward or reverse play is selected. (The solenoids should also actuate in the same way during record.)

If the forward solenoid does not actuate when forward operation is selected, check for +10 V at pin 16 of IC500. If the voltage is present, suspect Q652, D544 or the forward solenoid.

If the voltage is absent at pin 16 of IC500, check to make sure that the forward-play command is applied to IC500 from IC501 through IC504 when the FORWARD button is pressed. If not, suspect forward play switch S511, IC501, or IC504.

If the reverse solenoid does not actuate, check for +10 V at pin 17 of IC500. Then check Q651, D545, the reverse solenoid, and for a reverse command from S512 through IC501 and IC504.

On most decks, the reel motor should drive the supply and takeup reels through gears when forward or reverse play (or record) is selected.

If the reel motor does not operate in the forward-play mode, check for +10 V at pins 16 and 18 of IC500. If the voltage is absent, at either pin, check to make sure that the forward-play command is applied to IC500 from IC501 through IC504 when the FORWARD button is pressed. If not, suspect forward-play switch S511, IC501, or IC504.

If the voltage at pin 7 of IC650 is not −12.25 V, suspect Q653, ZD671, or ZD670. If the voltage is correct at pins 4 and 7 of

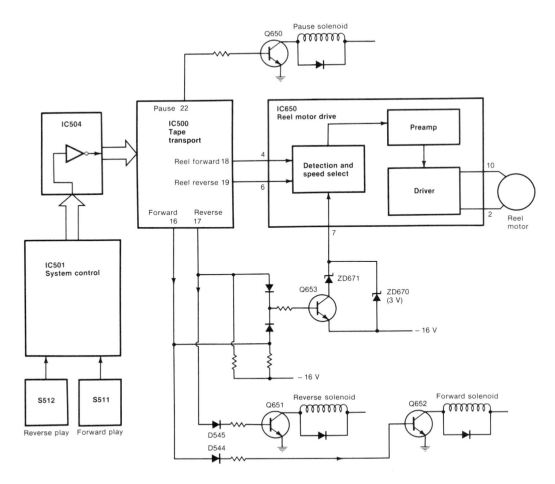

Fig. 4.30. Tape-transport troubleshooting diagram.

IC650, but not at pins 2 and 10, suspect IC650.

If the voltage is correct at pins 2 and 10 of IC650, but the reel motor does not turn, suspect the motor.

If the reel motor does not operate in the reverse-play mode, check for +10 V at pins 17 and 19 of IC500. Then check Q653, ZD671, ZD670, IC650, IC501, IC504, S512, and the reel motor.

4.6.3 Tape Transport Operates but No Sound Available in Playback

Figure 4.31 is the troubleshooting diagram. If the tape transport appears to be operating normally in all modes, but there is no sound during playback, first check the playback gain adjustment (Sec. 4.4.7), and turn up the front-panel *output* control,

RV40. This might cure the problem! If not, continue playing a known-good tape and monitor the audio at pins 1 and 7 of IC60 (about 100 mV typical).

If there is no audio output from IC60, check circuits from the heads to IC60, including Q61 (off) and Q62/Q63 (on).

If there is audio from IC60, check for audio at pins 17 and 18 of Dolby IC300. If not, check the audio path from IC60 to pins 7 and 8 of IC300.

Make certain that pin 24 of IC500 and pin 11 of IC300 are at −7 V. If not, suspect IC500. If pin 7 of IC500 goes high, IC300 goes into the record mode, rather than playback mode.

If there is audio from pins 17 and 18 of IC300, check for audio at RV40. If absent, make sure that Q40/Q41 have not been turned on (mute condition) by a signal at pin 27 of IC500.

If Q40/Q41 are not on, check the audio path from IC300 to RV40. Then check audio from RV40 to the *line out* jack and *phones* jack. If audio is available at RV40, but not at the jacks, suspect IC40.

4.6.4 Tape Transport Operates but No Record Operation

Figure 4.32 is the troubleshooting diagram. Always check playback (Sec. 4.6.3) and clear any problems before you check record. This applies to virtually all cassette decks. If there is no audio (or poor audio) during playback, the problem can be common to both record and playback. If the problem is only in record, you have quickly isolated the trouble to a few circuits (bias oscillator, record amp, etc.).

If audio is present during playback, but it is not possible to record audio, start by checking for audio at pins 14 and 15 of IC300. Also try curing the problem by record adjustments (Sec. 4.4.10), and turning up front-panel RECORD control RV01.

If audio is present at pins 14 and 15 of IC300, check the audio path from IC300 to the heads. Also make certain that pin 24 of IC500 and pin 11 of IC300 are high (about +6 V) to place IC300 in record mode.

If there is no audio at the input to IC50, make sure that Q50/Q51 have not been turned on (mute condition) by a signal at pin 27 of IC500.

If there is audio at the heads, but it won't record, check the bias oscillator. (As a general rule, if the tape can be erased, the oscillator and erase head are good. However, the bias signal may not be reaching the record/playback heads.) Check for an 85-kHz bias signal on both sides of C400 and RT400, as well as adjustment of RT400 (Sec. 4.4.10).

Keep in mind that the amount of bias signal depends on the type of tape selected. For example, the bias signal measured at C400 on our deck is about 3.4 V for normal tape, 5.2 V for chrome, and over 10 V for metal tape. This is determined by the *tape type* switch S5 setting.

If there is audio to the heads, and the

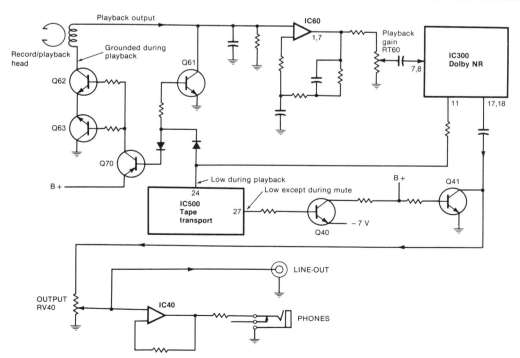

Fig. 4.31. No sound in playback troubleshooting diagram.

bias voltage is correct, suspect the heads. However, before you take the heads out, make sure that Q61 is turned on, and Q62/Q63 are off, to place the heads in a condition to record.

If there is no audio from pins 14 and 15 of IC300, trace the audio path from the *line*

in jack and *mic* (microphone) jack to IC300 through Q01, Q02, Q300, and IC02. Obviously, if you can record from *line in* but not from the *mic* jack, suspect IC02.

Keep in mind that Dolby NR switch S1 controls Q300 which, in turn, controls the Dolby filter. However, even if the filter circuit

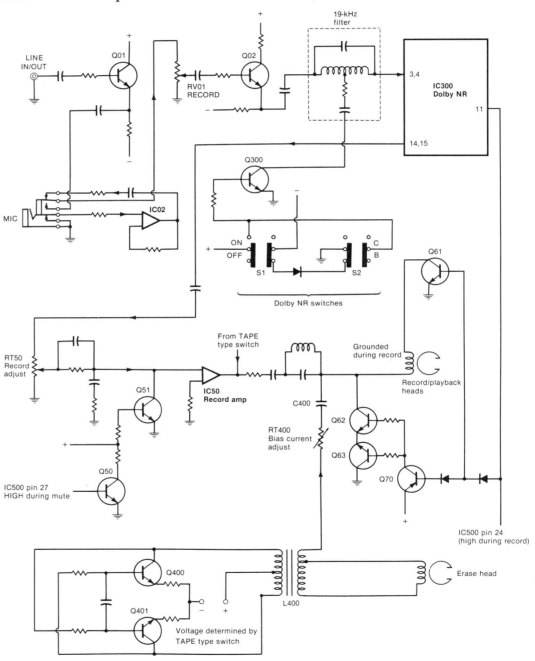

Fig. 4.32. No record operation troubleshooting diagram.

or Q300/S1 fails, you will probably be able to record, even though the recording is poor.

4.6.5 Front-Panel Fluorescent Display Inoperative

Figure 4.33 is the troubleshooting diagram. Front-panel fluorescent display FL200 (itself), and display drive IC200 are both suspect if the display is incorrect or absent, since IC200 controls FL200. Of course, if a particular input is absent or abnormal, the display cannot operate properly. So always check the input before you condemn the display!

If the fluorescent display is totally dark, check for a-c power to the filament at pins 1 and 47. Then check for grid drive or voltage at pins 33, 34, 36, and 37. (As a general tip, if any part of the display is on, it is reasonable to assume that FL200 is probably good, and getting power, but do not count on it.)

If the fluorescent display is on, but a particular display is inoperative, check the input signal to FL200 through IC200. If the input to IC200 is correct, but the display is not, check the segment signals from IC200 to FL200 (if you can find which segments are involved from the service literature; this is not always easy).

As an example, assume that there is no counter display, but other display functions are normal. The counter pulses originate at reel sensor IC503, as shown in Fig. 4.33. If the pulses do not appear at pin 18 of IC200, suspect IC503.

If the pulses are present, the problem could be in FL200, but is likely in IC200. If the information is available, check the counter segment outputs from IC200 to FL200. On our deck, counter information is applied on segments at pins 33 through 40 of IC200. Also note that a signal from IC501 is applied to IC200 through Q519 as a reset pulse for the counter.

Note that on the fluorescent display of our deck, the settings of Dolby selection switch S2 are fed directly to FL200, bypas-

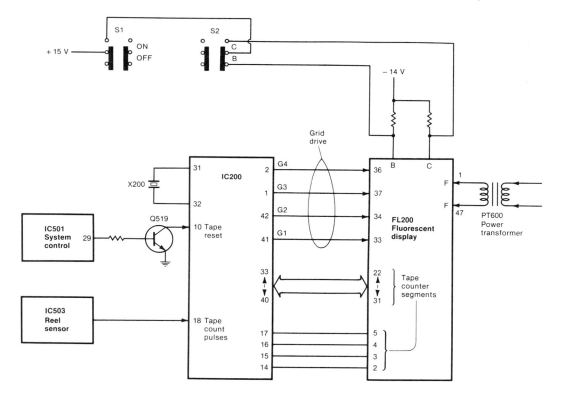

Fig. 4.33. Fluorescent display inoperative troubleshooting diagram.

sing IC200. Always look for such unusual connections.

4.6.6 Deck Stops Shortly After Start in All Modes

Figure 4.34 is the troubleshooting diagram. As discussed in Sec. 4.3.9, the tape-counting pulses from reel sensor IC503 are also applied to IC500/IC501. If the reel stops for any reason (mechanical problems, jammed reel, stuck tape, etc.), the pulses stop and IC500/IC501 shut down the tape drive—this creates a troubleshooting problem.

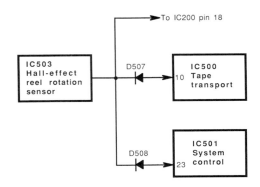

Fig. 4.34. Deck stops shortly after start troubleshooting diagram.

If sensor IC503 is defective, or the pulses do not reach IC500/IC501, the tape-transport system stops, even though there is no mechanical problem. Once the reel stops, there are no further pulses, so the system stops anyway!

The simplest way to check this condition is to monitor the pulses at pin 10 of IC500 and/or pin 23 of IC501, when the reel *first starts to rotate* from a stopped condition.

If the pulses are present (even briefly), but the tape transport starts and then shuts down, IC500/IC501 are the most likely suspects. (If the reel motor stops first, suspect IC500.) However, if there are no pulses when the reel starts, suspect IC503 and/or D507/D508.

4.6.7 Tape Transport Does Not Reverse Automatically

Figure 4.35 is the troubleshooting diagram. When the tape reaches the leader at either end, the tape-end sensor (LED/phototransistor) applies a signal to pin 9 of IC500. This causes IC500 to reverse the direction of the reel motor. (The capstan motor always rotates in the same direction, but either the forward or reverse capstan is used.)

If the tape does not reverse, first try correcting the problem by adjusting RT100, as described in Sec. 4.4.11.

If the problem is not corrected by adjustment of RT100, suspect the LED/phototransistor sensor, IC100, D100, D101 or the associated circuit.

Look for a low at pin 9 of IC500 when the leader is over the sensor. If pin 9 is low, but the tape does not reverse, suspect IC500.

4.6.8 No Music Detection During Search

Figure 4.12 is the troubleshooting diagram. If there is no scan-and-play operation, or if the tape does not stop at programmed selections, the music-detect circuits are suspect. However, before you go directly to music-detect, make sure that there is audio at pins 17 and 18 of IC300. If not, troubleshoot the playback circuits as described in Sec. 4.6.3.

If there is audio from IC300 at R30L/R30R, check at pin 6 of IC30 (or pin 8 of IC500) for about +10 V when music is present, and 0 V when there is no music. If practical, play a tape known to have both recorded and blank (no audio) sections.

If the voltage at pin 6 of IC30 switches between +10 and 0 V, suspect IC500.

If there is no change at pin 6 of IC30, check for a change in audio at pin 1 of IC30. The signal is very low at this input, but there should be a change between audio and no audio. If there is a change at pin 1, but not at pin 6, suspect IC30.

If the voltage at pins 1 or 6 of IC30 does not switch, select scan and play (press S&P,

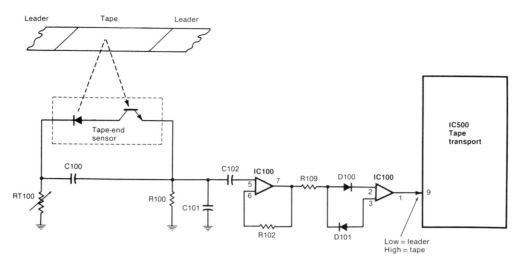

Fig. 4.35. No automatic tape reversal troubleshooting diagram.

and check for about +0.7 V at the base of Q30. If absent, suspect IC500 (check for a mute signal of about +0.7 V from pin 27 of IC500).

If the base of Q30 is at +0.7 V, but Q30 is not turned on, suspect Q30. Keep in mind that the signal at pin 1 of IC30 is attenuated drastically when Q30 is turned on.

CHAPTER 5

Troubleshooting and Repair of AM/FM-Stereo Tuners

This chapter is devoted to AM/FM-stereo tuners. Included are such subjects as the general description of a typical AM/FM-stereo tuner, typical tuner circuit descriptions, user control operation procedures and installation of stereo tuners, typical test/adjustment procedures, and examples of troubleshooting based on failure symptoms.

5.1 GENERAL DESCRIPTION OF A TYPICAL AM/FM-STEREO TUNER

Figures 5.1 through 5.3 show some typical AM/FM-stereo tuners. The tuner described here incorporates a number of modern features not found on all tuners, as well as the "typical features" found on most tuners. By studying all of these features, you should have no trouble in understanding any modern AM/FM tuner.

Modern tuners are essentially AM and FM-stereo radio receivers in a single package. Although most tuners have some audio amplification, the tuner output is generally applied to the speakers through an integrated amplifier such as described in Chapter 2.

Like all of the audio components described in this book, our tuner is under control of microprocessors (two in this case). The microprocessor circuits monitor and control all tuner functions via soft-touch buttons or controls on the front panel.

The majority of the tuner or receiver functions are performed by integrated circuits. For example, there are three major ICs in the FM section. These include an *FM tuner package* (that converts FM broadcast signals into IF signals, and provides tuning across the FM broadcast band), an FM IF *amplifier/detector IC*, and an *FM-multiplex decoder*. A single IC (AM IF amplifier/detector) is used in the AM section. The FM and AM circuits are followed by a dual-channel *audio amplifier IC* that provides amplification for both AM and FM stereo.

One feature found on most modern AM/FM tuners is a *quartz-synthesized tuning system*, also known as *frequency synthesis* or FS. With FS, exact tuning is assured by the accuracy of a crystal oscillator circuit within one of the microprocessors, and a

Fig. 5.1. Luxman Model T-02 PLL Frequency Synthesized FM-Stereo/AM Tuner. (Courtesy Luxman Division of Alpine Electronics of America, Inc.)

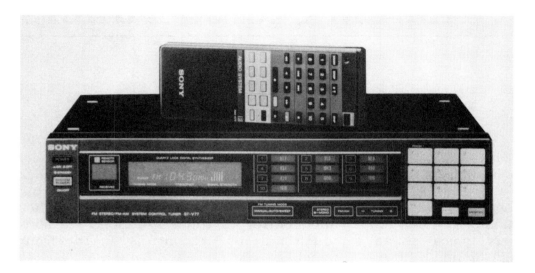

Fig. 5.2 Sony ST-V77 FM-Stereo/FM-AM system control tuner. (Courtesy Sony Corporation of America)

Fig. 5.3. Pioneer F-99X(BK) digital direct decoder stereo tuner. (Courtesy Pioneer Electronics USA, Inc.)

phase-locked loop, or PLL (also part of the microprocessor).

These circuits produce a preset frequency for the station selected, and fine tune the AM and/or FM sections for best reception. The FS signals are applied to the FM tuner package, to operate a *voltage-controlled oscillator* (VCO) within the package. In the AM section, the FS signals are applied to *voltage-variable diodes* (VVDs) or *volt-age-variable capacitors* (VVCs) that tune the AM-section input and local-oscillator circuits.

Our tuner has a front-panel fluorescent display that shows operating mode (AM or FM), operating frequency (kHz or MHz), and relative signal strength. If the FM-stereo broadcast signal is too weak for optimum reception, our tuner automatically switches from stereo to mono mode of operation.

The tuning or PLL microprocessor contains memory locations for 16 different stations (AM or FM) that may be programmed at random via the front panel. The user may then select any one of these channels for listening by entering the assigned station preset number. The PLL microprocessor remembers the preset stations indefinitely (as long as power is connected). The memory is retained for several days when power is removed.

When preset stations are programmed into the PLL-microprocessor memory, the user can *scan up or down* through 16 preset frequencies to select the desired AM or FM station.

The PLL microprocessor *remembers the last station listened to* and returns to that station when the tuner is again turned on. The last-channel memory is retained as long as power is applied or, in the case of power failure, for several days.

Search tuning, instead of preset channel scanning, is also available in the FM mode only. With search tuning, the user can search for a station of choice by pressing the front-panel TUNING UP/DOWN button. The FS tuning system automatically starts scanning at 200-kHz increments until a station is detected. At that time, the scanning function stops and waits for the user to enter an additional command.

The following specifications are for a "typical" AM/FM tuner, and are included here for reference. Always check the service literature for the tuner you are servicing.

FM Section

Frequency range: 87.9 to 107.9 MHz (in 0.2 MHz increments)

Sensitivity: 11.2 dBf

Signal-to-noise ratio: Mono 83 dB, Stereo 77 dB

Total Harmonic Distortion: Mono and Stereo 0.15%

Selectivity: 45 dB (±400 kHz)

Frequency response: 30 Hz to 15 kHz ±0.5 dB

Stereo separation: 45 dB @ 1000 Hz

Capture ratio: 1.0 dB

IF rejection ratio: 80 dB

Image rejection ratio: 45 dB

AM suppression ratio: 50 dB

Antenna terminal: 75 Ω unbalanced, and 300 Ω balanced

AM Section

Frequency range: 530 to 1630 kHz (in 10 kHz increments)

Sensitivity: 18 μV

Selectivity: 40 dB

Signal-to-noise ratio: 50 dB *Image rejection ratio:*

40 dB

5.2 USER CONTROLS, OPERATING PROCEDURES, AND INSTALLATION

Although the controls for most AM/FM tuners are standardized, there are differences. This section describes the basic user controls and operating procedures for a typical tuner. You must study the operating controls and indicators for any tuner you are troubleshooting.

5.2.1 External Connections

External connections between the tuner and stereo amplifier are usually made from the back of the tuner. In some cases, a pin cord is supplied with the tuner (or amplifier) for connection between the tuner L and R stereo outputs, and the corresponding inputs on the amplifier. Although the connections are very simple, certain precautions must be observed for all tuners.

Look for any color coding on the pin cord. Typically, red is used for the right channel, while white is used for the left channel (but do not always count on it). Also look for any ground terminals or leads that are part of the pin cord.

Figure 5.4 shows typical external connections between an AM/FM tuner and a stereo amplifier. Note that the amplifier shown has a-c power receptacles for a number of external components. Use a standard polarized wall outlet if necessary.

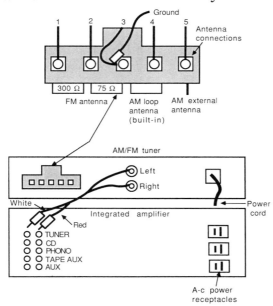

Fig. 5.4. External connections for a typical AM/FM tuner.

Do not connect the tuner to the *CD, aux, phono,* or *tape play* inputs of an amplifier. Instead, always use the *tuner* input (or whatever the tuner input is called on the amplifier). Generally, there is no damage if you connect the tuner to the wrong input. (A possible exception is the *phono* input.) However, the tuner output does not match the other audio components.

For example, the typical 500 or 600 mV output of a tuner is too high for the typical 5 mV of a turntable, and too low for the typical 2 V of a CD player. You can try a really novel

approach and use the input specified in the service literature!

Figure 5.4 also shows the antenna connections for a typical tuner. Note that there are five terminals involved.

Terminals 1 and 2 are for a 300-Ω FM antenna lead-in (or balun, TV/FM splitter, or other balanced FM signal source). Note that some tuners are provided with an FM dipole for indoor reception.

Terminals 2 and 3 are for a 75-Ω unbalanced or coax lead-in (center wire on terminal 2, shield on terminal 3).

Terminals 3 and 4 are for a built-in AM loop antenna.

Terminals 3 and 5 are for an external AM antenna. Use terminal 3 for ground, and terminal 5 for the single lead of the external AM antenna. Do not remove the loop from terminals 3 and 4 when using the external antenna.

On some older tuners, the power cord is used as the antenna. However, this is not found on most modern AM/FM tuners.

5.2.2 Typical Operating Controls

Figure 5.5 shows the operating controls and indicators for a typical AM/FM tuner. Compare the following with the controls and indicators of the tuner you are servicing.

Press the POWER button to turn the tuner on and off. None of the other controls function when power is off.

Press the UP side of the *tuning* button to tune the next higher frequency. Press the DOWN side of the *tuning* button to select the next lower frequency.

When AM is selected, press TUNING UP/DOWN momentarily to change the tuning frequency by 10 kHz. Hold the TUNING button to rapidly change the tuning frequency to the

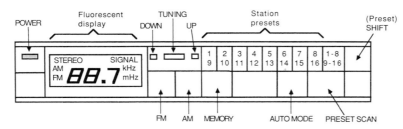

Fig. 5.5. Operating controls and indicators for a typical AM/FM tuner.

desired station. Audio is muted while the TUNING UP/DOWN button is pressed.

When FM is selected, the *auto mode* switch determines the method of tuning in the FM band. With the *auto mode* function on (the *auto mode* indicator on), pressing the TUNING UP/DOWN button causes the tuner to seek the next higher- or lower-frequency station. With *auto mode* in the mono function (the *auto mode* indicator off), the tuner operates as in AM mode, except that each station interval is 0.2 MHz (instead of 10 kHz). Also, the tuner output is mono audio, even if the station tuned in is broadcasting in stereo.

Preset stations may be selected using one of the preset buttons in conjunction with the SHIFT button. Press the SHIFT button to toggle between station presets 1 through 8, and 9 through 16. An indicator turns on showing the preset buttons are assigned to 1 through 8, or 9 through 16.

Press the FM button to change the tuning mode from AM to FM. It is not necessary to press FM when using the preset buttons, after the presets have been programmed.

Press the AM button to change the tuning mode from FM to AM. It is not necessary to press AM when using the preset buttons, after the presets have been programmed.

It is necessary to use the MEMORY button when programming the preset memory. First select AM or FM with the corresponding buttons. Then tune in the desired station with the TUNING UP/DOWN button. (The *auto mode* function must be on to tune FM-stereo stations.) Press the MEMORY button. The display should show the word "memory" for 5 seconds. Press the desired PRESET button within this 5-second interval to program the tuned station into memory. Repeat the programming process for each preset position.

Pressing the PRESET SCAN button causes the preset stations to be scanned. Each station is auditioned for 3 seconds before scanning continues. Release the PRESET SCAN button when the desired station is reached.

As shown in Fig. 5.5, the fluorescent display indicates the frequency tuned, the band selected, and the signal strength of the tuned station. The preset position is also displayed prior to the tuned frequency when the PRESET buttons are used.

5.3 TYPICAL AM/FM TUNER CIRCUIT DESCRIPTIONS

This section describes the theory of operation for a typical AM/FM tuner. All of the notes described in Sec. 2.3 apply here. In this section we concentrate on the circuits of a tuner similar to that shown in Fig. 5.5. Figure 5.6 is the block diagram of such a tuner.

In this section, we concentrate on main signal-path circuits that convert the AM and FM broadcast signals (from the antenna) into audio output (applied to the integrated stereo amplifier). Note that there is special emphasis on those circuits and ICs that control tuning (the PLL function). If you understand these circuits, you should have no trouble understanding operation of any modern AM/FM tuner.

We do not cover the power-supply circuits (which are similar to the power-supply circuits for most electronic equipment). Likewise, we do not dwell on the front-panel operating control and display circuits (which are similar, if not identical to the corresponding circuits on all of the other audio components discussed in this book). However, we do describe a number of circuits outside the main signal path that have direct bearing on the path.

5.3.1 Circuit Overview

As shown in Fig. 5.6, IC301 is both an amplifier and multiplex decoder, and is used in the audio path for AM and FM. The multiplex functions performed by IC301 are as described in Sec. 1.3.6 and shown in Fig. 1.18. Once audio reaches pin 2 of IC301, whether from the AM or FM section, IC301 produces corresponding audio at pins 6 and 7. IC301 has only one adjustment control.

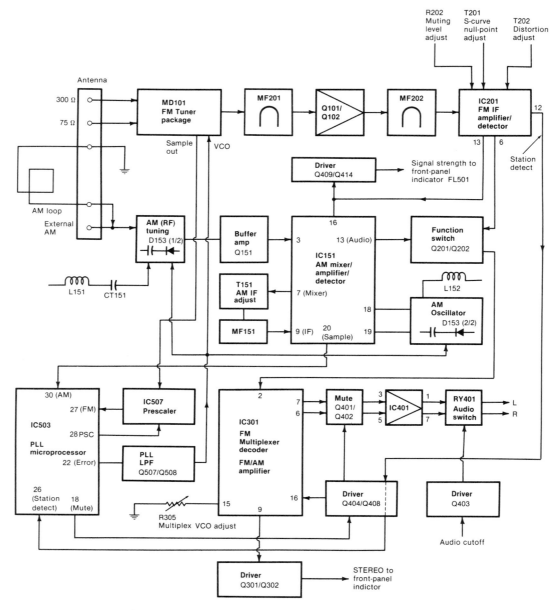

Fig. 5.6. Block diagram of typical AM/FM tuner.

This is the multiplex VCO adjust potentiometer, R305, connected at pin 15.

FM broadcast signals are applied to FM tuner package MD101. The IF output from MD101 is applied to the FM amplifier and detector IC201 through amplifiers Q101/Q102 and ceramic filters MF201/MF202. This amplifier/filter combination removes any amplitude modulation and passes only signal of the desired frequency.

IC201 has three adjustments: muting-

level adjustment R202, S-curve null-point adjustment T201 and FM distortion adjustment T202.

The audio output from the FM section is applied to multiplex decoder IC301 through Q201/Q202. IC301 functions as a mono amplifier when there is no FM stereo present, or when the stereo signal is too weak to produce proper FM.

AM broadcast signals are applied to AM buffer-amplifier Q151 through an RF circuit tuned by one section of D153. The output of Q151 is applied to AM IF amplifier/detector IC151. The mixer output of IC151 is tuned by AM IF adjust T151, and applied to the IF portion of IC151 through ceramic filter MF151.

The audio output from the detector of IC151 is applied to multiplex decoder IC301 through Q201/Q202. Note that IC301 functions as a mono amplifier when the AM mode is selected. Since there is no stereo signal present in the AM mode, IC301 shifts to mono operation, just as is the case when there is no FM stereo or the stereo is weak.

The FM section is tuned to the desired frequency (and locked to that frequency) by signals applied to MD101. The VCO signal (a variable d-c voltage, sometimes called the *error voltage*) from PLL microprocessor IC503 is applied to MD101 through Q507/ Q508. The IC503 error voltage shifts the MD101 oscillator as necessary to tune across the FM broadcast band, or to fine-tune MD101 at a selected station.

The frequency produced by MD101 is sampled and applied to the FM input of IC503 through prescaler IC507. (Operation of the prescaler is described in Sec. 5.3.2.) The sampled signal serves to complete the FM tuning loop. For example, if MD101 drifts from the frequency commanded by IC503, the error voltage from IC503 changes the MD101 oscillator as necessary to bring MD101 back on frequency.

A station-detect signal is produced at pin 12 of IC201. This signal is used to tell PLL microprocessor IC503 that an FM station has been located, and that the station has sufficient strength to produce good FM operation.

In between FM stations, or when the FM station is weak, pin 12 of IC201 goes high, turning on Q406. This causes pin 26 of IC503 to go low, and causes the audio to be muted.

When there is an FM station of sufficient strength, pin 12 of IC201 goes low, turning Q406 off, and causing pin 26 of IC503 to go high. Under these conditions, the audio is

unmuted, and IC503 fine-tunes the FM section for best reception of the FM station. The muting level is set by R202.

The AM section is also tuned to the desired frequency (and locked to that frequency) by signals from IC503 applied to the two sections of diode D153. This is the same error voltage applied to the VCO of FM tuner MD101. The IC503 error voltage shifts the RF and oscillator circuits as necessary to tune across the AM broadcast band.

The oscillator circuit of IC151 is adjusted by AM-covering adjustment L152, while the RF input circuit is tuned by tracking adjustments L151 and CT151.

The frequency produced by IC151 is sampled and applied to the AM input of IC503. The sampled signal serves to complete the AM tuning loop. For example, if the AM section drifts from the frequency commanded by IC503, the error voltage from IC503 changes both circuits controlled by D153 as necessary to bring the AM section back on frequency.

The output of both IC201 (FM) and IC151 (AM) are applied to front-panel fluorescent display FL501 through Q409-Q414. These outputs indicate the relative signal strength of AM or FM broadcast signals. Also note that when the FM multiplex decoder IC301 senses an FM-stereo signal of sufficient strength, IC301 applies a signal to the *stereo* display of FL501.

5.3.2 PLL Operation

Frequency synthesis, or *FS, tuning* provides for convenient push button or preset AM and FM station selection, with automatic station search or scan, and automatic fine-tune (AFT) capability. The key element in any FS system is the PLL that controls the variable-frequency oscillator and/or RF tuning, as required for station selection and fine-tuning. Note that the PLLs used in AM/FM tuners are essentially the same as those used in the FS tuners of TV sets and VCRs.

Figure 5.7 shows the basic PLL circuit.

PLL is the term used to designate a frequency-comparison circuit in which the output of a variable-frequency oscillator (VFO) is compared in frequency and phase to the output of a very stable (usually crystal controlled) fixed-frequency reference oscillator. Should a deviation occur between the two compared frequencies, or should there by any phase difference between the two oscillator signals, the PLL detects the degree of frequency/phase error, and automatically compensates by tuning the VFO up or down in frequency/phase until both oscillators are *locked* to the same frequency and phase.

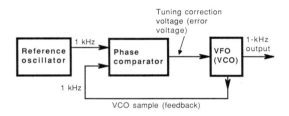

Fig. 5.7. Basic PLL circuit.

The accuracy and frequency stability of a PLL circuit depends on the accuracy and frequency stability of the reference oscillator (and on the crystal that controls the reference oscillator). No matter what reference oscillator is used, the variable-frequency oscillator of most PLL circuits is a volt-age-controlled oscillator, or VCO, where frequency is controlled by the error voltage.

5.3.3 Practical PLL Applications

Figure 5.8 shows how the PLL principles are applied to the AM section of our tuner. The 1-kHz reference oscillator of Fig. 5.7 is replaced by a reference signal (obtained by dividing down the PLL IC503 clock). This reference signal is applied to a *phase comparator* within IC503. The other input to the phase comparator is a sample of the AM signal at pin 30 of IC503 (obtained from pin 20 of IC151).

The output of the phase comparator is an *error signal* or *tuning correction voltage* applied through low-pass filter Q507/Q508 to the AM tuning circuits. The low-pass filter acts as a buffer between the comparator and tuning circuits.

Note that the AM sample is applied to the phase comparator through a *programmable divider* or *counter*. The division ratio of the programmable divider is set by commands from the front-panel operating controls (TUNING UP/DOWN, PRESET SCAN, etc.). In effect, the divider is programmed to divide the AM sample by a specific number.

This variable-divider function makes possible many AM local-oscillator frequencies. An AM station or frequency change is done by varying the division ratio with front-panel commands. This produces an error

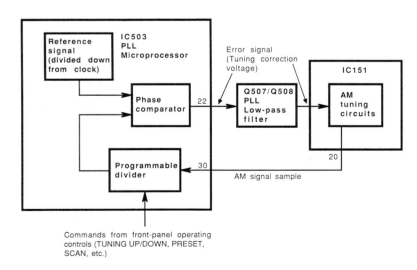

Fig. 5.8. PLL principles applied to practical AM/FM tuner.

signal that shifts the tuning circuits until the AM signal (after division by the programmable divider) equals the reference-signal frequency, and the tuning loop is locked at the desired frequency.

Figure 5.9 shows the PLL circuits for the FM section of our tuner. This circuit is more similar to the PLLs found in TV sets and VCRs, in that a *prescaler* is used. The system of Fig. 5.9 is generally called an *extended PLL*, and holds the variable oscillator frequency to some harmonic or subharmonic of the reference oscillator (but with a fixed phase relationship between the reference and variable signals).

The PLL of Fig. 5.9 uses a form of *pulse-swallow control* or PSC that allows the division ratio of the programmable divider to be changed in small steps. As in the case of AM, the division ratio of the programmable divider is determined by commands applied to IC503 from the front-panel controls.

The PSC system uses a very high-speed prescaler IC507, also with a variable division ratio. The division ratio of the prescaler is determined by the PSC signal from pin 27 of IC503, and can be altered as required to produce subtle changes in frequency needed for optimum station tuning (fine tuning) in the FM mode.

The PSC signal at pin 27 of IC503 is a series of pulses. As the number of pulses increases, the division ratio of the prescaler

also increases. When a given FM station or frequency is selected by the front-panel controls, the number of pulses on the PSC line is set by circuits in IC503 as necessary for each station or frequency. As a result, the overall division ratio for a specific FM station or frequency is the prescaler division ratio *multiplied* by the programmable-divider division ratio. The result of division at any FM station or frequency is a fixed output to the IC503 comparator when the FM tuner is set to the desired frequency.

5.3.4 Tuner Power Switching Circuits

Figure 5.10 shows the power switching circuits. These circuits are controlled by outputs from PLL microprocessor IC503. When POWER is pressed, pin 38 of IC503 goes high. This high is inverted by IC504 and applied to the bases of B+ power transistors Q417/Q418. Both Q417 and Q418 are turned on, applying the B+ power (about 13 V) to the various circuits.

The AM/FM switching is controlled by Q415/Q416 and the signal at pin 39 of IC503. When AM is pressed, pin 39 of IC503 goes low. This low is inverted by IC504 and applied to Q416, turning Q416 off. With Q416 off, Q415 turns on and applies B+ to the AM circuits. When FM is pressed, pin 39 of IC503 goes high. The high is inverted by IC504 and applied to Q416, turning Q416

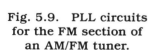

Fig. 5.9. PLL circuits for the FM section of an AM/FM tuner.

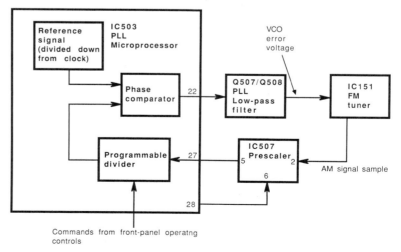

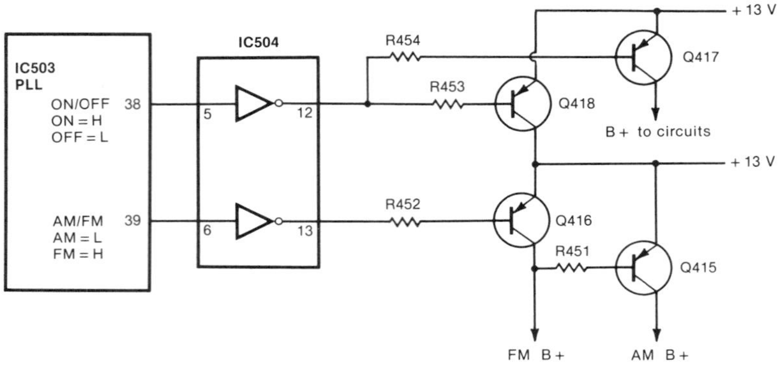

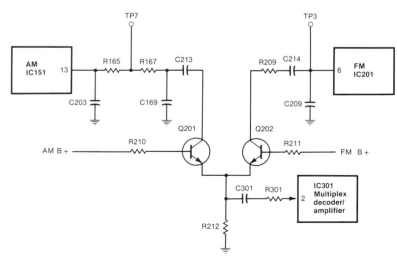

Fig. 5.10. Power switching circuits.

on. With Q416 on, B+ is applied to the FM circuits, but removed from the AM circuits since Q415 is turned off.

5.3.5 AM/FM Audio Output Switching Circuits

Figure 5.11 shows the AM/FM audio output switching circuits. These circuits select the FM or AM audio for input to multiplex decoder/amplifier IC301.

When FM is selected, FM B+ is applied to Q202, turning Q202 on. Since there is no B+ applied to Q201, the AM audio does not pass. However, FM audio present at pin 6 of IC201 is passed to pin 2 of IC301 through Q202, C301, and R301.

When AM is selected, Q201 is turned on, Q202 is turned off (blocking FM audio), and AM audio present at pin 13 of IC151 is passed to pin 2 of IC301 through Q201, C301, and R301.

5.3.6 Muting Circuits

Figure 5.12 shows the muting circuits. Four signals are used to mute the audio.

When the FM signal is weak, or between FM stations, pin 12 of IC201 goes high. This high is applied to Q406/Q407 which are connected as a Schmitt trigger. In the *auto* mode of FM tuning, the collector of Q407 goes high, turning Q404 on (through D402), and turning Q408 on (through R418). With Q408 on, B+ is applied to Q401/Q402, turning both Q401 and Q402 on. This grounds both the left- and right-channel audio lines, and mutes the audio.

When the FM signal of sufficient strength is tuned in during *auto mode,* pin 12 of IC201 goes low. This low turns Q406

Fig. 5.11. AM/FM audio output switching circuits.

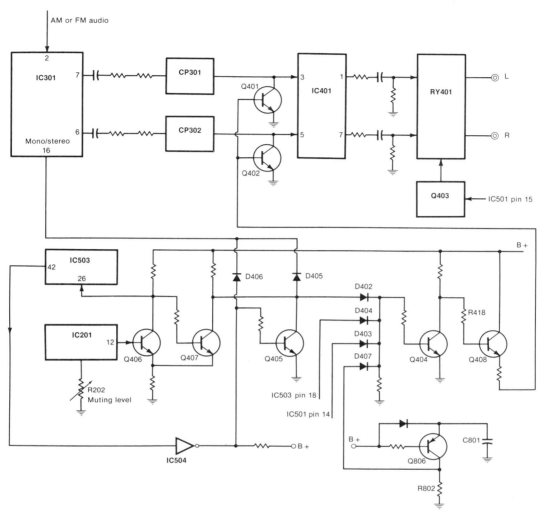

Fig. 5.12. Muting circuits.

off and Q407 on. With Q407 on, Q404, Q408, Q401, and Q402 are turned off to unmute the audio.

In the *mono mode,* pin 42 of IC503 goes low. This low is inverted to a high by IC504, turning Q405 on. With Q405 on, Q404, Q408, Q401, and Q402 are turned off. This removes the ground from the left- and right-channel audio lines, and unmutes the audio.

Note that the selection of auto or mono modes is determined by the status at pin 42 of IC503. When AUTO is selected (*auto mode* indicator on), pin 42 of IC503 goes high. This high is inverted to a low by IC504, and applied to IC301 at pin 16 through D406. This "tells" IC301 to operate as an FM-stereo multiplexer (left- and right-channel audio). The low from IC504 has no effect on Q405.

When MONO is selected (*auto mode* indicator off), pin 42 of IC503 is low. The low is inverted to a high by IC504. This turns Q405 on and mutes the audio as described earlier. The high from IC504 also "tells" IC301 to operate as a mono amplifier (same audio signal to both channels).

The audio can be muted (or unmuted) by signals from pin 18 of IC503 (for AM operation), and pin 14 of system-control microprocessor IC501 (when the tuner is used as part of a system).

The audio can also be muted by a temporary power interruption. During normal operation, C801 charges to the B+ level of about 13 V. If the B+ drops due to a momentary power interruption, Q806 turns on, and C801 discharges through Q806/R802. The temporary high across R802 turns Q404, Q408, Q401, and Q402 on to mute the audio (temporarily, until C801 discharges).

5.3.7 Fluorescent Display Circuits

Figure 5.13 shows the fluorescent display circuits. The segments of the fluorescent display are turned on sequentially in a time-sharing mode. However, the rate is high enough so that the segments appear to be on constantly.

Segments Sa through Sg are applied directly to fluorescent tube FL501 from IC503. Segments D6 through D2 are applied to FL501 through buffers within IC506. The S and D segments produce all displays (frequency, operating mode, etc.) except for stereo indication and relative signal-strength.

When an FM-stereo station (of sufficient

strength) is received, pin 9 of IC301 goes low. This turns Q301 and Q502 on, allowing B+ to be applied to the stereo segment of FL501 (turning on the *stereo* display).

A sample of the AM and FM audio signal is applied to Q414. Variations in AM/FM signal strength cause Q409 through Q413 to turn on, supplying B+ to segments S1 through S5. This provides a display of relative signal strength.

5.4 TYPICAL TEST/ADJUSTMENT PROCEDURES

This section describes the test/adjustment procedures for a typical AM/FM tuner. All of the notes described in Sec. 2.4 apply here. In this section, we concentrate on the procedures for a tuner similar to that shown in Fig. 5.5.

5.4.1 FM IF Adjustment (Field Procedure)

Figure 5.14 is the adjustment diagram. The purpose of this procedure is to set the IF

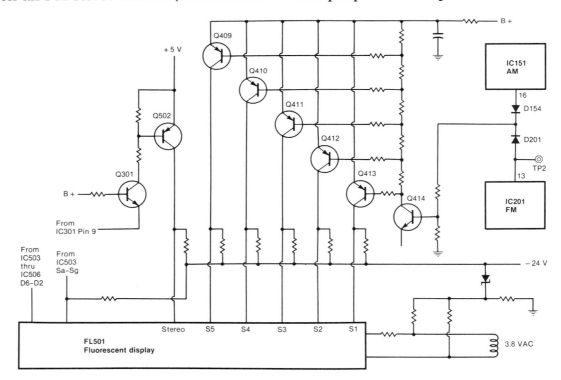

Fig. 5.13. Fluorescent display circuits.

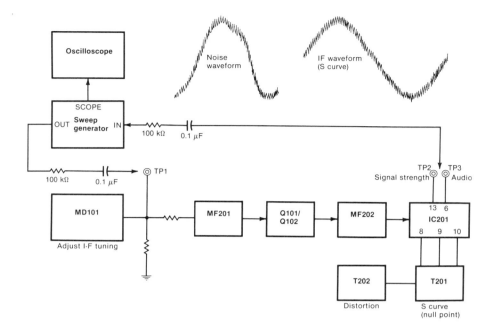

Fig. 5.14. FM IF adjustment diagram (field procedure).

circuits of the FM section, when the tuner is serviced in the field. Of course, the procedure can be used at any time, but a preferred procedure is described in Sec. 5.4.2.

With the sweep generator connected to TP2, adjust the sweep generator for 10.7 MHz with a 200-kHz sweep width. Adjust the generator output amplitude for a weak signal that produces noise as shown on the noise waveform of Fig. 5.14.

Using a nonmetallic alignment tool, adjust the IFT (IF tuning) of the MD101 FM tuner so the IF waveform (S curve) of Fig. 5.14 is maximum.

Move the sweep generator to TP3, but leave the frequency and output amplitude as previously set. If necessary, reduce the oscilloscope gain.

Alternately adjust T201 for a symmetrical S curve, and T202 for linearity between the positive and negative peaks of the IF waveform.

5.4.2 FM IF Adjustment (Shop or Preferred Procedure)

Figure 5.15 is the adjustment diagram. Start by performing the field adjustment as described in Sec. 5.4.1.

Adjust the FM generator (connected to

the 300 Ω antenna terminals as shown in Fig. 5.15) for 97.9 MHz, modulated by 1 kHz with 75-kHz deviation (100% modulation, mono). Adjust the generator output amplitude for 65.2 dBf.

The term dBf (often found in modern FM tuner specifications) is the power level measured in dB, referenced to one *femtowatt* (10^{-15} watt). Assuming a lossless transmission cable and balun or other termination, the formula for the FM generator output voltage is as follows:

$$V = \sqrt{\begin{array}{l}(\text{antilog dBf/1}) \times (10^{-15}) \times \\ (\text{generator output impedance})\end{array}}$$

which should not take you more than three or four days to calculate.

Adjust the tuner to 97.9 MHz (as indicated on the front-panel fluorescent meter), and adjust T201 for 0 V ±50 mV on the d-c null meter (connected between TP4 and TP5).

Adjust T202 for minimum distortion on the distortion meter (connected to the left-channel audio-output jack or terminal).

Work between T201 and T202 until you get minimum distortion, and (hopefully) 0 V ±50 mV on the d-c null meter.

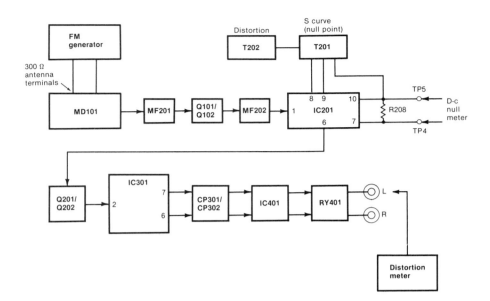

Fig. 5.15. FM IF adjustment diagram (shop procedure).

5.4.3 FM Muting Level Adjustment

Figure 5.16 is the adjustment diagram. This adjustment sets the signal threshold for audio muting in the FM auto mode (where the audio should be muted in between stations and on weak stations).

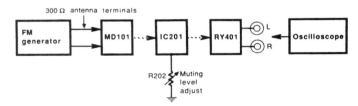

Fig. 5.16. FM muting level adjustment diagram.

Adjust the FM generator (connected to the 300-Ω antenna terminal as shown in Fig. 5.16) for 97.9 MHz, modulated by 1 kHz with 75-kHz deviation. Adjust the generator output amplitude for 33 dBf.

Adjust the tuner to 97.9 MHz (as indicated on the front-panel fluorescent meter). Place the tuner in FM auto mode (press AUTO MODE and check to make sure that the *auto mode* indicator turns on).

Adjust R202 until the audio is muted. Then slowly readjust R202 until the audio is just unmuted.

5.4.4 FM Multiplex VCO Adjustment and Distortion Test

Figure 5.17 is the adjustment/test diagram. This adjustment sets the 19-kHz pilot VCO in IC301, and checks the resultant distortion.

Adjust the FM generator (connected to the 300-Ω antenna terminal as shown in Fig. 5.17) for 97.9 MHz with no modulation. Adjust the generator output amplitude for 65.2 dBf.

Adjust the tuner to 97.9 MHz (as indicated on the front-panel fluorescent meter). Place the tuner in FM auto mode (press AUTO MODE and check to make sure that the *auto mode* indicator turns on).

Adjust R305 for 19 kHz ±50 Hz as indicated on the frequency counter connected to TP8.

Leave the tuner and FM generator set at 97.9 MHz. Apply 1-kHz modulation to the FM generator left channel (with a pilot-carrier deviation of 6 kHz, and a total deviation of 75 kHz).

Adjust the IFT of MD101 (using a nonmetallic alignment tool) for minimum distortion (as indicated by the distortion meter connected to the left-channel audio output jack or terminal). Do not adjust the IFT of

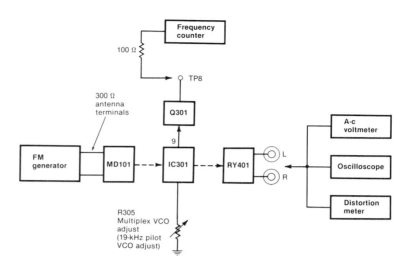

Fig. 5.17. FM multiplex VCO adjustment and distortion test diagram.

MD101 more than one-quarter turn from the setting established in Sec. 5.4.1.

Remove the left-channel modulation from the FM generator, and apply the same modulation to the right channel. Monitor the right-channel audio output with the distortion meter, and check to make sure that the distortion is approximately the same for both channels.

5.4.5 AM IF Adjustment

Figure 5.18 is the adjustment diagram. The purpose of this procedure is to set the IF circuits of the AM section.

Adjust the sweep generator frequency to 450 kHz. Increase the generator output until a waveform appears on the oscilloscope. Do not overdrive the IF section. Adjust T151 un-

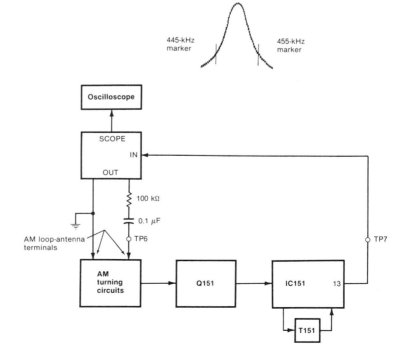

Fig. 5.18. AM IF adjustment diagram.

til the waveform is as shown in Fig. 5.18 (maximum at 450 kHz).

5.4.6 AM Local Oscillator Confirmation

Figure 5.19 is the adjustment diagram. The purpose of this procedure is to check to make sure that the tuning voltage (error voltage from PLL IC503) applied to the AM section is correct. Normally, it is not necessary to adjust the local oscillator, but the tuning voltage should be checked after any service in the AM section.

Adjust the tuner to 1630 kHz (as indicated on the front-panel fluorescent meter).

Check to make sure that the DVM (connected to TP9) reads less than 23 V.

Adjust the tuner to 530 kHz, and confirm that the TP9 voltage is 1.8 V ±0.3 V.

If the reading at 530 kHz is out of tolerance, adjust L152 for an error voltage of 1.8 V ±0.1 V. Then check to make sure that the error voltage is less than 23 V with the tuner at 1620 kHz.

5.4.7 AM Tracking Adjustment

Figure 5.20 is the adjustment diagram. The purpose of this procedure is to adjust the RF input circuits of the AM section for proper tracking across the AM broadcast band.

Adjust the generator (connected to the AM external antenna input) for 600 kHz, modulated with 400 Hz at 30%. Set the generator output level as necessary for a reading on the a-c voltmeter (connected to the left- or right-channel audio output). Use the mini-

mum output from the generator that produces a satisfactory reading.

Adjust the tuner to 600 kHz (as indicated on the front-panel fluorescent meter). Adjust L151 for maximum output on the a-c voltmeter.

Adjust the tuner to 1400 kHz, and adjust CT151 for maximum output.

If necessary, work between L151 and CT151 for maximum output at 600 and 1400 kHz. These two adjustments usually interact.

5.5 TYPICAL TROUBLESHOOTING PROCEDURES

This section describes the troubleshooting procedures for a typical AM/FM tuner. All of the notes described in Sec. 2.5 apply here. In this section, we concentrate on the circuits of a tuner similar to that shown in Fig. 5.5.

The following paragraphs are a collection of trouble symptoms that match the troubleshooting trees found in the service manual for a typical AM/FM tuner. After selecting the symptom that matches the tuner you are servicing, follow the steps in the corresponding troubleshooting procedure.

Before you launch into any troubleshooting, perform the preliminary checks as described in Sec. 4.6.1.

5.5.1 PLL Troubleshooting

Before we get into specific trouble symptoms, let us discuss the PLL circuits, since these circuits are common to most modern AM/FM tuners. A failure in the PLL IC, or in

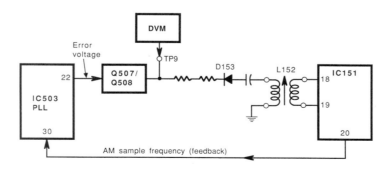

Fig. 5.19. AM local-oscillator adjustment diagram.

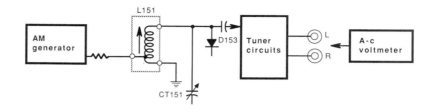

Fig. 5.20. AM tracking adjustment diagram.

the frequency-synthesis (FS) circuits controlled by the PLL, can cause many trouble symptoms. Unfortunately, a failure in other circuits can cause the same symptoms.

For example, assume that you operate the TUNING UP/DOWN buttons and see that the front-panel frequency display varies accordingly, but the AM or FM section does not tune across the corresponding band (no stations of any kind are tuned in). This can be caused by a PLL failure, or by a failure of the commands to reach the PLL IC503 (even though the commands are displayed).

This creates a special troubleshooting problem for AM/FM tuners with PLL. Here is an approach that can be applied to most tuners, without regard to the exact method of PLL tuning.

The most common symptoms for failure of the PLL are a *combination of no stations received* (on both AM and FM) and *noisy audio* (audio not muted as you tune across the broadcast band). Of course, not all tuners have both auto and mono mode as does our tuner, and not all muting circuits operate in exactly the same way. However, the following approach can be applied to the basic PLL problem.

First, make certain that the operating controls are properly set for a particular PLL function. For example, on our tuner, you must be in the auto mode (AUTO MODE button pressed, *auto mode* indicator on) before the PLL will seek FM stations as you tune across the FM band with the TUNING UP/DOWN buttons. If you have selected mono (*auto mode* indicator off), or the circuits have gone into mono because of a failure, the PLL tunes across the FM band in 200 kHz increments, whether stations are present or not. Always look for some similar function on the tuner you are servicing.

When you are certain that the controls are properly set, and that there is a true malfunction, the next step in troubleshooting PLLs is to isolate the problem to the tuning circuits or the PLL circuits. There are two basic approaches.

The first approach is to apply a frequency-change command to the PLL, and see if the error voltage and/or sample voltage changes accordingly.

For example, to check the AM section of our tuner (Fig. 5.8) press the TUNING UP/DOWN buttons and see if the voltage at pin 22 of IC503 changes as the frequency display changes. If not, suspect IC503 (or the circuits between the front-panel TUNING UP/DOWN buttons and IC503.

If the error voltage at pin 22 of IC503 changes, check to make sure that the frequency of the signal at pin 30 of IC503 (or pin 20 of IC151) also changes as the frequency display changes.

If the frequency does not change at pin 30 of IC503 (or pin 20 of IC151) with changes in error voltage, suspect the tuning circuits, D153, Q151, IC151 and/or low-pass filter Q507/Q508. Figures 5.18 and 5.19 show the relationship of the circuits involved.

To check the FM section of our tuner (Fig. 5.9) using this same technique, press the TUNING UP/DOWN buttons and see if the error voltage at the VCO input of MD101 changes as the frequency display changes. If not, suspect IC503 and/or IC507. You can also check to make sure that the PSC pulses at pin 28 of IC503 change, but this is usually more difficult to monitor.

If the error voltage applied to the VCO input of MD101 changes, check to make sure that the frequency of the signal at pin 2 of IC507 (or the sample-frequency output of

MD101) and pin 27 of IC503 changes as the frequency display changes.

If the frequency does not change at the sample-frequency output of MD101 with changes in error voltage, suspect MD101. If the frequency does change at MD101 (and pin 2 of IC507), but not at pin 27 of IC503, suspect IC507. (It is also possible that IC507 is not receiving proper PSC pulses from pin 28 of IC503.)

The alternate technique for troubleshooting PLL circuits is to apply a *substitute tuning voltage* or error voltage to the tuning circuits, and see if the tuning circuits respond by producing the correct frequency. Although this sounds simple, there are some considerations.

First, you must make certain that the substitute tuning voltage is in the same range as the error voltage. For example, the error voltage in our tuner varies from about 1 V to 20 V (at the tuning circuits). You can cover this range with a typical shop-type variable d-c supply. (However, the shop supply can possibly load the tuning circuit with unwanted impedance, reactance, etc.).

Keep in mind that if you apply a lower voltage, the circuits will not respond properly. If you apply a voltage higher than the tuning-circuit range, the circuits can be damaged.

Although a number of tuners use circuits similar to our tuner (the MD101 tuner package is quite common), the tuning circuits are not the same for all tuners. (Some tuners combine the AM and FM functions in a single package.) Of course, if you are lucky, you can find the error-voltage range in the service literature, often in the adjustment chapter.

If the tuner has a *station-detect* function (most tuners do, at least in the FM section), you can use this feature together with a substitute tuning voltage to isolate PLL problems. Simply vary the substitute tuning voltage across the range, and see if stations are detected. For example, in our tuner (Fig. 5.12), you can check at pin 12 of IC201 and/or pin 26 of IC503 for a change of status

each time a station is tuned in and out. Pin 26 of IC503 should go high, and pin 12 of IC201 should go low, each time an FM station of sufficient strength is tuned in. The status of the pins should reverse when the station is tuned out.

5.5.2 Tuner Does Not Turn On

Figure 5.10 is the troubleshooting diagram. If the tuner does not turn on when POWER is pressed (assuming that the fuses are good, the power cord is plugged in, the power-supply circuits are good, and the circuits between the POWER button and IC503 are good), check for a high at pin 5 of IC504 and/or pin 38 of IC503. If missing, suspect IC503.

Check for a low at pin 12 of IC504, and at the bases of Q417/Q418. If missing, suspect IC504, R453, and R454.

If the bases of Q417/Q418 are low, check for about +13 V at the collectors. If missing, suspect Q417/Q418.

5.5.3 Either AM or FM Cannot Be Selected

Figure 5.10 is again the troubleshooting diagram. Press the front-panel AM button, and check to make sure that pin 39 of IC503 and pin 6 of IC504 are low. If not, suspect IC503.

Check for a high at pin 13 of IC504, and at the base of Q416. If missing, suspect IC504 and R452.

If the base of Q416 is high, Q416 should be off and Q415 should be on. The collector of Q415 should be at or near +13 V, while the collector of Q416 should be substantially lower (near zero). If not, suspect Q415, Q416, and R451.

Now press the FM button, and check to make sure that pin 39 of IC503 and pin 6 of IC504 are high. If not, suspect IC503.

Check for a low at pin 13 of IC504, and at the base of Q416. If missing, suspect IC504 and R452.

If the base of Q416 is low, Q416 should be on, and Q415 should be off. The collector of Q416 should be at or near +13 V, while the collector of Q415 should be zero. If not, suspect Q415, Q416 and R451.

5.5.4 AM Audio Good, No FM Audio

Figure 5.11 is the troubleshooting diagram. If you get AM audio, but not FM audio, it is fair to assume that the circuits from R212 through to pin 2 of IC301 (and beyond to the audio output terminals) are good. The first place to trace FM audio is at pin 6 of IC201 (TP3) and at the base of Q202.

If there is no audio at pin 6 of IC201 (or TP3) suspect the FM circuits. Check the FM PLL circuits as described in Sec. 5.5.1. If necessary, go through the FM adjustments as described in Secs. 5.4.1 through 5.4.4. Pay particular attention to the FM muting level adjustment of Sec. 5.4.3.

If there is audio at pin 6 of IC201 (or TP3) but it does not appear at the emitter of Q202, suspect C209, C214, R209, R211, and Q202. Make certain that Q202 is turned on by FM B+. (The base of Q202 should be about 3 to 4 V.)

If there is FM audio at pin 2 of IC301, but no audio at the tuner output terminals, suspect the muting circuits (Sec. 5.5.6).

5.5.5 FM Audio Good, No AM Audio

Figure 5.11 is the troubleshooting diagram. If you get FM audio, but not AM audio, it is fair to assume that the circuits from R212 through to pin 2 of IC301 (and beyond to the audio output terminals) are good. The first place to trace AM audio is at pin 13 of IC151, TP7, and at the base of Q201.

If there is no audio at pin 13 of IC151 or TP7 suspect the AM circuits. Check the AM PLL circuits as described in Sec. 5.5.1. If necessary, go through the AM adjustments as described in Secs. 5.4.5 through 5.4.7.

If there is audio at pin 13 of IC151, but not at TP7, suspect C203 and R165.

If there is audio at TP7, suspect C169, C213, R167, R210, and Q201, if the audio does not appear at the emitter of Q201. Make

certain that Q201 is turned on by AM B+. (The base of Q201 should be about 3 or 4 V.)

If there is AM audio at pin 2 of IC301, but no audio at the tuner output terminals, suspect the muting circuits (Sec. 5.5.6).

5.5.6 Audio Muting Problems

Figure 5.12 is the troubleshooting diagram. The audio muting functions of a tuner can present troubleshooting problems, particularly the FM section. In most tuners, there is an operating mode where the FM is muted between stations, or when stations are too weak to provide good stereo operation (such as the auto mode in our tuner). This same function may, or may not, be available in AM. Likewise, most tuners have a mode where the audio is not muted under any circumstances (weak stations, no stations, etc.).

Obviously, if the tuner never mutes in any mode, there is a problem in the muting circuits. However, if the muting circuits are defective, and mute the audio under all circumstances (or under the wrong circumstances) that can lead you to believe there are no stations of sufficient strength to unmute the audio, or that the circuits ahead of the muting function are bad. So the first step in troubleshooting the muting circuits is to make some preliminary isolation steps.

In our tuner, start by checking for audio at pins 2, 6, and 7 of IC301. If there is no audio at pin 2, check the front-end circuits as described in Secs. 5.5.4 and 5.5.5. If there is audio at pin 2, but not at pins 6 and 7 of IC301, suspect IC301.

If there is audio at pins 6 and 7 of IC301, trace the audio through to the left- and right-channel audio output terminals.

If the audio drops off at pins 3 and 5 of IC401, it is possible that Q401/Q402 are turned on by a muting signal from Q408/Q404.

If audio is available at pins 1 and 7 of IC401, but not at the tuner audio output terminals, it is possible that RY401 has been turned off by a low at pin 15 of IC501.

Once satisfied that the audio path from

IC301 to the output terminals is good, select the auto mode (press AUTO MODE so that the *auto mode* indicator turns on). Check to make sure that pin 42 of IC503 goes high. If not, suspect IC503, or the circuits between the AUTO MODE switch and IC503.

Check to make sure that pin 16 of IC301 is low (in the auto mode). If pin 16 of IC301 is high, IC301 operates as a mono amplifier, rather than an FM-stereo multiplex/decoder. However, IC301 should pass audio in either mode (auto or mono).

Check the base of Q404. If the base is low (zero volt) the audio should be unmuted. If not, suspect Q404/Q408. If the base is high (about 0.6 V) the audio should be muted. If not, suspect Q404, Q408, Q401, and Q402.

With the auto mode selected, the base of Q404 should go high between stations, and low only when an FM station of sufficient strength is tuned in. If this does not appear to be the case, try correcting the problem by adjustment of the muting level (R202) as described in Sec. 5.4.3. If that does not cure the problem, check to make sure that pin 12 of IC201 goes high and low as you tune across the FM band. If not, suspect IC201.

If pin 12 of IC201 changes status as FM stations are tuned in and out, but the base of Q404 does not change status, suspect Q406/Q407.

Also make certain that Q405 has not been turned on by a defect. Q405 should be on only when mono mode is selected (*auto mode* indicator off). If Q405 is on, Q406/Q407 and the signal at pin 12 of IC201 have no effect on the base of Q404. However, Q404 can be turned on to mute the audio by a high from pin 18 of IC503, pin 14 of IC501, or across R802.

5.5.7 No Signal-Strength Indication

Figure 5.13 is the troubleshooting diagram. If there is no signal-strength indication on the front-panel fluorescent meter,

but audio is available at the output terminals, check for signals at the base of Q414, at pin 16 of IC151 (AM mode), and pin 13 of IC201 (FM mode).

If signals are available at the base of Q414, but not at fluorescent display FL501, suspect Q409 through Q414 or FL501.

If signals are missing during AM, but available during FM, suspect IC151 and D154. If signals are missing during FM only, suspect IC201 and D201.

5.5.8 No Stereo Indication

Figure 5.13 is the troubleshooting diagram. If there is no stereo indication on the front-panel fluorescent display, but stereo is available at the output terminals, check for a low at pin 9 of IC301. If the low is available, but the *stereo* display is not on, suspect Q301/Q502 or FL501.

5.5.9 No Automatic Search Operation During FM Mode

Figure 5.12 is the troubleshooting diagram. First, make certain that you are in the FM auto mode. (There is no AM auto mode.) If necessary, press FM and AUTO MODE. Make sure that the *FM* and *auto mode* indicators are on. (That might cure the problem!)

Next, check to make sure that the front-panel *stereo* indicator is on when an FM station is tuned. It is possible that the station is not broadcasting FM, or that the signal is not sufficient for good FM operation.

With an FM station tuned in during auto mode, and the *stereo* indicator on, check to make sure that pin 12 of IC201 is low and pin 26 of IC503 is high.

If pin 12 of IC201 is not low, suspect IC201. If pin 12 of IC201 is low, but pin 26 of IC503 is not high, suspect Q406.

If pin 26 of IC503 is high, but the FM tuning does not stop when the front-panel *stereo* indicator turns on, suspect IC503. Check the PLL functions of IC503 as described in Sec. 5.5.1.

CHAPTER 6

Troubleshooting and Repair of CD Players

This chapter is devoted to compact disc (CD) players. Included are such subjects as special safety precautions in CD player service, the general description of a typical CD player, typical CD player circuit descriptions, user-control operation procedures and installation of CD players, typical test/adjustment procedures, and examples of troubleshooting based on failure symptoms.

6.1 SPECIAL SAFETY PRECAUTIONS IN CD PLAYER SERVICE

In addition to all of the precautions discussed in Chapter 1, the *laser diodes* used in CD players require special consideration during service. Direct exposure to a laser beam can cause permanent eye injury, or skin burns, as can exposure to any very intense light source. To make this more of a hazard, the laser-diode light beam is invisible (in contrast to the red light beam produced by the laser tubes used in video disc players). Since you cannot see a laser-diode light beam, you are never really sure when the beam is present.

The operator (or customer) of a CD player is never exposed to the laser beam, even when the disc compartment is open. (There are interlocks that cut power to the laser when the disc compartment is open.) This is not necessarily true for the servicer. If you go inside to get at the laser (by opening the disc compartment, removing covers, etc.), and keep power on the laser diode (by overriding interlocks, jamming switches, etc.) the beam may get you!

Don't panic, but please keep on your toes. Start by looking for any laser warning labels. A typical warning label is a triangle containing a bright star, possibly with a beam radiating from the star). This is combined with a note such as "*danger*, invisible laser radiation when open and interlock failed or defeated. *Avoid direct exposure to beam.*" Then check the service literature for any cautions concerning the laser diodes, particularly in handling and adjustment. (We discuss both of these in this chapter.)

Whatever precautions you take for yourself, also make sure that all shields and covers are in place, and that interlocks are working before you turn a CD player over to the customer. Besides a potentially dangerous beam, a laser diode produces strong electromagnetic radiation. This will not hurt people, but can be dangerous to magnetic tape, some wristwatches, and anything affected by magnetic fields.

The laser beam from the diodes is focused onto the compact disc through a lens that is part of the optical system or pickup assembly. The lens is usually called the *objective* lens (or possibly the object lens). No matter what it is called, the lens must be clean and free of moisture. Try not to touch the lens surface, and keep the disc compartment closed, except when inserting and removing the disc. Sound quality can be degraded if too much dirt or dust accumulates on the lens. Dirt and moisture can be wiped away with a soft cloth. Dust can be removed with an air blower such as used on a camera lens.

Keep in mind that the laser diode is an electrostatically sensitive (ES) device, similar to any MOS/CMOS part, and should be so treated during service. This includes placing a conductive sheet on the workbench, using wrist straps, etc. The laser diode is usually part of the optical system or pickup assembly, and most CD player manufacturers recommend replacement of the complete assembly as a package, and do not supply replacement parts. Often, the manufacturers ship the replacement pickup in a bag made of conductive material that you can use on the bench to prevent static breakdown.

There are some very specific precautions you must observe when adjusting and testing the laser diodes. We discuss these in Sec. 6.5.

6.2 GENERAL DESCRIPTION OF A TYPICAL CD PLAYER

Figures 6.1 through 6.3 show some typical CD players, which are a very specialized form of phonograph or record player. A CD player plays prerecorded discs (carrying music, speech, etc.) through a conventional hi-fi stereo system (amplifier, equalizers, loudspeakers, etc.). The compact disc is single-sided, 4.75 in. (120 mm) in diameter, and can contain up to about 60 minutes of stereo sound.

The CD player uses a *light beam/optical pickup* instead of the pickup arm found on LP turntables, and spins at a high speed (about 200 to 500 rpm) compared to the typical 33⅓ or 45 rpm for LP. Unlike LP, CD players can provide immediate access to audio at any part of the disc (in addition to providing superior sound, even to PCM digital recordings), and you can program a CD player to reproduce only selected portions of the recorded material.

Figure 6.4 is the interface block diagram of a typical CD player. Before we get into the fascinating details, let us consider some basic differences between CD and LP players.

Fig. 6.1. Luxman D-405 Duo-Beta digital audio compact disc player. (Courtesy Luxman Division of Alpine Electronics of America, Inc.)

Fig. 6.2. Magnavox CDB850 compact disc player. (Courtesy N.A.P. Consumer Electronics Corp.)

First, when a CD is played, a light beam is driven by a servo-operated pickup motor across the disc, and is focused onto the disc by a servo-focused objective lens. The light beam reflects off microscopic pits and flats on the disc underside. These pits are coded with music or other audio, as well as synchronization and identification data. The beginning of a CD player is near the center, and the light beam moves outward toward the disc edge as the program plays.

The objective lens is part of a pickup assembly. There are two basic types of pickup assembly. In one, the optical system is mounted at the end of a rotating arm. The arm and lens are rotated (by the servo drive motor) so that the lens moves from disc center to edge. The rotating arm pickup has generally been replaced by the pickup shown in Fig. 6.5. With this newer configuration, the optical system (including the objective lens) is part of a slide assembly (also called the sled) which is driven across

the disc underside by a servo-operated motor.

Besides the pickup assembly drive motor, a typical CD player also has a turntable drive motor to spin the disc, and a loading motor to insert and remove the disc from the player.

There is no physical contact between the disc and pickup, so CDs last forever (in theory). Instead of physical contact, the optical readout uses a laser beam generated by a small, low-power diode made of aluminum gallium arsenide (AlGaAe) that emits an invisible infrared light. The objective lens that focuses the beam acts like the lens of a microscope to form the beam into a spot slightly less than 1 μm in diameter. The beam is then reflected from the pits and flats back through the lens and optical system onto photodiodes to reproduce the digitally recorded information.

In forming recorded information, the original audio is sampled 44,100 times per

Fig. 6.3. Pioneer PD-M6(BK) multiplay compact disc player.
(Courtesy Pioneer Electronics USA, Inc.)

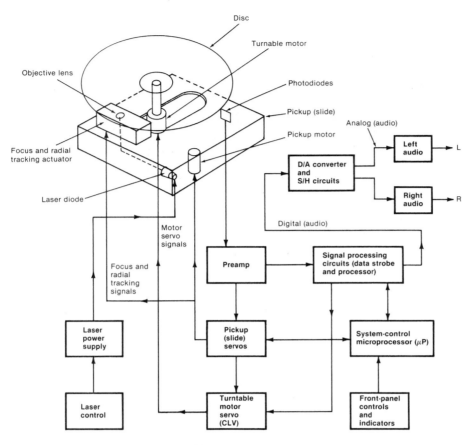

Fig. 6.4. Interface block diagram of a typical CD player.

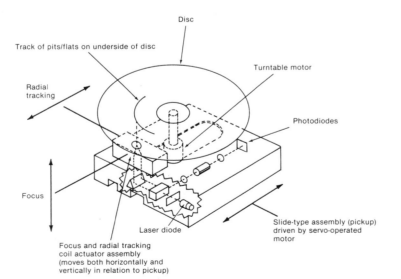

Fig. 6.5. Relationship of slide-type pickup to disc and turntable motor.

second (over twice the usual 20 kHz audio range). The composition (frequency, level, etc.) of each separate signal sample is then converted into a binary format (a series of 1s and 0s). This form of storage is called PCM, pulse code modulation, but is not to be confused with the PCM of other digital recordings.

The digital signal composition used in CD is measured on a scale of 2^{16}, or 65,536 gradations, and the result is expressed as a 16-place binary number. This 16-bit CD system offers a wider dynamic range in which to express the sample signal than other PCM digital recordings (which generally use a 13-bit system). In theory, the dynamic range of the 16-bit system is almost 98 dB. Most CD player manufacturers claim about a 90 to 95 dB dynamic range.

The CD system carries left- and right-channel stereo information separately, with two sets of information aligned successively on a continuous spiral track (from disc center to outer edge). There is a fixed time interval between the two sets of information, so only one information-carrying track is required. This separation of channels in CD reduces crosstalk (a common problem in LP where each groove contains two signals that must be read simultaneously). In theory, CD crosstalk is zero. Realistically, a channel separation of 90 dB (and better) is possible with CD.

Figure 6.6 shows the relationship of the lens and beam to the track of pits and flats. Note that the length of the pits and flats determines the information contained on the track. The pits and flats can vary in length from about 1 to 3 μm. The analog waveform shown below the pits and flats represents the decoded signal after D/A (digital-to-analog) conversion. The pits reflect less light than the flat area, and the length of the two vary to re-create the original audio signal.

6.2.1 Optical Pickup

Figure 6.7 shows the basic elements of the optical system used in the slide-type pickup. The laser diode produces the beam that is applied to the reflective surface of the disc through a series of lenses, prisms, gratings, and possibly mirrors. The beam is then reflected back through the optics to photodiode detectors (typically 6 photodi-

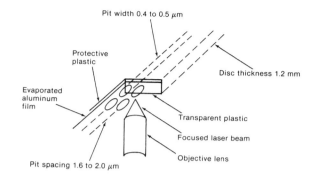

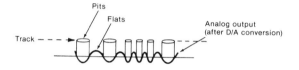

Fig. 6.6. Relationship of lens and beam to the track of pits and flats.

odes). The detector produces an output that corresponds to the audio stored on the disc, as well as tracking and focus signals.

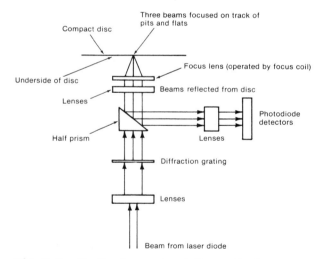

Fig. 6.7. Basic elements of the optical system.

Radial Tracking It is essential that the laser beam follows the track of pits and flats as the optical pickup is drawn across the disc by the pickup motor, regardless of any possible disc eccentricity. This is called radial tracking, and usually involves a radial tracking coil (also called a tracking actuator coil, or TAC). The coil is operated by a tracking servo to move the lens (and beam) as necessary.

The radial tracking system uses the 3-beam (or 3-spot) principle shown in Fig. 6.8. The main spot is used for maintaining proper focus, and retrieving the digital information. The two subspots are used to maintain radial tracking, and are generated by passing the laser beam through a defraction grating, and then through the lens system.

When the laser is reflected from the disc surface, the two subspot laser beams fall upon two optical sensors (often designated TRA and TRC). The TRA and TRC signals are compared within a microprocessor that produces a tracking error voltage (TER). The TER signal is applied to the TAC through an amplifier.

The TER error voltage is zero as long as disc tracking is precise. However, if even the slightest radial tracking error is detected, the input differential between TRA and TRC produces an output. This output is fed to the radial tracking servo and coil that move the objective lens (at right angles to the track) as necessary to correct the position of the main laser beam. In most slide-type pickups, the radial tracking coil moves the optical system (lenses, etc.) in relation to the remainder of the pickup assembly to restore tracking. In a typical CD player, radial tracking is maintained within 0.1 μm.

Automatic Focus The laser beam must remain focused on the disc surface to accurately read the information. The optical pickup provides for automatic focusing of the beam to compensate for vertical movement of the disc. The focusing system moves the objective lens (toward, or away from, the disc), if the laser beam is not focused precisely (within ± 1 μm) on the pits and flats.

Automatic focus (or AF) uses the astigmatism principle. In the simplest of terms, the main laser beam is detected by four equally spaced photodiodes shown in Fig. 6.9. (These same diodes also reproduce the audio signal.) If the main beam is properly focused, the beam spot is round, and all four diodes receive the same amount of light (and produce signals of the same strength).

If the beam is not properly focused, the beam spot is elliptical, and the four diodes receive different amounts of light (and produce different outputs). The outputs from the four diodes are summed in error amplifiers, and represent the focus error. This error (if any) is fed to a focus coil (or focus actuator) that moves the objective lens as necessary to correct the focus.

6.2.2 Signal Processing

The block diagram of Fig. 6.4 shows the sequence of signal processing within a typical CD player. We discuss all of these circuits further in Sec. 6.4. For now, let us run through the signal sequence quickly.

The *photodiode* output is amplified in a

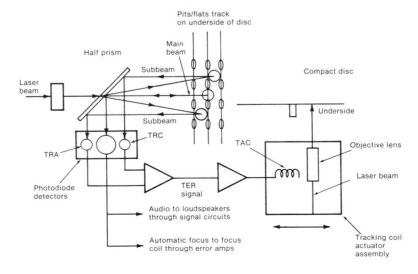

Fig. 6.8. Radial tracking principles.

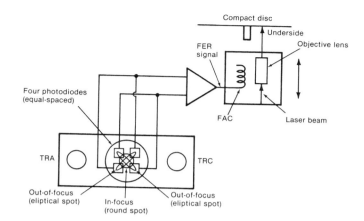

Fig. 6.9. Automatic focus principles.

preamp stage, and is applied to a *data strobe* circuit that discriminates between 1s and 0s. The data strobe also extracts and separates the sync signals from the music or other audio. (Sync signals are encoded along with the music at the time of disc manufacture, making it possible to reproduce audio at selected points on the disc track, among other functions.)

A *data processor* or *signal processor* follows the data strobe. The processor has multiple functions: demodulation of the signal data, error detection and correction, determination of the 1 or 0 status, compensation for possible missing parts of the sync signal, RAM control, rearranging of data for temporary storage in the RAM, and overall control of the signal processing circuit.

When a CD is recorded, the music or other audio is *interleaved* before recording on the disc. In simple terms, the audio is scrambled at the time of recording, and unscrambled (by the CD player) at the time of playback. This scrambling and unscrambling process provides a form of error correction known as CIRC or cross interleaved Reed-Solomon code. Actually, CIRC involves both interleaving and the addition of parity bits.

We will not go into CIRC here since we are far more concerned with troubleshooting CD players than the recording process. If you really want a fascinating discussion of CIRC, read the author's best-selling *Com-*

plete Guide to Compact Disc (CD) Troubleshooting and Repair (1986). However, you should have some knowledge of the encoding and recording process to understand how a CD player works.

Figure 6.10 shows the relationship between the encoding and recording formats. As you can see, a very complex encoding scheme is used to transform the digital data to a form that can be placed on the disc. Each 16-bit word is divided into two 8-bit symbols. These symbols are scrambled in a predetermined way. Then error correction, sync, and a subcode are added. The subcode is used to store index and time information (such as which program or music passage appears after a given playing time).

The combined recording signals are then modulated by a process known as *eight-to-fourteen bit modulation* (EFM). The 8-bit information is changed to 14-bit data by means of a ROM-based lookup table. Three merging bits are added to each word (now containing 17 bits), sync, and subcode data. The encoded data bits are then recorded onto the disc as the series of pits and flats.

Keep in mind that interleaving or scrambling is done by the recording equipment during CD manufacture, and cannot be changed by the CD player. It is the player's job to restore the original signal condition according to information recorded on the disc.

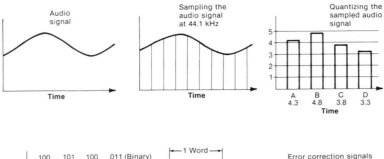

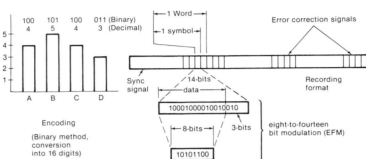

Fig. 6.10. Relationship between the encoding and recording formats.

As shown in Fig. 6.4, a *D/A converter* follows the data processing circuits. The D/A converter transforms the digital signal back into an analog signal. The converted analog signal is then restored to pure two-channel audio by a *sample-and-hold* (S/H) circuit, and applied to the left and right *stereo outputs* (generally on the rear panel). Most CD players also include a headphone jack for audio on the front panel.

In most CD players, the laser used in the optical pickup has a separate laser power supply and power control circuits as shown. Also, the system-control circuits shown in Fig. 6.4 control overall operation of the player. The system-control circuits accept commands from the user operation controls, and display the corresponding functions on front-panel indicators. Generally, the system control functions are produced by a microprocessor IC (typically a 64-pin LSI).

In addition to the signal circuits, CD players have several servo circuits. One servo controls disc turntable speed (to maintain a *constant linear velocity*, or CLV, rather than a constant speed) by locking the motor speed to signals recorded on the disc. (This function is sometimes called *tangential tracking*.) Other servos control radial track-

ing, focus of the optical system, and pickup motor speed.

6.2.3 Constant Linear Velocity (CLV)

To maintain a CLV of 1.3 m per second, the rotational speed of the disc is progressively changed from about 500 rpm at start-up (center) to about 200 rpm at the outside edge of the disc. The data stream is kept at a constant rate by a memory circuit (usually part of a microprocessor IC).

The memory is allowed to fill to one-half capacity. Then data bits are taken from the memory at the same rate as incoming data, thus maintaining the half-full condition. If incoming data bits are received at too fast a rate, the memory exceeds the half-full condition, and an error signal is developed. This error signal is applied to the turntable (disc) motor, and disc speed is reduced until the memory remains at half-full condition. The opposite occurs if the disc slows down.

With this half-full memory circuit, the rotational speed change of the disc has no effect on the rate of speed that the data bits are removed from memory. As a result, disc speed changes are not detected in the reproduced sound.

6.2.4 Features of a Typical CD Player

Keep in mind that the features described here are found on most, but not all, CD players. This can be a problem, particularly when you first begin CD player service. There is nothing more frustrating than troubleshooting a failure symptom when the player is supposed to work that way! Try studying the service literature.

Many CD player manufacturers claim that their player is "computer controlled" or "under control of a built-in computer." In reality, the "computer" is a system-control microprocessor (μP) IC that makes possible all of the features we describe here. However, the major function of the system-control μP is *random memory programming* that allows the user to program and store in memory up to 15 individual program selections.

CDs are digitally encoded at the beginning of the program material so the player will know the length of the audio. Also encoded at the beginning of each selection is an individual code that identifies the location of the particular selection. This system of identification (sometimes known as the *disc directory*) allows each selection of the disc to be accessed (by the system-control μP) on command.

The player normally plays from the beginning of the disc to the end. However, if only certain selections are desired, these parts of the program can be selected, stored, and played as many times as desired. This is done by the system-control μP that reads the codes on the disc (transmitted along with the audio), and causes the player to reproduce only the desired selections, and in the desired sequence.

Typically, there are indicators on the front panel that show such conditions as total disc playing time, elapsed playing time, number and total time of the program entered (via random memory programming), and possibly the track or index numbers being played.

Play of the entire disc, or play of a random memory programming sequence, can be repeated continuously on most CD players. For play of the entire disc, you push the repeat control at any point prior to or during play of the disc. After the full disc is played, the pickup returns to the beginning and begins play again. Repeat play of the random memory programming sequence is generated in the same way.

If a CD player has *memory stop*, you can mark any point on the disc for instant location with the FB (fast backward) control. In either play or pause modes (we discuss operating procedures in Sec. 6.3), you mark the current disc location (the beginning of a favorite program, for example) by pushing the memory stop control. The point can then be returned to by pushing the FB control (in either play or pause). The pickup moves back to the memory stop location, and the player automatically goes into the pause mode. You then push the play control to start play from the memory stop point.

With *disc scanning*, the player is placed in the scan mode when the play control and FF (fast forward) or FB are operated simultaneously. This causes a brief sample of the current program to be played. Then the pickup advances to a point approximately 30 seconds ahead (or behind) in disc play time, and another brief sample is played. This process continues as long as the FF or FB controls are engaged.

With *self-program search*, you skip forward and backward to locate the beginning of each program on the disc. Typically, you press the FF control once, and the pickup advances to the beginning of the next program (and begins playing the disc at that point). When you press the FB control once, the pickup moves back to the beginning of the current program to begin play. If you press the FB control twice, the pickup moves back to the beginning of the previous program to begin play (on some CD players).

CD players are available in both *front load* and *top load models*. Likewise, there are variations in both models. However, the *front load with horizontal tray* has become the most popular configuration for state-of-the-art CD players.

The tray is operated by a *loading motor.* One touch of an open/close button moves the tray out to a position where the disc can be inserted (or removed). Another touch of the button causes the tray to be pulled in, and positions the disc over the turntable.

Keep in mind that on virtually all CD players, there are circuit breakers and/or safety switches (interlocks) that prevent operation of drive motors, and the laser, when the disc tray (or other cover) is open. It is essential that you find the physical location of these interlocks before you start servicing (for your own safety, if nothing else). We discuss such circuits in Sec. 6.4.

6.3 USER CONTROLS, OPERATING PROCEDURES, AND INSTALLATION

Although CD players are not usually difficult to operate or install, the basic procedures may be a mystery to those totally unfamiliar with CD players. This section describes the basic user controls and operating procedures for a typical CD player. You must study the operating controls and indicators for any CD player you are troubleshooting.

Before we launch into a typical operating sequence, here are some precautions that apply to all CD players.

6.3.1 Transit Screw

Most CD players have a transit or transport screw used to hold the pickup in place when the player is moved or shipped. Without such a screw, the pickup can move back and forth, causing possible damage to the delicate optics. The transit screw is accessible from the bottom on most CD players.

Make certain to remove or loosen the transit screw before using the player. (Generally, the screw is of the captive type that is not removed, but not always.) Equally important, be sure to install the transit screw when transporting or shipping the player.

On a front-load player, the transit screw can be installed only when the optical pickup is in one position (the at-rest or secured position). This usually means turning on the power, shutting the tray, and then tightening the screw.

The transit screw can produce problems for the service technician. When the customer brings in the player, the customer will probably forget to tighten the screw, possibly damaging the optics. The opposite occurs if the service technician tightens the screw upon returning the player to a customer. When the customer gets the player home, he or she will probably call with a complaint that the player "no longer works after you fixed it." You must patiently explain these facts to the customer. (In any event, do not lose the screw.)

6.3.2 External Connections

External connections between the CD player and stereo amplifier are usually made from the back of the player. In most cases, a pin cord is supplied with the player for connection between the player's L and R stereo outputs, and the corresponding inputs on the amplifier. Although the connections are very simple, certain precautions must be observed for all players.

Never connect the player to the *phono* input of an amplifier. Instead, use the *CD, aux,* or possibly the *tape play* inputs. The player output is about 2 V which can damage the amplifier and/or speakers, and will over drive the amplifier.

Even on those CD players where the output is adjustable, the player impedance (about 50 kΩ) is best matched to the *CD/aux* or *tape* inputs. As in the case of any audio component, always switch off the power before making or breaking connections between the player and amplifier.

Before connecting the player to a power source, check to make sure that the operating voltage of the player is identical with the voltage of the local power supply. Players designed for world-wide use can be operated at

120, 220, and 240 V. The operating voltage is selected by special connections and/or switch settings, so check the service/operating literature.

6.3.3 Installation and Care of CD Players During Service

The following notes are a supplement to (but not a substitute for) the operating and installation sections of the player service literature.

CD players produce strong magnetic fields. Do not place video or audio cassettes on or near the player.

If the player is brought directly from a cold to a warm place, or is placed in a very damp room, moisture may condense on the optical pickup lenses. The player will not operate properly (if at all) should the lenses become fogged. You can wipe off the objective lens, but not the other lenses in the optical system. Try removing the disc and leave the player turned on for about an hour to evaporate the moisture.

Never use solvents such as benzine, thinner, or the commercial cleaners (or anti-static spray) intended for LP records on a compact disc. Any of these can eat through the CD sealant, and destroy the disc. (There are cleaners designed specifically for CDs, such as the Nagaoka CD-1100K cleaning system from Microfidelity Inc.)

CDs are in no way as delicate as LP records, but discs still require some care in handling. Hold the discs by the edges, avoid touching the rainbow-colored surface, and try to keep discs clean.

Some CD players cause interference to radio and TV reception (although this is not supposed to happen). If this happens, try moving the CD player a few feet from the radio or TV.

A special problem for those not familiar with CD players involves *setting the volume control.* This is because background noise on a CD player is practically nil. If you crank up the volume, either on the player or amplifier, while listening to a portion of the disc where no audio signals are recorded (or to very low-level audio), the speakers may be damaged when that portion of the disc with peak signals is played (and you can imagine what happens to your eardrums when listening with headphones!).

Figure 6.11 shows the operating controls and indicators for a typical front-load CD player with full programming (the most popular type of player). Compare the following

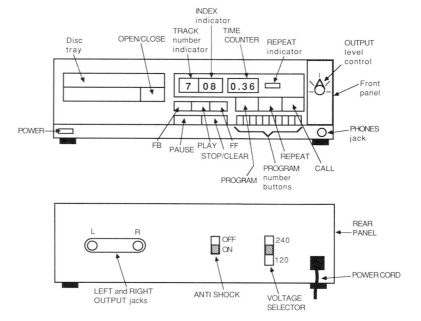

Fig. 6.11. Operating controls and indicators for a typical front-load CD player.

with instructions you find in the literature for the player you are servicing. Note that this player has an *antishock feature* not found in all players.

Make sure that the *voltage selector* is in the proper position (120 or 240 V) before connecting the rear-panel power cord.

Power is applied to the player, and all of the indicators turn on when you press the POWER button. When the POWER button is pressed again, power is removed and all of the indicators turn off.

To load or unload a disc, you press the OPEN/CLOSE button. The power must be on for the OPEN/CLOSE button to operate.

Unless otherwise programmed or interrupted, the disc is played from program 1 to the last program when the PLAY button is pressed. The *play* indicator turns on during play.

To interrupt play on a temporary basis, press the PAUSE button. Press the PLAY button to resume play. The *pause* indicator turns on during the pause interval.

To stop play, press the STOP/CLEAR button. This also removes any programming from the memory, so do not use the STOP/CLEAR button if you want only a temporary pause.

To select a program sequence, press the PROGRAM button and then select the desired program sequence by pressing individual PROGRAM number buttons. (The programs are usually listed by a number system on the disc or jacket.)

Press the FF (fast forward) button for quick forward play. Press the FB (fast back) button to reverse play quickly.

Connect the rear-panel *right* and *left* output jacks to the stereo amplifier input terminals (*CD, aux* or *tape play*), *but not to the phono* input. Connect stereo headphones to the front-panel *phones* jack.

On this player, the front-panel *output* level control sets the output level to both the headphones and amplifier input terminals (rear panel). Some players have separate controls for headphone and amplifier signals. The *output* control permits you to ad-

just the volume level to match that of other audio components that may be played through the stereo (LP turntable, cassette deck, tuner, etc.).

Press the REPEAT button to perform repeat play. Under these conditions, the entire programmed sequence is repeated (on this player). So, if you want only one or more selections, program those particular numbers and use the REPEAT button. The *repeat* indicator turns on during repeat operation.

Press the CALL button to check the programmed numbers before you start play. If you press the CALL button during play, the *next program* to be played is shown on the *track* and *index* number indicators.

The *track* number indicator shows the track number being played or, during programming, the track numbers of programmed selections. The *index* indicator shows the index number of the selections being played. (Not all discs have both track and index numbers.)

On some discs, it is more convenient to locate a particular program by playing time. The *time counter* shows the playing time in minutes (MIN) and seconds (SEC) from the start of play (beginning of the disc).

Set the *antishock* switch to OFF, unless the player is subject to excessive vibration and/or the disc has excessive eccentricity (center hole enlarged, disc warped, etc.) "Sound skipping" can be produced by either of these conditions. With the *antishock* switch ON, antishock circuits compensate for both vibration and disc eccentricity.

When troubleshooting a "sound skipping" symptom, keep in mind that antishock circuits can actually increase skipping if the disc is *badly scratched*. First, try turning the antishock switch OFF. If this cures the trouble, then check the disc.

6.4 TYPICAL CD PLAYER CIRCUIT DESCRIPTIONS

This section describes the theory of operation for a typical CD player. All of the notes described in Sec. 2.3 apply here. In this section, we concentrate on the circuits of a player similar to that shown in Fig. 6.11 (front-load with a slide-type optical system). Figure 6.12 is the block diagram of such a player.

Note that most of the circuits are in IC form, which is true of modern CD players. Some early model players use more discrete-component circuits. We discuss the discrete-component circuits here so that you will have a better understanding of what goes on inside the IC. As you read through the circuit descriptions, compare them with the ICs shown in Fig. 6.12.

6.4.1 Radial Tracking Circuits

Figure 6.13 shows some typical radial tracking circuits in discrete form (compare this to Figs. 6.8 and 6.12). The laser is split into three beams that are focused on the disc surface. When there is proper tracking, the center or main beam is focused directly on the track. The two tracking beams (also called the first-order beams) are focused above and below, and slightly offset from the center beam.

Half of each tracking beam is focused on the pit circumference, with the other half focused on the mirrored area between the pit circumference. The two tracking beams are picked up by two separate photodiodes (TRA and TRC) that produce corresponding signals.

TRA is applied to op amp IC66 connected as a current-to-voltage converter. The converter gain is set by tracking servo offset potentiometer R63. The output of the TRA converter is applied to one input of a comparator within IC1.

TRC is also converted to a voltage by IC63, and applied to IC1 through a 30-μs delay network, CP3/CP4. The time delay is necessary because the tracking circuits require that the TRA and TRC beams analyze the same point on the disc. The voltage outputs from the TRA and TRC converters must reach the input of IC1 at the same time.

When there is proper tracking, TRA and

TRC are equal and the IC1 comparator output is zero. If the main beam drifts, the converter outputs are different, and the comparator output varies above or below 0 V. The IC1 output is called the tracking error or TER signal, and is applied to the TAC tracking coil through IC3 and IC4.

6.4.2 Automatic Focus (AF) Circuits

Figure 6.14 shows some typical automatic focus (AF) circuits in discrete form (compare this to Figs. 6.9 and 6.12). The AF circuits use the center (or brightest) beam produced by the laser. (This same beam is used to detect audio and program information recorded on the pits and flats.) The center beam illuminates on a four-quadrant photodiode.

When properly focused, the focus lens (Fig. 6.7) makes the beam illuminate equally on all four quadrants. If the beam focuses above the track, the lens makes the beam elliptical, and illuminates quadrants 2 and 4 brighter than 1 and 3 (or vice versa, if the beam focuses below the track). The focus circuit moves the lens up or down as necessary to maintain proper focus.

The outputs from two pairs of photodiodes are applied to the inverting input of two comparators within IC1. The outputs of the first pair of comparators are applied to the inputs on a second pair of comparators. One of the second comparators is for detection, and produces a signal at pin 28 of IC1 (as discussed in Sec. 6.4.3). For now, concentrate on the focus output (FER) at pin 6 of IC1.

When in focus, the beam illuminates all quadrants equally. The two photodiode comparators see the same voltage, and the comparator outputs are at the same level. These equal-level voltages are applied to the focus comparator, and the output at pin 6 of IC1 is zero (actually at a fixed d-c reference).

If the beam goes out of focus, either the even (2,4) or odd (1,3) quadrants become brighter, and produce a positive or negative voltage deviation from a zero reference. This produces an S-curve (similar to an FM discriminator) called the focus error signal, or FER. The FER is amplified by IC4 and IC10, and applied through FET-type analog switch Q7 to IC15.

Q7 is turned on by a high from the focus-ok or FOK output of IC1. The AND gate within IC1 produces the FOK output only when all three inputs (two comparators, and the laser monitor input) are present. The FER signal from IC15 is applied to the focus coil through

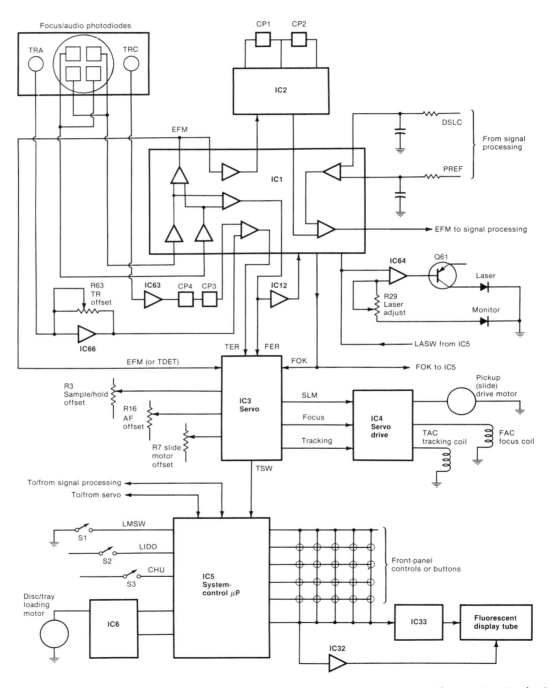

Fig. 6.12. **Typical**

amplifiers. The focus coil moves the lens up or down to get proper focus.

When the disc is first loaded, a rough focus is produced by the focus-up/down or FUD signal from the system-control μP. The FUD consists of two square-wave pulses (with a period of 1s) that are applied to IC15 through integrator R12/C15. This drives IC15 and the push-pull amplifier to move the lens up and down two times.

The first time the lens starts to move, the laser turns on. The lens stops when a $\overline{FOK}$ signal is applied from inverter IC25 to IC15. If no disc is detected (no reflection) the first time, the lens moves toward the disc a second time (on the second FUD pulse). The system-control μP shuts the system down if no disc is detected a second time.

6.4.3 Audio Detection and EFM Signal Generation

Figure 6.15 shows the circuits used to detect audio and other program information recorded on the disc. The circuits of Fig. 6.15 are mostly in discrete form (compare this to Fig. 6.12). When a pit is present, the main beam is absorbed, and no reflection occurs. When a pit is not present (a flat), the beam reflects back to the four-quadrant diode. The diode outputs are amplified by IC1 and appear at pin 28.

The signal at pin 28 is further amplified by IC3, and is returned to IC1 as the EFM signal (also called the *HF signal*, the *RF signal*, or the *eye pattern*). Although the EFM signal appears to be sine waves at this point (at TP11), the signals are digital. The desig-

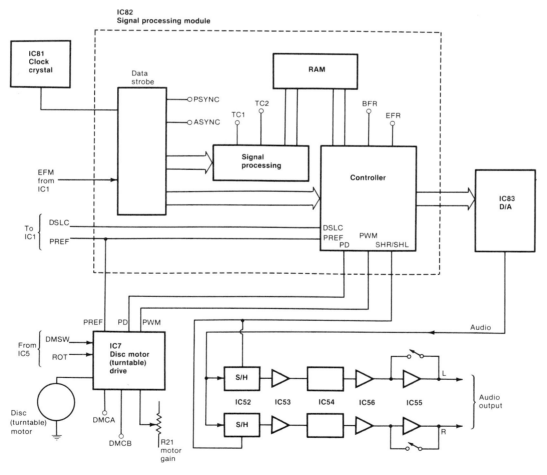

CD player block diagram.

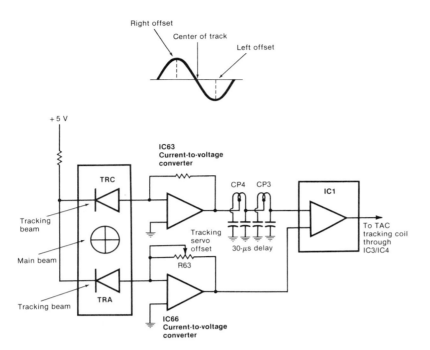

Right offset
Center of track
Left offset

Fig. 6.13. Typical
radial tracking
circuits.

nations 3T, 4T, etc., refer to three times the
period required to read the pit, four times,
the period, etc. The limits of 3T through 11T
are set by specifications.

The EFM signal returns to IC1 at pin 26,
and is applied to pin 23 through an AGC
amplifier. The EFM signal exits IC1 at pin
23, and enters an equalization network (actually a transverse filter) composed of Q3,
Q4, Q5, CP1, CP2, and IC5). The transverse
filter assures that the 3T signal (high frequency) is equal in amplitude with the 11T
signal (low frequency).

The filter output is applied to a comparator in IC1 at pin 20. The comparator
shapes the EFM signal into square waves
(known as the EFMS or EFM-square-wave
signal). The EFM signal is compared to a d-c
threshold voltage developed by circuits
within IC1 and the signal-control logic ICs
(discussed in Sec. 6.4.4).

The EFMS signal is applied to the strobe
and processor portion of the signal-control
logic. The controller portion of the signal-
control logic develops two square-wave signals: the data slice level control or DSCL
(with variable duty cycle) and the preference
pulse or PREF (with fixed duty cycle). DSCL

and PREF are combined by an amplifier
within IC1, and produce an error voltage
that becomes the threshold voltage for the
EFM comparator.

6.4.4 Signal-Control Logic Circuits

Figure 6.16 shows the signal-control
logic circuits which process the digital signal before application to the D/A converter
(where the digital information is converted
to audio). Typically, the signal-control circuits are contained within three or four ICs
(compare Figs. 6.12 and 6.16).

The following is a brief description of
the major functions performed within the
three major ICs. Keep in mind that the functions cannot be altered, adjusted, or even
checked, since the circuits are not accessible. At best, you can check input and output
functions at the IC pins during troubleshooting (as we do in Sec. 6.6).

The data strobe processor IC82 detects
and generates sync pulses derived from the
EFMS signal. Error correction and detection
processor IC83 demodulates the EFM signal, and unscrambles the signal back to the
original 16 bits. (This processing is known
as C1 and C2 decoding, in CD specifica-

tions.) IC83 also processes control and data information.

Controller IC84 governs many digital circuit functions, although the main function is to address memory locations in external RAM IC85. IC84 also outputs the 16 bits of digital data (representing the original audio, but in digital form) to the D/A converter.

6.4.5 D/A Converter and Audio Section

Figure 6.17 shows the D/A converter and audio circuits. The D/A converter, IC86, is a 16-bit device (using the familiar R-2R ladder with op-amp summing), and is capable of producing 65,536 audio output levels. The audio is amplified by IC87, and mutliplexed into right and left channels by sample-and-hold (S/H) circuits within IC88, under control of IC84.

When the left channel is in the sample status (audio from IC86 is passing), the right channel is being held (audio not passing), and vice versa. The S/H outputs are amplified by IC89, and applied through low-pass filter CP51 to amplifier IC53. CP51 produces a sharp dropoff between 20 and 25 kHz, so any signals above the audio range (that might produce distortion) are rejected. IC53 and IC54, which are preamp ICs with equalization or emphasis networks, filter and amplify the audio. In some players, the net-

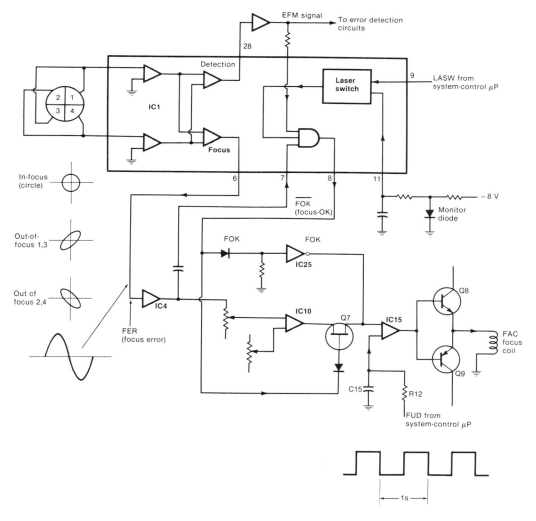

Fig. 6.14. Typical automatic focus circuits.

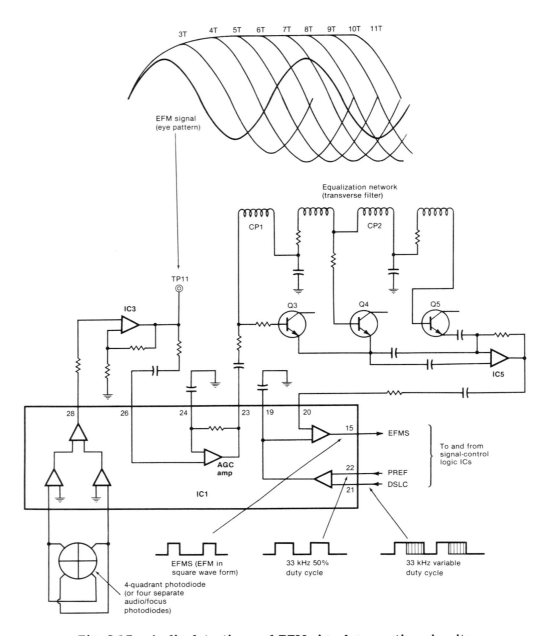

Fig. 6.15. Audio detection and EFM signal generation circuits.

works are under control of relays and switches (such as RY52 in Fig. 6.17).

In the player of Fig. 6.17, there are both fixed and variable outputs on the rear panel (audio to the amplifiers) and a variable output at the front panel (audio to headphones). In most players, the audio can be muted by relays. In the player of Fig. 6.17, the audio outputs are applied through RY51 under control of an MU2 signal (from system-con-

trol IC61). The same MU2 signal is also used to mute the digital signal path.

6.4.6 Pickup Motor Control

Figure 6.18 shows the slide or pickup motor control circuits in discrete form (compare this to Fig. 6.12). A motor is required to keep the beam moving across the disc at a constant rate, even though the disc speed changes. The radial tracking error or TER

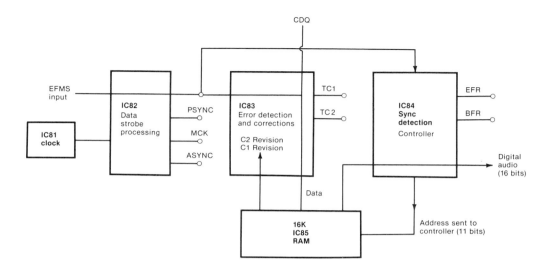

Fig. 6.16. Signal-control logic ICs.

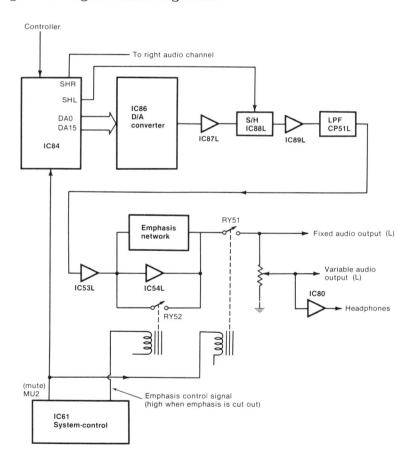

Fig. 6.17. D/A converter and audio circuits (left channel).

signal is applied to the slide motor as a fine control (not the main drive signal). The TER signal is applied through Q50, low-pass filter IC20, analog switch Q20, amplifier IC21, and drive transistors Q23/Q24.

The direction of current through the

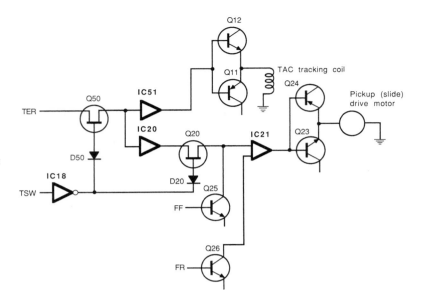

Fig. 6.18. Pickup (slide) motor control circuits.

motor (and the direction of motor rotation) is set by the polarity of the signal applied to Q23/Q24. Note that the TER signal is passed only when there is a TSW (tracking switch) signal from the system-control μP. The TSW signal is inverted by IC18, and applied to Q50 (through D50) and Q20 (through D20), permitting the TER signal to pass.

During fast-forward or fast-reverse operation, the pickup must move at a faster rate than during normal play. On some players, the fast operation also occurs during "search," when moving from one out-of-sequence program to another. The increased pickup speed is produced by FF and FR pulses from the system-control μP. The FF and FR pulses, applied through Q25 and Q26, produce inputs to IC21 much larger than the inputs from Q20. This results in increased current through Q23/Q24, and increases the pickup motor speed.

6.4.7 Laser Monitor and Control

Figure 6.19 shows the laser monitor control circuits. Most players include circuits to monitor and control the amount of light emitted by the laser. This is necessary for proper performance of the optical system. For example, a low output from the la-

ser diode can produce tracking errors, as well as audio dropouts.

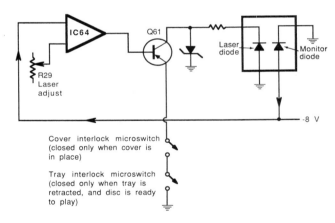

Fig. 6.19. Laser monitor and control circuits.

In Fig. 6.19, the output of a monitor diode is applied to the input of a comparator within IC64. The other input to IC64 receives an adjustable reference voltage, set by potentiometer R29. The output of IC64 is applied to the laser diode through drive transistor Q61.

If the laser diode output goes below the desired reference level, the monitor diode output decreases, and the IC64 output goes less positive. This increases laser drive current supplied by Q61, increasing the laser diode output back to normal. The opposite occurs if the laser diode output increases. The laser diode output can be set to an optimum value with R29 (as discussed in Sec. 6.5).

The laser diode is cut off completely when the outer cover is removed, or when the tray is in the extended position (ready to insert or remove a disc). This prevents the user from being exposed to laser radiation. In the circuit of Fig. 6.19, the laser is controlled by two series-connected microswitches. Both switches must be closed (player cover in place and tray retracted, ready to play) before drive transistor Q61 can pass comparator IC64 output to the laser diode.

6.4.8 Turntable Drive Motor

Figure 6.20 shows the turntable or disc drive motor control circuits in discrete form (compare this to Fig. 6.12). In CD players, the disc is rotated at a *varying speed* so that the rate at which the track is kept moving, with respect to the pickup, is constant.

These speed variations are necessary since there is less data on the tracks near the inside of the disc (start) than near the outside (end).

Most CD players use some form of unitorque motor with Hall-effect elements to get the variable speed. This is similar to the speed control circuits for turntables (Chapter 3). Of course, with turntables, you want a constant speed, instead of the constant linear velocity or CLV required for CD players. Typically, disc speed varies from about 480 rpm (inside) to 210 rpm (outside) so as to maintain a CLV of about 1.25 to 1.3 meters per second.

In the circuit of Fig. 6.20, the Hall-effect outputs are fed back through control elements to the motor drive windings, and thus maintain the desired speed. The Hall-effect elements are also fed currents (from a controller under the direction of the system-control μP) to vary the speed at the desired rate. CLV circuits within the controller monitor the EFM signal to determine the rate at which information is passing, and then pro-

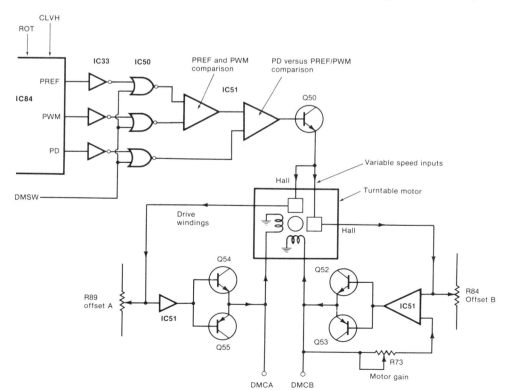

Fig. 6.20. Turntable or disc drive motor control circuits.

duce the necessary signals to maintain the desired rate of speed.

Figure 6.21 shows the relationships of the signals that control the drive circuits in Fig. 6.20. The outputs of the Hall-effect elements are applied to the motor windings through Q52, Q53, Q54, Q55, and amplifiers within IC51. R84 and R89 provide for offset or balance adjustments. R73 sets the gain (and thus the motor speed).

Operation of the disc motor control can be divided into two phases: when power is first applied (sometimes called the *start-servo phase*), and when the disc motor reaches the desired speed (the *regular-servo phase*).

When power is first applied, the disc motor runs free, the DMSW and CLVH signals are low, and the ROT output is high (as shown in Fig. 6.21). Under these conditions, the motor begins to accelerate, and turn at a constant velocity. IC84 produces essentially similar outputs at PWM, PREF, and PD.

After a free-run period (set by the system-control µP), ROT goes low and the motor starts to accelerate. The EFM signal is read by IC84, and compared to a reference. The difference between the reference and the EFM is the PWM output from IC84.

During the acceleration portion of this start-up period, the PWM duty cycle (which varies above and below 50%, as determined by motor speed) is compared with the PREF signal (which has a fixed duty cycle). The result of this comparison is applied to the motor circuits to control speed.

When the disc motor reaches the desired speed (the regular-servo phase), the PWM signal has a 50% duty cycle, and the pickup reads the disc data at a constant linear velocity (Fig. 6.21). This condition is maintained within a ±1% accuracy by means of the PD pulse from IC84. The duty cycle of the PD pulse is set by comparison of the EFM signal to a reference within IC84. In turn, the PD signal is compared with the output from the PWM and PREF comparator. The result of this comparison is applied to the motor to maintain the ±1% accuracy.

6.4.9 Electro-Mechanical Functions of CD Players

The electro-mechanical components in a CD player perform two major functions:

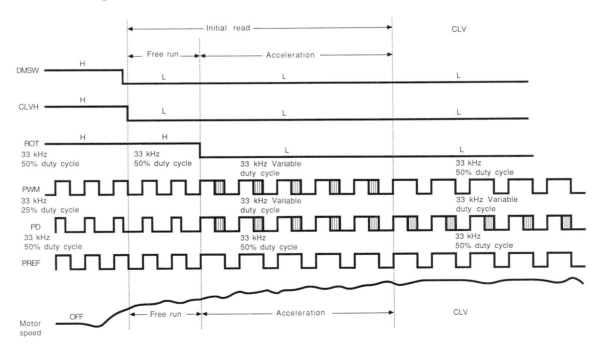

Fig. 6.21. Relationship of turntable motor control signals.

loading and unloading the disc, and driving the optical pickup across the disc. For example, in the player of Fig. 6.11 (which represents about 90% of the CD players being manufactured today), the tray is opened by a drive motor (in response to pushing the OPEN/CLOSE button), a disc is inserted (manually) within the tray, the tray and disc are returned within the player (by the drive motor), and then the disc is installed on the turntable (by the same drive mechanism, and usually the same drive motor). Some players use an additional motor to clamp or "chuck" the disc onto the turntable.

Operation of drive motors is controlled by limit switches, and the system-control µP. So, when you are troubleshooting any mechanical function, you must study *both* the mechanical drawings and the wiring you find (hopefully) in the service literature. The following paragraphs describe both the me-

chanical and electrical functions of a typical CD player. Again, keep in mind that these descriptions must be compared with the descriptions found in (or omitted from) service literature.

Figures 6.22 and 6.23 show the major mechanical components, and the associated wiring, respectively. Note that most of the components are part of a unit mechanism secured to the mainframe by two rails.

The tray is moved out of the player front panel on crossed rollers by the loading motor (LIDM). This action also raises the spring-loaded clamp or chuck. A disc is installed manually in the tray, and the tray is pulled within the player by the LIDM. This action also lowers the clamp so that the disc is pressed against the turntable motor assembly. In most players, the coil assembly can be separated from the turntable motor, and replaced as a separate component.

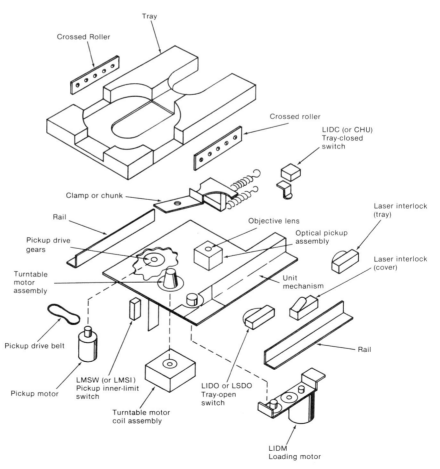

Fig. 6.22. Basic mechanical and electro-mechanical components of a CD player.

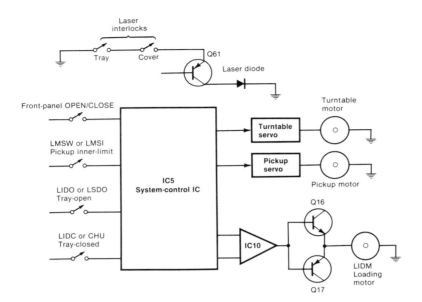

Fig. 6.23. Electro-mechanical wiring and control circuits.

The LIDM motor receives open/close drive signals from the system-control μP through IC10 and Q16/Q17. In turn, the system-control μP receives indicator signals from the tray-open (LSDO) switch and the tray-closed (LIDC) switch.

The LIDC switch is actuated only when the tray is in, and the clamp is in the fully down position. (LIDC is identified as the chuck or CHU switch in some literature, just to confuse you.)

The LSDO switch is set to actuate when the tray has just reached the correct open limit, and thus cuts off the loading motor through operation of the system-control μP.

The LIDC or CHU switch (or whatever it is called) actuates when the tray is fully in, and the clamp is fully down. This cuts off the loading motor.

The optical pickup assembly is driven across the disc by the pickup motor, connected to the pickup drive gears by a belt. On most players, the belt can be replaced when covers are removed, without removing the pickup or motor.

The system-control μP receives a signal from the pickup inner-limit (LSMI) switch, which is set to actuate and turn off the drive motor when the pickup reaches the inner limit (start) of the disc. (Again, to confuse

you, the LMSI switch is often called the LMSW switch.)

In most players, the entire unit mechanism can be replaced as an assembly. Some manufacturers also recommend replacement of the motors and limit switches (and they describe the procedures for replacement/adjustment). The mechanical section is one area where most CD player service literature is very good (if only the theory and troubleshooting sections were that clear!).

We do not dwell on mechanical replacement/adjustment here. However, as a practical matter, never disassemble the unit mechanism of a CD player beyond that point necessary to replace or adjust a given part. Likewise, never make any adjustments unless the troubleshooting procedures lead you to believe that adjustment is required.

6.5 TYPICAL TEST/ADJUSTMENT PROCEDURES

This section describes the test/adjustment procedures for a typical CD player. All of the notes described in the introduction to Sec. 2.4 apply here. In this section, we concentrate on the procedures for a player similar to that shown in Fig. 6.11. Figure 6.12 is the block diagram of such a player. We start with laser diode adjustments, which is always a good point to start on any type of CD player.

6.5.1 Laser Diode Test/Adjustment

Normally, the laser diode need not be adjusted or tested unless (1) the pickup has been replaced or (2) troubleshooting indicates a laser problem. So, before you suspect the laser, consider the following points.

Even though the laser beam is invisible, the diffused laser beam is often visible at the objective lens. (The lens appears to glow when the beam is on.) Also, when power is first applied to the optical circuits, the objective lens moves up and down two (or possibly three) times to focus the beam on the disc, as described in Sec. 6.4.2. So, if you see the objective lens move when power is first applied, it is reasonable to assume that the laser is on and producing enough power to operate the optics.

Of course, this brings up some obvious problems. First, on most players, if you open the disc compartment and gain access to see the lens, you must override at least one interlock. Next, many players have some provision for shutting down the player optics if there is no disc in place (Sec. 6.4.2) so you must override this feature.

Most important
NEVER, NEVER LOOK DIRECTLY INTO THE OBJECTIVE LENS WITH POWER APPLIED! KEEP YOUR EYE AT LEAST 12 INCHES FROM THE LENS!

The purpose of the lens is to focus the beam sharply into the disc. The lens can also do the same job for your eye!

The service literature for early model CD players sometimes recommends monitoring the laser with a light meter. However, it is more practical (and much easier) to adjust the laser diode output until you get an EFM signal of correct amplitude. This not only checks the laser but also checks the photodiodes and IC amplifiers following the photodiodes.

Figure 6.24 is the diagram for testing

and adjusting the laser diode using the EFM signal. Before you make the adjustment, set R29 to minimum, and then increase the setting as required. Also, note that chuck switch S3 must be in the closed (tray in) position before power is applied to Q61 and the laser. You must override S3 manually during adjustment. If S3 is in the tray-open position, the laser has no power and system-control μP IC5 receives a +5-V signal to shut the system down.

1. Connect the oscilloscope as shown in Fig. 6.24. With this connection, you are monitoring the EFM signal (after the photodetector output is preamplified by IC1). As discussed, the EFM signal (at this test point) is also applied to the tracking, focus and pickup motor servos, as well as to the signal processing circuits.

2. Load a disc in the player and select the PLAY mode. The EFM signal should appear on the scope, and produce a waveform similar to that of Fig. 6.24.

3. Adjust R29 until the EFM signal level is 0.7 V (or as specified in the service literature, typically 0.5 to 0.9 V).

Be aware that laser diodes can be damaged by current surges (as can any semiconductor). Typically, the laser diodes used in CD players have drive current limits in the 40- to 70-mA range, possibly 100 mA. Generally, 150 mA is sufficient to damage (if not destroy) any CD laser diode. This can present a problem since laser diodes may require more drive current to produce the required light, as the diode ages. Some service literature spells out "safe" limits of laser drive current.

The simplest way to check laser diode drive current is to measure the voltage across a resistor in series with the diode, such as R23 in Fig. 6.24, then calculate the drive current. For example, if the recommended laser diode current is 40 to 70 mA, and the series resistance is 22 ohms, the voltage should be between 0.88 and 1.54 V.

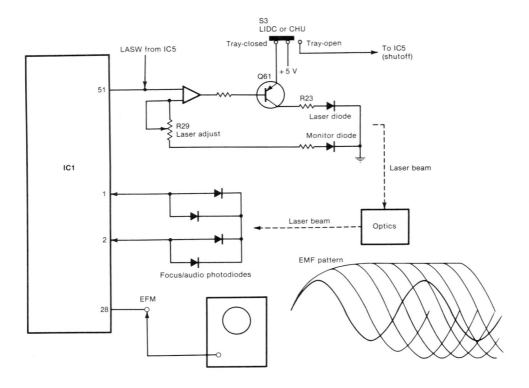

Fig. 6.24. Laser diode test/adjustment diagram (using EFM).

You can make this check before adjustment of the diode, and you *should* make the check after adjustment (to make sure that you have not exceeded the safe drive limits).

6.5.2 Pickup Motor Offset Adjustment

This adjustment is not available on all CD players. When available, the adjustment sets the point where the pickup accesses the beginning of the disc (the disc directory). If the adjustment is not correct, the program information may not be read properly.

Note that this adjustment controls the pickup motor servo, and is not to be confused with the inner-limit microswitch. However, the two adjustments are interrelated. For example, if you set the micro-switch so that the pickup motor cannot reach the disc inner limit, the servo cannot be adjusted to access the full disc directory.

1. Monitor the voltage at test point TP15 with a d-c voltmeter, as shown in Fig. 6.25. With this connection, you are monitoring the motor gain output from servo. IC3.

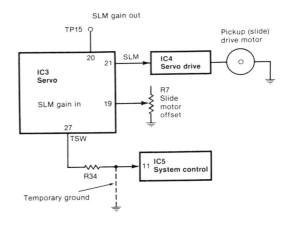

Fig. 6.25. Pickup motor offset adjustment diagram.

2. Load a disc in the player and select the PLAY mode.

3. While the disc is playing, connect a jumper between the junction of R34 and IC5-11 to ground. This simulates a low TSW signal to system-control IC5. If the TSW line is high, IC5 shuts the system down.

4. Set the player to STOP. After about 10 seconds, measure the d-c level at TP15, and

adjust R7 so that the reading is 0 V ±50 mV. Adjust R7 in small increments and wait for the voltage level to stabilize before continuing to adjust. (Make sure to remove the jumper from the junction of R34 and IC5.)

6.5.3 Tracking Servo Offset Adjustment

Figure 6.26 is the adjustment diagram. With this setup, you are monitoring the EFM signal, and adjusting the optical pickup (through the servo and tracking actuator coil) so that the laser beam is properly centered on the tracks (as indicated when EFM is maximum). Note that R63 sets the offset of the two tracking photodiodes but not the four remaining focus/audio photodiodes.

1. Load a disc in the player and select the PLAY mode. The EFM should produce a waveform on the scope (similar to that shown in Fig. 6.24).

2. Adjust R63 until the EFM is maximum (optical pickup centered on the tracks).

On some players, the display may become erratic and the audio will mute, after making this adjustment. If the display is erratic, set the player to STOP, and then go back to PLAY. This should eliminate the erratic display.

6.5.4 Focus Offset Adjustment

Figure 6.27 is the adjustment diagram. With this setup, you are again monitoring the EFM, but you are now adjusting the optical pickup (through the servo and focus actuator coil) so that the laser beam is properly focused on the tracks (as indicated by maximum EFM). Note that R16 sets the offset of the four focus/audio photodiodes, but not the two remaining tracking photodiodes.

1. Load a disc in the player and select the PLAY mode. The EFM should produce a waveform on the scope as shown.

2. Adjust R16 until the EFM is maximum (optical pickup focused on the tracks).

Again, if the display becomes erratic after this adjustment, stop and restart the player.

6.5.5 Disc Motor Hall Gain Balance

Figure 6.28 is the adjustment diagram. With this setup, you are monitoring the drive signals to both coils A and B of the disc motor (from motor drive IC7).

1. Load a disc in the player and select the PLAY mode.

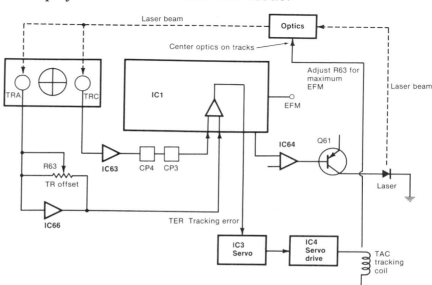

Fig. 6.26. Tracking servo offset adjustment diagram.

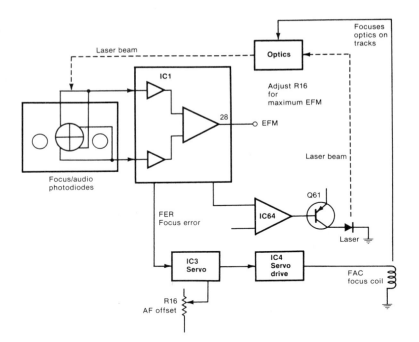

Fig. 6.27. Focus servo offset adjustment diagram.

2. Adjust R21 so that the output levels at TP18 (DMCA) and TP17 (DMCB) are equal. Usually DMCA and DMCB are about 2 V (p-p).

6.5.6 Sample-and-Hold Offset Adjustment for TER

Figure 6.29 is the adjustment diagram. This adjustment, not available on all players, is not to be confused with the sample-and-hold audio circuits. The S/H circuits shown in Fig. 6.29 are located in pickup servo IC3, and control the tracking error or TER signals (described in Sec. 6.4.1).

With the setup of Fig. 6.29, you play a disc with a simulated defect, and adjust TER signals to produce the best response (minimum audio dropout). The effect is simulated by placing a black (nonreflective) tape on the mirror side of the disc. You then monitor the EFM and adjust for minimum dropout (hopefully no dropout).

You can make this adjustment by ear. The simulated defect produces a chattering or ticking in the audio. You adjust for minimum noise. The scope is generally more accurate (or you can monitor both ways). Do

not turn up the volume with a simulated defect. The noise is unbearable!

1. Load a disc and select the PLAY mode.
2. Adjust R3 for minimum audio dropout on the EFM display, or for minimum chattering in the audio, or both.

Note that with such a defect, a portion of the EFM display is cut out (typically a notch or wedge, starting from the top, as shown), no matter how you set R3. However, you should be able to eliminate all (or most) of the audio dropout (as indicated by a cutout at the bottom of the EFM display). If you get considerable dropout at all R3 settings, IC1 may be defective.

6.6 TYPICAL TROUBLESHOOTING PROCEDURES

This section describes the troubleshooting procedures for a typical CD player. All of the notes described in Sec. 2.5 apply here. In this section, we concentrate on the circuits of a player similar to that shown in Fig.

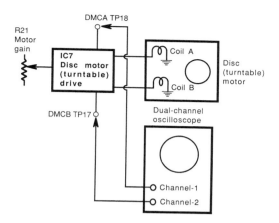

Fig. 6.28. Disc motor Hall gain balance adjustment diagram.

6.11. Figure 6.12 is the block diagram of such a player.

The following paragraphs are a collection of trouble symptoms that match the troubleshooting trees found in the service manual for a typical CD player. After selecting the symptom that matches the player you are servicing, follow the steps in the corresponding troubleshooting procedure.

6.6.1 Preliminary Troubleshooting Checks

It is always a good idea to make a few preliminary checks before you go into the

player with soldering tools. Here are some examples.

1. The transit or shipping screw must be removed or loosened before the player can operate normally.

2. If practical, check to make sure that the customer's stereo system is operating normally before you do any extensive service.

3. Cleaning the objective lens should be a routine part of servicing. A dirty objective lens can cause a variety of symptoms (intermittent or poor focus, skipping across the disc, erratic play, excessive dropouts, to name a few).

4. These same symptoms can also be caused by a defective disc. Try a known good disc, first.

5. Do not replace the pickup assembly, or make any adjustments on the pickup, before checking for mechanical problems that can affect the pickup. For example, look for binding at any point on the pickup travel, indicating that the rails or guides are adjusted too tightly. (Figure 6.22 shows the relationship of the rails to remaining components on a typical CD player.) At the other extreme, if you hear a mechanical "racheting" or "chattering" when the pickup is

Fig. 6.29. S/H offset adjustment diagram.

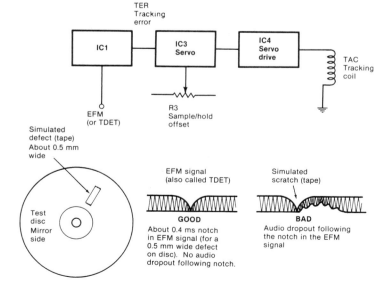

moved, the rails may be too loose. (Note that player literature generally gives all mechanical adjustment procedures in boring detail, so we will not repeat the procedures here.)

6. It is assumed that if you have such obvious symptoms as "none of the front-panel LEDs turn on when the POWER switch is pressed," you will check the fuses (right after you have checked to make sure that the power cord is plugged in).

7. It is also assumed that you will check for bad solder connections, broken copper bands, loose or unseated boards, and the like (cleaning the module and board contacts with a pencil eraser, as necessary).

8. Finally, before you get too far into troubleshooting, you should check the various power supply voltages if entire sections (or functions) appear to be inoperative. This means that you must be able to locate the power-supply circuits on the schematic and/or block diagram, and measure the voltages. (If you cannot do either of these, do not bother to read the rest of this chapter!)

6.6.2 Tray Refuses To Open or Close

Figure 6.30 is the troubleshooting diagram. If the tray does not open or close, first check to make sure that system-control μP IC5 is getting signals from front-panel *open/close* switch S18. If not, suspect S18 and/or the wiring between S18 and IC5.

Next, check to make sure that the loading motor receives a signal from pin 12 of IC6 when S18 is pressed. If so, suspect the motor. If not, you have a problem between IC5 and the motor (through IC6).

Check for signals at pins 10 and 11 of IC6 each time S18 is pressed, and that the signals invert (pin 10 high and 11 low, then vice versa). Check for corresponding inverted signals at pins 33 (open) and 34 (close) of IC5. If absent, or if the signals do not invert when S18 is pressed, suspect IC5.

If the tray opens, but not fully, check when LIDO switch S2 actuates, as indicated

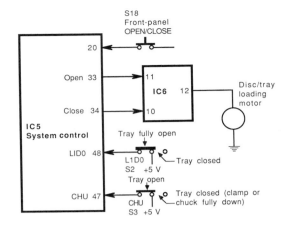

Fig. 6.30. Tray open/close troubleshooting.

by a low-to-high change at pin 48 of IC5. If necessary, adjust S2 (as described in the service manual; see Fig. 6.22 for location of LIDO S2). Before making any adjustments, check for a mechanical condition that might prevent the tray from opening fully (binding gears, jammed cross rollers, improperly adjusted rails, etc.).

If the tray opens fully, but the loading motor does not stop, the problem is almost always an improperly adjusted S2 (although IC5 could be at fault).

If the tray closes, but not fully, and the clamp or chuck does not hold the disc in place on the turntable, check to see if CHU switch S3 actuates, as indicated by a high-to-low change at pin 47 of IC5. If necessary, adjust S3. First, check for mechanical problems (something in the clamp or chuck hinges and tray, wiring that has worked its way out of place, etc.).

If the tray closes, and the clamp or chuck goes fully down, but the loading motor does not stop, the problem is likely an improperly adjusted S3, but could be IC5. Look for a high-to-low change at pin 47 of IC5, which should occur when the tray is fully in, and the clamp is down on the disc.

6.6.3 Laser Diode Troubleshooting

Figure 6.31 is the troubleshooting diagram. The laser diode must produce a proper beam if the CD player is to perform all functions correctly. If the beam is absent, there is no EFM signal. If the beam is weak, EFM is weak. If the monitor diode does not monitor the laser diode properly, the beam can shift to an incorrect level (high or low) without being sensed by the laser-drive circuits. Any of these conditions can cause improper tracking which, in turn, can produce an even weaker EFM.

Always look at the laser circuits first when you have mysterious symptoms with no apparent cause (improper tracking that cannot be corrected by adjustment, excessive audio dropout with a known good disc, etc.). Start with laser diode adjustment. This should show any obvious problems in the laser circuits, and also tell if the EFM signal is good. (An EFM signal of proper amplitude generally means a good laser.)

If the laser appears to be completely dead (no glow at the objective lens, no EFM, no movement of the focus when power is first applied), check to make sure that Q61 is getting ±5 V through CHU switch S3. If not, suspect S3 (or adjustment of S3). When S3 is in the OPEN position, ±5 V is applied to pin 47 of IC5 to show that the tray is open and/or the clamp is not fully down. This disables a number of IC5 system-control functions (including LASW). When the clamp is fully down, S3 moves to the CLOSE position, and the laser diode receives power through Q61.

If power is applied to the laser diode, look for an LASW signal (low) at pin 51 of IC5. If LASW is absent (high), suspect IC5. If present, check for a signal at pin 5 of IC64

from the monitor diode. If abnormal, suspect the monitor diode and/or R29.

If signals are present at both pins 5 and 6 of IC64, look for drive signals at pin 7 of IC64, and the base of Q61. If absent, suspect IC64. If present, suspect Q61.

6.6.4 Pickup Does Not Move to Inner Limit when Power Is Applied, Disc Directory Not Read Properly.

Figure 6.32 is the troubleshooting diagram. On most front-load CD players, the pickup moves to the inner limit (disc start) when power is first applied. The system-control μP applies a temporary SLR (reverse) signal to the pickup motor. In Fig. 6.32, the temporary SLR is generated by a reset circuit (Q1, Q3, and Q4) and applied at pin 24 of IC5. This produces a temporary SLR at pin 60 of IC5 (that is applied to the motor through IC3, IC64, and IC4), and causes the pickup to move inward until inner-limit LMSW S1 is actuated.

If the pickup appears to move to the inner limit when power is applied, but the disc directory is not read properly (say that the total playing time, or number of programs on the disc is not given on the front-panel display), try correcting the problem by adjustment of the motor offset (Sec. 6.5.2) before going into the circuits.

If the pickup does not move when power is first applied (you may not be able to see the pickup, but you should hear the motor) check for SLR at pin 60 of IC5. If absent,

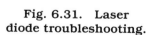

Fig. 6.31. Laser diode troubleshooting.

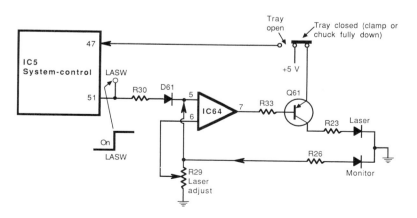

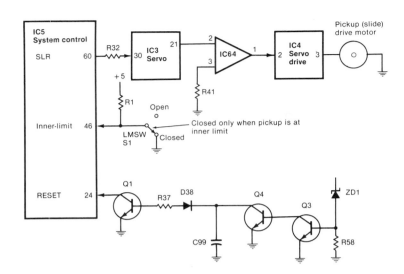

Fig. 6.32. Pickup inner-limit troubleshooting.

suspect IC5 or the reset circuit. If you get SLR, but the motor does not run, suspect IC3, IC64, IC4, and the motor itself.

Check for motor drive voltage at the output of IC4, and at the motor. If the motor runs, but the pickup does not move, look for mechanical problems (jammed gears, binding rollers, improperly adjusted rails, etc.).

If the pickup moves, but does not reach the inner limit, check when LMSW S1 actuates, as indicated by a high-to-low change at pin 46 of IC5. If necessary, adjust S1. Before adjusting S1, check adjustment of the pickup servo offset as described in Sec. 6.5.2. If the offset can be adjusted so that the pickup accesses the disc properly (disc directory can be read in full), S1 is probably adjusted correctly. On most players, LMSW switch S1 does not go out of adjustment, except when the pickup is replaced (or when there has been tampering).

If the pickup reaches the inner limit, but the motor does not stop, the problem is almost always one of an improperly adjusted LMSW switch, S1. A possible exception is where IC5 is defective, and not responding to the low at pin 46.

6.6.5 Pickup Does Not Focus Properly

Figure 6.33 is the troubleshooting diagram. On most front-load players, when play

first begins, the focus actuator coil receives a focus up-down (FUD) signal from IC5 through IC3 and IC4. The FUD pulses move the focus actuator up and down two or three times as necessary to focus the beam on the disc. Once focus is obtained, a focus-ok (FOK) signal is generated by IC1, and applied to both IC5 and IC3. If FOK is not received after two or three trys, IC5 shuts the system down and play stops (turntable off, pickup moves to inner limit). Note that this also occurs when there is no disc in place, so the FOK function also serves as a disc detector for most front-load players. (There are a few players that use a separate disc detector system.)

If focus is obtained, the focus error (FER) signal from IC1 is applied to the focus actuator through IC3 and IC4. The FER signal keeps the pickup focused on the disc. On most players, when the pickup reaches the outer limit (where there are no tracks), focus is lost, the FOK signal is removed, and IC5 shuts down the system.

If you suspect problems in the automatic focus (AF) circuits, install a disc, select PLAY, and check to make sure that the pickup moves up and down two or three times, and then settles down. If not, check the laser (and adjust the laser if necessary). Then make a quick check of the focus coil—try checking the tracking coil at the same time, since you will probably need to pull

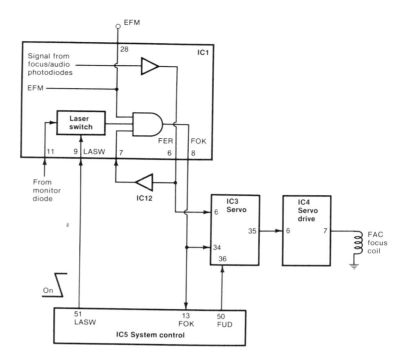

Fig. 6.33. Focus
troubleshooting.

the same connector from the pickup to reach the focus coil wiring.

Measure the resistance of the focus and tracking coils with an ohmmeter. Typically, the focus coil is about 20 Ω, while the tracking coil is 4 Ω. The actual resistance depends on the pickup. However, if you get an open or short, or a resistance that is way off, the coils are suspect. On some players, you can see a *very slight* movement of the objective lens when the ohmmeter is connected to the coils.

If the coils appear good, and the problem cannot be corrected by adjustment, check the focus servo as follows.

If the FUD pulses are not present just after PLAY is selected, suspect IC5. Check for pulses at pin 50 of IC5, pins 35 and 36 of IC3, pins 6 and 7 of IC4 and at the focus coil.

Next, check for FOK signals at pin 8 of IC1, pin 13 of IC5, and pin 34 of IC3. (Keep in mind that if IC5 does not get an FOK signal, the system should shut down.) If the FOK signals are absent at pin 8 of IC1, suspect IC1, or possibly the four focus/audio photodiodes. Also, the FOK signal is not generated unless there is an LASW signal applied to pin 9 of IC1 (from IC5) and a sig-

nal from the monitor diode (as well as EFM and FER).

Next, check for FER signals at pins 6 and 7 of IC1. If FER signals are present at pin 6, but not at pin 7, suspect IC12. If FER signals are absent at pin 6, suspect IC1, or possibly the photodiodes.

If you suspect the focus/audio photodiodes, monitor the EFM signal at the EFM test point (pin 28 of IC1). If EFM is good, it is reasonable to assume that all four photodiodes are good. Typically, EFM is about 0.75 V at this point, but could be between 0.5 and 1.0 V, depending on the player.

Keep in mind that if the photodiodes, focus coil, tracking coil, or any parts of the pickup are defective, you must replace the entire pickup assembly, on most players.

6.6.6 Pickup Does Not Track Properly

Figure 6.34 is the troubleshooting diagram. In most players, it is very difficult to separate tracking and focus servo problems. For example, unless there is an FOK signal applied to IC3, the tracking error (TER) signal does not pass to the tracking coil. Both

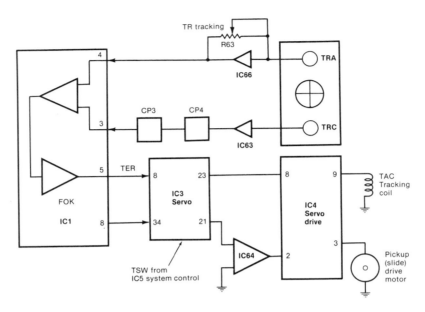

Fig. 6.34. Tracking servo troubleshooting.

the focus and tracking servos use the laser beam as a source of error signal (although different photodiodes are used). To make it worse, TER is also used by the pickup motor as a fine speed control (this takes place in IC3). If TER is lost, both the radial tracking coil and pickup motor have no control signals. Either condition can produce symptoms of improper tracking.

First try to correct any tracking problems with adjustment. Next, make a quick check of the tracking coil. Then see if the pickup moves to the inner limit when power is first applied. (This confirms that the pickup motor, reset circuit, and basic servo are good.) If the motor and coil are good, and adjustments do not correct the problem, check the following.

Check the TER signal from the source (tracking diodes) to the tracking coil and pickup motor. (Note: TER is not applied to the pickup motor in all players.)

IC3 is usually at fault if TER does not reach IC4. However, before you pull IC3, re-

member that IC3 must receive a number of signals before TER can pass. FOK and TSW are two such signals. (In some players, the TER signals are also analyzed for errors in IC3.) If FOK or TSW are absent or abnormal, or if there are excessive errors in the TER signals, IC3 is cut off and TER signals do not pass. So always check the signals and voltages at the pins of IC3 (using the service manual values) before you decide IC3 is bad.

6.6.7 Disc Motor (Turntable) Does Not Rotate Properly

Figure 6.35 is the troubleshooting diagram. It is easy to tell if the turntable is not spinning, and you can usually pin down the cause of such total failure. For example, you can easily check for DMCA and DMCB drive signals to the motor windings.

The problem is not quite that simple if the motor rotates, but you are not sure of the correct speed (especially since the motor speed is constantly changing). You must rely on waveform measurements and adjustments. So the first step in disc motor circuit troubleshooting is to perform the adjustments. However, before you decide there is a problem in the disc motor control circuits, consider the following.

The DMSW, CLVH, and ROT signals must come from system-control μP IC5 before IC82 can apply disc motor control signals to IC7. In most players, if IC5 does not get an FOK (and possibly a TOK) from the focus and tracking circuits, the DMSW, CLVH, and ROT signals are set (high) to prevent IC82 and IC7 from passing the PREF, PWM, and PD signals to the motor. (Typi-

cally, both DMSW and CLVH are made low to turn on the disc motor when PLAY is selected, and ROT goes low about 1 second later.) If all three signals remain high after PLAY is selected, check for FOK and TOK to IC5. If only one of the three signals is abnormal, IC5 is most likely at fault.

If you get the DMCA and DMCB drive signals, and the motor is turning (indicating that DMSW, ROT, and CLVH are good), but you are unable to set the output levels as described, check all of the waveforms associated with the disc motor control circuit as follows.

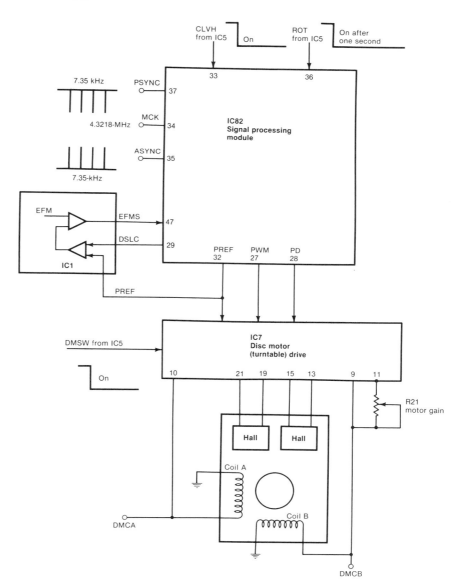

Fig. 6.35. Disc motor (turntable) troubleshooting.

Check PWM, PREF, and PD from IC82. If any are absent or abnormal, suspect IC82. Next, trace the signals between IC7 and the motor. Suspect IC7 if any or all signals are abnormal. If all signals appear to be normal (check the service manual for waveforms and amplitude), suspect the disc motor (probably the Hall elements, but possibly the windings).

Also note that PREF is applied to IC1, along with the DSLC signal from IC82, to form the EFMS signal (that is returned to IC82). IF EFMS is absent, IC82 does not produce PREF, PWM, and PD signals. (If EFMS is absent, you will probably have several other problems.)

You can make a quick check of EFMS by comparing the signals at pin 37 (PSYNC) and pin 35 (ASYNC) of IC82 using a dual-trace scope. As shown in Fig. 6.35, both signals should be synchronized with each other. If not, or if either signal is missing, suspect IC82.

In most modern players, the disc motor control circuits are closely related to the signal processing circuits. A failure in signal processing can appear as a failure in disc motor control. So if you are unable to locate a problem in the disc motor, check the signal processing circuits.

6.6.8 Signal Processing Circuit Problems

Figure 6.36 is the troubleshooting diagram. A failure in signal processing can cause a variety of failure symptoms in both audio and disc motor control circuits. Likewise, a failure in system control can appear as a failure in signal processing. From a practical standpoint, there is no sure way to tell if the problem is in signal processing, system control, disc motor, or audio. However, there are some checks that can help you pin down the problem.

First, check for audio at D/A converter IC83 output (pin 17). You should get both left- and right-channel audio (at a very low level). If you get no measurable audio at this point, suspect signal processing. If there is measurable audio, the problem is likely in the audio circuits (Sec. 6.6.9).

Next, if there are excessive audio dropouts (with a known good disc), and the front-panel indications are not normal (such as the time code not changing as the disc continues to rotate), the problem is likely in signal processing. Check all of the waveforms to and from the signal processing circuits shown in the service literature. Pay particular attention to the following (using Fig. 6.36 as a guide).

Check for a 4.3218-MHz MCK signal at pin 34 of IC82. If missing, check the crystal and IC81.

Check for 7.35-kHz PSYNC and ASYNC signals at pins 37 and 35 of IC82. The ASYNC signal should be present only during PLAY, but PSYNC should be available in both STOP and PLAY.

Make certain that PREF and DSLC are supplied to IC1 and returned to IC82 as square-wave EFMS signals. If EFMS is missing, check for high-frequency EFM signals at pin 20 of IC1.

Check all signals (ROT, CLVH, etc.) between IC5 and IC82 shown in Fig. 6.36. It is not practical to analyze the waveforms of these signals. However, if you can measure a data stream on each line with a scope, it is reasonable to assume that the signal is correct. If one or more of these signals is missing, suspect IC82 or IC5, or both.

Remember that a signal from IC5 can depend on a signal from IC82, and vice versa. So you may have to replace both ICs to find the problem. Also remember that IC5 may not produce the signals unless other signals (such as FOK and TOK) are applied to IC5.

Before you pull IC82, check the TC1 and TC2 signals at pins 11 and 10 of IC82. Both of these test points (that indicate the accuracy of the C1- and C2-decoding processes within IC82) should produce a 7.35-kHz signal during stop, but then drop to 200 Hz or less when PLAY is selected. If not, suspect IC82.

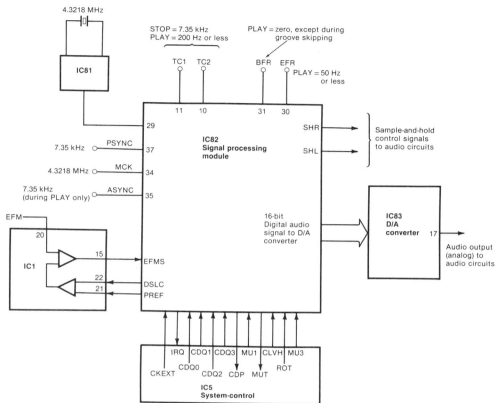

Fig. 6.36. Signal processing troubleshooting.

Next, check the BFR and EFR signals at pins 31 and 30 of IC82. Both of these test points show the accuracy of the sync and detection functions within IC82. In PLAY, BFR should always be zero, except under conditions of excessive groove skipping. In PLAY, EFR may produce a signal, but at a frequency below 50 Hz. The EFR and BFR signals are undefined during STOP.

6.6.9 Audio Circuit Problems

Figure 6.37 is the troubleshooting diagram. The first check of the audio circuits is to monitor the output of the D/A converter at pin 17 of IC83. Next, check the sample-and-hold SHR and SHL signals from IC82. If the SHR and SHL signals are present, and there is audio at pin 17 of IC83, but there are audio problems, trace the audio signal from D/A converter IC83 to the headphones and/or rear-panel output jacks. Note that the level for audio at both the rear-panel jacks and

headphones is controlled by R41. Compare this to the circuits shown in Fig. 6.17.

Look for any muting or emphasis signals from IC5 and/or IC82. For example, if MU3 from IC5 is low, Q52 does not conduct, and relay RY52 remains open. This prevents audio from passing to the output. In some players, a mute signal is also applied to the signal-control circuits to prevent digital information from passing to the D/A converter, resulting in no audio from the converter.

Note that the emphasis network is controlled by RY51 and Q51 which, in turn, receive a control signal from pin 41 of IC82. If the disc is recorded with (or without) emphasis, this is sensed by circuits within IC82, and the emphasis network is cut in (or out) as required.

6.6.10 Programming and Operating Problems

Programming or operating problems can usually be traced to the front-panel op-

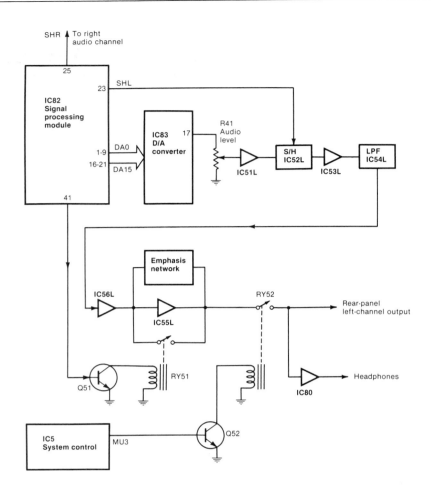

Fig. 6.37. Audio troubleshooting.

erating controls or indicators, the system-control μP, or the wiring between these components, so we do not go into such problems here. For example, if you press PROGRAM, REPEAT, etc., and the player does not respond properly, check to make sure that the system-control μP receives the command from the front-panel switch or button. If not, check the corresponding switch and wiring. If the command is received, but the system-control μP does not produce the corresponding command to player circuits, suspect the μP.

Some players have two system-control μPs. One μP receives front-panel commands, while the other μP applies commands and instructions to the player circuits. There may also be separate system clocks. However, the present trend is to combine all functions into one system-control μP (typically a 64-pin LSI).

Finally, if a programming or operating function can be selected, but you do not get the corresponding front-panel indication (typically a fluorescent display or LED), check the circuits to the display (including any driver ICs, such as shown in Fig. 6.12).

Index

MORE
FROM
SAMS

☐ Audio IC Op-Amp Applications (3rd Edition)   *Walter G. Jung*

This updated version of a classic reference will be welcomed by recording and design engineers and hobbyists using audio signal processing. This new edition covers the changes that have marked the Op-Amp field over the last few years and includes new devices such as the OP-27/37 and application ICs for automobile stereo and audio testing. The update also includes new applications circuitry to illustrate current usage, among them differential input/output IC devices. Jung is a recognized expert in his field and is the author of the definitive *IC Op-Amp Cookbook*.
ISBN: 0-672-22452-6, $17.95

☐ Basics of Audio-Visual Systems Design   *Raymond Wadsworth*

Newcomers to the audio-visual industry will find indispensable information presented here. System designers, architects, contractors, equipment suppliers, students, teachers, consultants. . .all will find these NAVA-sanctioned fundamentals pertinent to system design procedures. Topics include image format, screen size and performance, front versus rear projection, projector output, audio, and the effective use of mirrors.
ISBN: 0-672-22038-5, $15.95

☐ The Complete Guide to Car Audio
Martin Clifford

Car audio systems are becoming almost as complex as home sound systems. Choices abound, but quality varies. This book describes car audio system components and helps you plan your own system. Sections on installation, noise control, and theft protection complete this valuable reference.
ISBN: 0-672-21820-8, $9.95

☐ Electronic Music Circuits
Barry Klein

Understand music synthesizers and how they work, then build your own. Each component in the synthesizer system is explained and illustrated. The components are ultimately combined into a do-it-yourself sample system with suggestions for modifications and enhancements.
ISBN: 0-672-21833-X, $16.95

☐ Modern Recording Techniques (2nd Edition)
Robert E. Runstein and David Miles Huber

Engineers and students alike will find this a valuable guide to state-of-the-art developments and practices in the recording industry. This revised edition reflects all the latest equipment, controls, acoustics, and digital effect devices being used in modern recording studios. It explores the marriage of video and audio multi-track studios and illustrates sound and studio capabilities and limitations.
ISBN: 0-672-22451-8, $18.95

☐ Principles of Digital Audio
Ken C. Pohlmann

Here's the one source that covers the entire spectrum of audio technology. Includes the compact disk, how it works, and how data is encoded on it. Illustrates how digital audio improves recording fidelity. Starting with the fundamentals of numbers, sampling, and quantizing, you'll get a look at a complete audio digitization system and its components. Gives a concise overview of storage mediums, digital data processing, digital/audio conversion, and output filtering. Filled with diagrams and formulas, this book explains digital audio thoroughly, yet in an easy-to-understand style.
ISBN: 0-672-22388-0, $19.95

☐ Sound System Engineering (2nd Edition)
Don Davis and Carolyn Davis

This reference guide is written for the professional audio engineer. Everything from audio systems and loudspeaker directivity to sample design applications and specifications is covered in detail.
ISBN: 0-672-21857-7, $39.95

☐ The Home Satellite TV Installation and Troubleshooting Manual
Frank Baylin and Brent Gale

For the hobbyist or electronics buff, this book provides a comprehensive introduction to satellite communication theory, component operation, and the installation and troubleshooting of satellite systems—including the whys and wherefores of selecting satellite equipment. The authors are respected authorities and consultants in the satellite communication industry. If you are among the 100,000 people per month who are installing a satellite system, you'll want to have this book in your reference library.
ISBN: 0-672-22496-8, $29.95

☐ How to Read Schematics (4th Edition)
Donald E. Herrington

More than 100,000 copies in print! This update of a standard reference features expanded coverage of logic diagrams and a chapter on flowcharts. Beginning with a general discussion of electronic diagrams, the book systematically covers the various components that comprise a circuit. It explains logic symbols and their use in digital circuits, interprets sample schematics, analyzes the operation of a radio receiver, and explains the various kinds of logic gates. Review questions end each chapter.
ISBN: 0-672-22457-7, $14.95

☐ John D. Lenk's Troubleshooting & Repair of Microprocessor-Based Equipment
John D. Lenk

Here are general procedures, techniques, and tips for troubleshooting equipment containing microprocessors from one of the foremost authors on electronics and troubleshooting. In this general reference title, Lenk offers a basic approach to troubleshooting that is replete with concrete examples related to specific

equipment, including VCRs and compact disc players. He highlights test equipment and pays special attention to common problems encountered when troubleshooting microprocessor-based equipment.
ISBN: 0-672-22476-3, $21.95

☐ Know Your Oscilloscope (4th Edition)
Robert G. Middleton
The oscilloscope remains the principal diagnostic and repair tool for electronic technicians. This book provides practical data on the oscilloscope and its use in TV and radio alignment, frequency and phase measurements, amplifier testing and signal tracing, and digital equipment servicing. Additional material is provided on oscilloscope circuits and accessories. A vital reference for your workbench.
ISBN: 0-672-21742-2, $11.95

☐ Ku-Band Satellite TV: Theory, Installation, and Repair
Frank Baylin and Brent Gale
This book is a complete step-by-step guide to the theory, installation, and servicing of Ku-Band satellite receivers for engineers, laymen, and hobbyists. Written in an understandable, easy-to-read manner, this book discusses satellite components, equipment selection guidelines, converting C-Band to Ku-Band, and basic troubleshooting.
ISBN: 0-672-22565-4, $22.95

☐ Semiconductor General-Purpose Replacements (6th Edition)
Howard W. Sams Engineering Staff
Assembled by Howard W. Sams engineers, this handy guide gives over 281,000 general-purpose replacements by registered type numbers, part numbers, and other ID numbers for servicing electronic equipment. All major types of semiconductors are covered including bipolar transistors, field-effect transistors, diodes, rectifiers, integrated circuits and miscellaneous devices. Also provided is a comprehensive index to identification numbers.
ISBN: 0-672-22540-9, $12.95

☐ Troubleshooting with the Oscilloscope (4th Edition)   *Robert G. Middleton*
One of the quickest and least costly ways to troubleshooting most electronic equipment is to use an oscilloscope — properly. In this book, now in its fourth edition, the author not only provides correct step-by-step procedures on the use of an oscilloscope but combines these with specific facts of television receiver troubleshooting.
ISBN: 0-672-21738-4, $11.95

☐ Television Symptom Diagnosis (2nd Edition)   *Richard W. Tinnel*
This easy-to-use text provides you with a basis for entry-level servicing of monochrome and color TV sets. It focuses on identification of abnormal circuit operations and symptom analysis.
ISBN: 0-672-21460-1, $15.95

☐ Tube Substitution Handbook (21st Edition)   *Howard W. Sams Engineering Staff*
This guide contains more than 6000 receiving tube and 4000 picture tube direct substitutes in both color and black and white. Also includes 300 industrial substitutions for receiving tubes, and 600 communications substitutes. Includes pinouts. Special Piggyback Edition: Includes a regular handbook plus a pocket-size handbook for carrying ease.
ISBN: 0-672-21746-5, $5.95
Piggyback Ed.
ISBN: 0-672-21748-1, $6.95

☐ Televison Servicing with Basic Electronics   *Joseph G. Sloop (EIA)*
Use this introductory text to learn how to quickly isolate a television servicing problem and then troubleshoot that section to repair your TV in a minimum number of steps. The book uses block diagrams and troubleshooting charts to help guide you through the information. It covers the basic math required for TV servicing, covers test equipment, discusses the importance of public relations and emphasizes safety for the technician.
ISBN: 0-672-21859-3, $16.95

☐ The Sams Hookup Book: Do-It-Yourself Connections for Your VCR
Howard W. Sams Engineering Staff
Here is all the information needed for simple to complex hook ups of home entertainment equipment. This step-by-step guide provides instructions to hook up a video cassette recorder to a TV, cable converter, satellite receiver, remote control, block converter, or video disk player.
ISBN: 0-672-22248-5, $4.95

☐ Cable Television (2nd Edition)
John Cunningham
With this text, engineers and technicians can learn to examine each component in a cable system, alone and in relation to the system as a whole. Sections include component testing, troubleshooting, noise reduction, and system failure.
ISBN: 0-672-21755-4, $15.95

☐ The Cheap Video Cookbook
Don Lancaster
The logical sequel to *TV Typewriter Cookbook*, this book demonstrates ways to get words, pictures, and code from your computer to your TV without the need for electronic modifications.
ISBN: 0-672-21524-1, $8.95

☐ The Hidden Signals on Satellite TV (2nd Edition)
Thomas P. Harrington and Bob Cooper
This is the authoritative guide that details satellite services available and demonstrates how to access and use such non-video signals as audio channels, news services, teletext services, and commodity and stock market reports. Don't pass up the hidden world illuminated for you by this valuable book.
ISBN: 0-672-22491-7, $19.95

☐ Image Tubes   *Illes P. Csorba*
This text provides a wealth of valuable, hard-to-find data on electron optics, imaging, and image intensification systems: image tube theory, design, construction, and components.
ISBN: 0-672-22023-7, $44.95

☐ North American Radio-TV Station Guide (15th Edition)   *Vane A. Jones*
Sams brings you the only complete, up-to-date, pocket-sized guide to every radio and TV station in the U.S., Canada, Mexico, and the West Indies. The facts are indexed by each station's geographic location, call letters, and frequency. A handy reference for pilots, mariners, tourists, salesmen, truckers, and broadcasting professionals.
ISBN: 0-672-22296-5, $9.95

☐ The Satellite TV Handbook

Anthony T. Easton

Learn how to legally and privately cut your cable TV costs in half, see TV shows that may be blacked out in your city, and pick up live and unedited network TV shows. Shows how to buy or build and aim your own satellite antenna.
ISBN: 0-672-22055-5, $16.95

☐ TV Antennas and Signal Distribution Systems   *M. J. Salvati*

This book will be an invaluable aid to help you select and install TV antenna and signal distribution systems. Not just a picture collection of antennas and components, it is packed with easy-to-understand information on using these systems to produce high-quality TV reception. Performance tested and practical, the book covers everything from basic principles and practical aspects of antenna systems to signal optimization techniques.
ISBN: 0-672-21584-4, $11.95

☐ Introduction to Satellite TV

Chris Bowick and Tim Kearney

Covers business and technical aspects of satellite systems, receiving antennas (including feedtypes and mounts), LNAs and converters for home reception, and receiver operation. Appendices provide additional help on satellite location, antenna aiming, and the Direct Broadcast System.
ISBN: 0-672-21978-6, $9.95

☐ The Ku-Band Satellite Handbook

Mark Long

This book will be the industry standard for Ku-Band satellite technology—the future of satellite communications. Intermediate level users, technicians, and satellite professionals will learn the various aspects of the transmission and reception of video, voice, and data signals by commercial communications satellites operating on frequencies within the 11- to 12-GHZ range.
ISBN: 0-672-22522-0, $18.95

☐ Satellites Today   *Frank Baylin*

Here are the history of satellite communications, the costs of satellite systems, system components, legal questions that have been and remain to be decided, and up-to-date coverage of the latest developments in satellites.
ISBN: 0-672-22492-5, $12.95

☐ Digital Satellite Communications

Dr. Tri T. Ha

This resource is indispensable for satellite, communication, and electrical engineers, as well as serious students investigating this challenging new field. In-depth, concrete instruction and analysis help you keep pace with the technological advances in this sophisticated communications category including orbit analysis, satellite construction, earth station equipment, and signals and networking enhancement.
ISBN: 0-672-22547-6, $54.95

☐ Reference Data for Engineers: Radio, Electronics, Computer, and Communications (7th Edition)

Edward C. Jordan, Editor-in-Chief

Previously a limited private edition, now an internationally accepted handbook for engineers. Includes over 1300 pages of data compiled by more than 70 engineers, scientists, educators and other eminent specialists in a wide range of disciplines. Presents information essential to engineers, covering such topics as: digital, analog, and optical communications; lasers; logic design; computer organization and programming, and computer communications networks. An indispensable reference tool for all technical professionals.
ISBN: 0-672-21563-2, $69.95

☐ Electronic Test Instruments: A User's Sourcebook   *Robert Witte*

This book goes beyond the details of how to operate test equipment. It also explains why a particular instrument is used for a task, how it works, and what is being measured. From simple meters to spectrum analyzers, this manual offers practical techniques and shortcuts that illustrate how to use the latest digital instruments necessary for understanding, designing, or troubleshooting electronic circuits and systems. It also details how to make measurements with enough background and theory to achieve that goal.
ISBN: 0-672-22483-6, $14.95

☐ The Complete Guide to Video

Martin Clifford

For lay readers who want to turn their TV into a complete entertainment center, this guide presents practical tips on using the TV set with a video camera, VCR, videotape, and videodisc player. Learn how standard commercial TV signals can be augmented with cable and satellite reception with ease. Projection TV, video component connections, and video terminology are also included.
ISBN: 0-672-21912-3, $15.95

☐ Home Video Handbook (3rd Edition)

Charles Bensinger

Video system integration and use are the themes here. Learn how to hook the components together to make your camera, VCR, videodisc, projection TV, and/or satellite receiver a system you can be proud of. Includes tips on how to buy the best equipment for your needs and receive the greatest benefits.
ISBN: 0-672-22052-0, $13.95

☐ Video Cameras: Theory & Servicing

Gerald P. McGinty

This entry-level technical primer on video camera servicing gives a clear, well-illustrated presentation of practical theory. From the image tube through the electronics to final interface, all concepts are fully discussed.
ISBN: 0-672-22382-1, $14.95

☐ Video Production Guide   *Lon McQuillin*

For those who want to learn how video production really works, this book contains real-world applications. Pre-production planning, creativity and organization, people handling, single and multi-camera studio and on location production, direction techniques, editing, special effects, and distribution of the finished production are addressed. This book is designed for working and aspiring producers/directors, broadcasters, schools, CATV personnel, and others in the industry.
ISBN: 0-672-22053-9, $28.95

☐ Video Tape Recorders (2nd Edition)

Harry Kybett

This book shows you how to operate and service helical VTRs and includes numerous examples of recorder circuitry and mechanical transport systems.
ISBN: 0-672-21521-7, $14.95